endorsed for

SALTERS HORNERS
AS/A level Physics

THIRD EDITION

Brooke Weston BW
Coomb Road
Great Oakley
Corby
Northants NN18 8LA

tel 01536 396366 fax 01536 396867
email enquiries@brookeweston.org

ALWAYS LEARNING

PEARSON

Published by Pearson Education Limited, 80 Strand, London WC2R 0RL

www.pearsonschoolsandfecolleges.co.uk

Copies of official specifications for all Edexcel qualifications may be found on the website: www.edexcel.com

Text © University of York, developed by University of York Science Education Group, 2015

Designed by Elizabeth Arnoux, Pearson Education Ltd
Typeset by Wearset Ltd, Boldon, Tyne and Wear
Original illustrations © Pearson Education
Illustrated by Pantek Arts, Maidstone, Kent; Wearset Ltd, Boldon, Tyne and Wear
Cover design by Juice Creative
Picture research by Caitlin Swain
Cover photo © Shutterstock/videodoctor

The rights of the authors to be identified as authors of this work have been asserted by them in accordance with the Copyright, Designs and Patents Act 1988.

First edition published 2000
Second edition published 2008
This edition published 2015
19 18 17 16 15
10 9 8 7 6 5 4 3 2 1

British Library Cataloguing in Publication Data
A catalogue record for this book is available from the British Library

ISBN 978 1 447 99098 7

Printed in Slovakia by Neografia

Websites
Pearson Education Limited is not responsible for the content of any external internet sites. It is essential for tutors to preview each website before using it in class so as to ensure that the URL is still accurate, relevant and appropriate. We suggest that tutors bookmark useful websites and consider enabling students to access them through the school/college intranet.

From the Publisher

In order to ensure that this resource offers high-quality support for the associated Edexcel qualification, it has been through a review process by the awarding body to confirm that it fully covers the teaching and learning content of the specification or part of a specification at which it is aimed, and demonstrates an appropriate balance between the development of subject skills, knowledge and understanding, in addition to preparation for assessment.

While the publishers have made every attempt to ensure that advice on the qualification and its assessment is accurate, the official specification and associated assessment guidance materials are the only authoritative source of information and should always be referred to for definitive guidance.

Edexcel examiners have not contributed to any sections in this resource relevant to examination papers for which they have responsibility.

No material from an endorsed book will be used verbatim in any assessment set by Edexcel.

Endorsement of a book does not mean that the book is required to achieve this Edexcel qualification, nor does it mean that it is the only suitable material available to support the qualification, and any resource lists produced by the awarding body shall include this and other appropriate resources.

Picture credits
The authors and publisher would like to thank the following individuals and organisations for permission to reproduce photographs:

(Key: b-bottom; c-centre; l-left; r-right; t-top)

123RF.com: Eugene Tochilin 115t, jukree boonprasit 82l/5, Mike Flippo 82l/2, Sergei Lemtal 75; **Alamy Images:** Angelo Hornak 86, Art Directors & TRIP 133, Aurora Photos 230, Bon Appetit 110cl, 121tr, David O'Shea 107, Heritage Image Partnership Ltd 206, James Davies 15, John Pilkington 190, John Wedrychowski. Adams Picture Library 88tl, Lee Dalton 146, Mary Evans Picture Library 109, Mira 229l, Piero Cruciatti 28c, Robert Harding Picture Library Ltd 189, Tony Lilley 80r; **AMSAT-UK:** 145l; **Ancient Art & Architecture:** 188l, 188r; **Chris Butlin:** 111; **Cambridge Science Media:** 212-a, 212-b, 212-c; **Corbis:** 13/ Philip and Karen Smith/Ocean 24, Lester V. Bergman 211, Lisi Niesner/Reuters 134, Nigel Cattlin/Visuals Unlimited 125, Robert Harding World Imagery 41; **CSC Scientific Company, Fairfax, Virginia:** 110bl; **DK Images:** Dave King 64; **Eyewire:** 82cl, 82cr; **Getty Images:** Adrian Dennis/AFP 4, 27, Alexander Hassenstein 32cr, Arthur Tilley/The Image Bank 13r, BanksPhotos 149, Derek Trask/Photolibrary 19b, Helene Wiesenhaan/Contributor 229r, Hugh Threlfall/Photolibrary 114b, James Balog/The Image Bank 19t, John Giustina/Photodisc 29b, Juan Silva/The Image Bank 110tl, Kolbz/E+ 16, Leon Neal 204, MCT 3r, Michael Steele 44, Popperfoto/Contributor 219c, rollover 29t, Science & Society Picture Library/Contributor 251r, Stocktrek Images 171, Stuart Franklin - FIFA 232; **Imagemore Co., Ltd:** 78l, 82l/6; **Instron Corporation:** 122, 123; **Jonathan Sanderson:** Institute of Physics (The Institute does not endorse this textbook)/National STEM Centre 70; **Joost D. de Bruijn:** Taken from PNAS article Osteoinductive ceramics as a synthetic alternative to autologous bone grafting/PNAS 248bc; **Kruss Optronic GmbH:** 131; **NASA:** 142, 162tr, 162b, 163br, Marshall Space Flight Center 143, 163t; **Otto Bock HealthCare PLC:** 242; **PhotoDisc:** Tony Gable. C Squared Studios 82c, Tony Gable. C Squared Studios. 78r, 82l/1; **Photolibrary.com:** Corbis 265t; **Reuters:** Benoit Tessier 2l; **Rex Features:** 32cl, 36, Andy Hooper/Daily Mail 32c, APA- PictureDesk GmbH 3l, James D. Morgan 82bl, Tina Norris 243t; **Science & Society Picture Library:** Science Museum 121-br; **Science Photo Library Ltd:** 228, 251c, 269b, Andrew Lambert Photography 215t, Astrid & Hanns-Frieder Michler 216l, Chris Gallagher 277, David Campione 268, Dr David Wexler, coloured by Dr Jeremy Burgess 215c, Dr Jeremy Burgess 88cl, 88bl, Dr Kari Lounatmaa 215b, Erich Schrempp 91, ESA/Rosetta/Philae/CIVA 168, Food & Drug Administration 119, Jan Hinsch 212, John Reader 219cl, Lockheed Martin Corporation/NASA 163bl, Loren Winters/Visuals Unlimited, Inc. 46, Mauro Fermariello 243b, Maximilian Stock Ltd 216r, NASA 144c, 151, 162tl, 233, Natural History Museum, London 219cr, NYPL/Science Source 207, Schleichkorn/Custom Medical Stock Photo 269t, SIU 244l, Steve Gschmeissner 213l, 213c, Susumu Nishinaga 213r; **Shutterstock.com:** Ansis Klucis. 78c, Dieter H 106, Lucky Business 37, melis 40l, Monkey Business Images 266, Pete Saloutos. 32tl, Peter Bernik 13l, Vasilyev 181, Vereshchagin Dmitry 82l/3, Vlad61 235, Vladimir Sazonov 251br; **South Oxfordshire Archeological Group:** 191; **Sozaijiten:** 82l/4; **Stable Micro Systems:** 120t, 120b; **STFC:** 144t, 144b; **Surrey Satellite Technology Ltd:** 145r; **The Education Group:** 130c, 130r; **Tony Sherborne:** 40r; **University of York Science Education Group:** Dr Swinbank 92; **Veer/Corbis:** Elina Manninen 121cl, Greg Epperson 19c, Norbert Suto 32l, pedrosala 170, saddakos 121r, Stocksnapper 121cr; **Werner Forman Archive Ltd:** 218t, 218b; **www.dappolonia.com:** 198; **www.phys.unsw. edu.au/jw/patterns2.html:** E. Bossy and R. Carpentier 80 i, 80 ii, 80 iii, 80 iv, 80 vi; **Xylem Inc. 2014 – Bellingham + Stanley:** 128; **York Archaeological Trust:** 205t, 205b

Cover images: *Front:* **Shutterstock.com:** videodoctor

All other images © Pearson Education

Picture research by: Caitlin Swain

We are grateful to the following for permission to reproduce copyright material:

Figures
Figure 2.1b from Audacity®, Audacity® software is copyright © 1999-2015 Audacity Team. The name Audacity® is a registered trademark of Dominic Mazzoni. Website: http://audacity.sourceforge.net/. It is free software distributed under the terms of the GNU General Public License; Figure 4.25 Microsoft Excel screen shot frame, Microsoft product screenshot frame reprinted with permission from Microsoft Corporation; Figure 5.11 from Resistive tomography survey showing vertical 'slices', http://zond-geo. ru/wp-content/uploads/ZondRes2d_5.png, with permission from Alex Kaminsky, Zond Software Ltd; Figure 5.54 from Helical states of nonlocally interacting molecules and their linear stability: a geometric approach, *Journal of Physics A: Mathematical and Theoretical*, Volume 44, Issue 5 (Benoit, S., Holm, D.D. and Putkaradze, V. 2011), IOP Publishing, http://dx.doi.org/10.1088/1751- 8113/44/5/055201; Figure 6.17 after Stress-strain tests on bone samples, http://hansmalab.physics.ucsb.edu/macrobone.html, image from Paul Hansma's Research Group; Figure 6.22b from Test Certificate, Orthoplastics PUR - 1020 Medical Grade UHMWPE, Orthoplastics Ltd.

Text
Pearson Education for the use of Edexcel copyright material. Extract on page 19 Copyright © 2015, Johanna Kirkham.

Every effort has been made to contact copyright holders of material reproduced in this book. Any omissions will be rectified in subsequent printings if notice is given to the publishers.

Many people from schools, colleges, universities, industries and the professions have contributed to the Salters Horners Advanced Physics (SHAP) project and the preparation of SHAP course materials.

Authors of this edition

Jonathan Allday (The Royal Hospital School, Ipswich)
Christina Astin (The King's School, Canterbury)
Hovan Catchactoor (Reigate College, Surrey)
Ian Francis (Rode, Somerset)
Helen Hare (Rooks Heath College, South Harrow)
Neil Jaques (Bancroft's School, Essex)
Jan Hatherell (Hardenhuish School, Wiltshire)
David Neal (Barton on Humber, Lincs)
Chris Pambou (City & Islington College, London)
Siôn Peters-Flynn (John Leggott College, Scunthorpe)
Nicky Robinson (Reigate College, Surrey)
David Swinscoe (City & Islington College, London)
Bernard Taylor (Bede College, Teesside)
Carol Tear (York)

Project director and general editor

Elizabeth Swinbank (University of York)

Acknowledgements

We would like to thank the following for their help and support with the preparation of this edition.

Joanna MacDonald (University of York)
Robin Millar (University of York)
Audrey Strong (The Salters Institute)

Authors of previous editions

This third edition is based on previous editions and incorporates the work of the following authors:

Jonathan Allday	Alasdair Kennedy	Tony Sherborne
Chris Butlin	Bob Kibble	Richard Skelding
Steven Chapman	Paul Lee	Sandy Stephens
Steve Cobb	Maureen Maybank	Wendy Swarbrick
Tony Connell	Averil Macdonald	Elizabeth Swinbank
Howard Darwin	Graham Meredith	David Swinscoe
Nick Fisher	David Neal	Carol Tear
Frances Green	Chris Pambou	Clare Thomson
Greg Hughes	Kerry Parker	Nigel Wallis
Neil Jaques	David Sang	

Sponsors

We are grateful to the following for sponsorship that has continued to support the Salters Horners Advanced Physics project after its initial development and has enabled the production of this edition.

The Worshipful Company of Horners
The Worshipful Company of Salters

Advisory Committee for the initial development

Prof. Frank Close
Prof. Cyril Hilsum FRS
Prof. Robin Millar
Prof. Sir Derek Roberts FRS

Contents

CONTENTS

HOW TO USE THIS BOOK

Context-led study

This book covers the first year of a two-year A level course and the AS. SHAP is a context-led approach to the Edexcel AS and A level Physics specification.

Each chapter starts by looking at particular situations in which physics is used or studied, and then develops the physics you need to learn to explore this 'context'.

We have tried to select contexts to give you some idea of how physics can help improve people's lives, how physics is used in engineering and technology, and how physics research extends our understanding of the physical world at a fundamental level. These will show you just some of the many physics-related careers and further study that might be open to you in the future.

Within each chapter, you will develop your knowledge and understanding on one or more areas of physics. In later chapters, you will meet many of these ideas again – in a completely different context – and develop them further. In this way, you will gradually build up your knowledge and understanding of physics and learn to apply key principles of physics to a variety of contexts. Each chapter includes the following features:

Main text

This presents the context of each teaching unit and explains the relevant physics, as you need it.

Within the main text, some words are printed in **bold**. These are key terms relating to the physics. We suggest that you make your own summary of these terms (and others if you wish) as you go along. Then you can refer back to your summary when you revisit a similar area of physics later in the course and when you revise for exams.

There are references to relevant websites in this book. We have made the links available on our website at www.pearsonhotlinks.co.uk. Search for Salters Horners AS/A level Physics or ISBN 978 1 447 99098 7.

Activities

The text refers to many Activities. These include practical work, the use of ICT, reading, writing, data handling and discussion. Some activities are best carried out with one or more other students, while others are intended for you to do on your own. For some activities, there are handout sheets giving further information, details about apparatus and so on.

> ### ⚙ ACTIVITY 4 NON-UNIFORM MOTION
> Use ticker tape, a stop-frame video or a camcorder to record your own motion when sprinting from a crouched start and plot a graph of your displacement against time.
>
> Calculate your velocity in each small interval between dots or between frames, and so also calculate your acceleration in each small time interval.

Questions

There are two types of Questions in this book:

- Some are intended for you to do as you go along, as a self-check or perhaps for homework; the answers to these questions appear at the end of each chapter.

- Questions on the whole chapter are intended as a summary to what you have learned in each chapter: your teacher will provide the answers to these questions.

Once you have had a go at a question, check your answer. If you have gone wrong, use the answer (and the relevant part of the book chapter) to help you sort out your ideas. Working in this way is not cheating; rather, it helps you to learn.

MATHS REFERENCE

Manipulating powers on a calculator

See Maths note 1.4

Maths notes

Maths references in the margin will direct you to the Maths notes at the end of the book, which are to help you with the maths needed in physics. This may involve calculations, rearranging equations, plotting graphs, and so on. You will probably have covered most of what is required at GCSE, but you may not be used to applying it in physics. The Maths notes summarise the key maths ideas that you need and show you how to apply them to situations in physics.

PRACTICAL SKILLS REFERENCE

Recording data

See Practical skills note 3.2

Practical skills references

These references in the margin direct you to guidance notes on practical skills at the end of the book. The notes set out a framework for carrying out practical work and give guidance on particular aspects of such work. They draw attention to points that you need to consider when preparing for and carrying out the task and when writing a report.

STUDY NOTE

For guidance on using *Audacity*, see *The Sound of Music* Additional Sheet 2.

Study notes

These notes in the margin are intended to help you get to grips with the physics. For example, they indicate links with other parts of the course.

Getting the most from your ActiveBook

Your ActiveBook is the perfect way to personalise your learning as you progress through your A level Physics course. You can:

- access your content online, anytime, anywhere;
- use the inbuilt highlighting and annotation tools to personalise the content and make it really relevant to you;
- search the content quickly.

Highlight tool

Use this to pick out key terms or topics so you are ready and prepared for revision.

Annotations tool

Use this to add your own notes, for example links to your wider reading, such as websites or other files. Or make a note to remind yourself about work that you need to do.

Link the learning

At the end of each chapter there is the opportunity to revisit and consolidate the physics you have already learned. The questions and activities will help you connect different aspects of your learning from across the course and apply your knowledge to new contexts. A table of achievements shows exactly what material you've covered in the chapter, so you can recap what you've learned at glance.

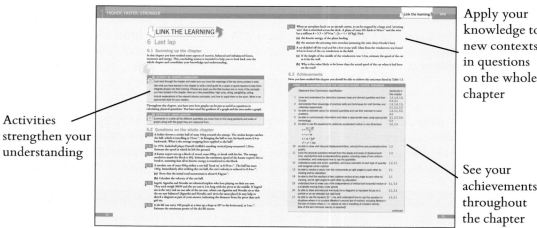

Activities strengthen your understanding

Apply your knowledge to new contexts in questions on the whole chapter

See your achievements throughout the chapter

Further investigations

Alongside your A-level work, you might have the opportunity to carry out a major piece of investigative work for an Extended Project qualification (EPQ).

As you proceed through the course, keep a note of any areas you might like to pursue; we have included some suggestions under the heading Further investigations, but any unanswered question that intrigues you could form the basis of an EPQ.

FURTHER INVESTIGATION

Explore the behaviour of various materials that appear 'bone-like', such as cuttle-fish bone (available from pet shops), seaside rock and 'oasis' (used in flower arranging). Try to measure the Young modulus and ultimate compressive strength. Observe the way they fracture. Comment on their resemblance (or otherwise) to real bone.

WORKING AS A PHYSICIST

Throughout this course, you will be developing your knowledge and understanding of what it means to work scientifically in the context of physics and its applications.

The examples, questions and activities in each chapter will help you to become increasingly competent in manipulating quantities and their units, in planning, carrying out and evaluating practical experiments, and in communicating your knowledge and understanding of physics. The *Maths notes* are written to help you to build up your skills in handling quantities and units, and the *Practical skills* references are designed to support your investigative and practical work.

You will also learn more about the ways in which the scientific community, and society as a whole, use physics and contribute to its progress. You will study many applications of physics in a wide variety of situations, and you will see how the risks and benefits of those applications are evaluated. You will also learn more about the ways in which the scientific community operates to validate new knowledge relating to physics, and to ensure that work on physics and its applications is carried out with integrity.

By the time you have completed your AS or A level course, you will have developed your knowledge of *Working as a Physicist*, and these *Achievements* will be tested in the examinations. Table 1 lists the requirements for *Working as a Physicist*, copied from the examination specification, and refers to sections of the book where they are addressed. Note that these are not *all* the places that involve *Working as a Physicist* – that would make Table 1 very large. Rather, Table 1 lists the sections where aspects of *Working as a Physicist* are first introduced, where they are treated in most detail or where there are activities or questions specifically designed to help with these parts of your course. As you progress through the course, you will revisit these statements several times, helping you to build up your skills and to develop a broad and deep knowledge of what it means to work as a physicist. The lists of *Achievements* at the end of the chapters include some further examples of where particular aspects of *Working as a Physicist* are addressed.

Table 1 *Achievements* for *Working as a Physicist*

Statement from examination specification		Chapter	Section(s)
1	know and understand the distinction between base and derived quantities and their SI units	Maths notes	2
		HFS	1.4, 2.3, 3.1
		MUS	2.2
		EAT	2.2
		SPC	2.1, 2.3
		DIG	1.2
2	demonstrate their knowledge of practical skills and techniques for both familiar and unfamiliar experiments	Practical skills	all
		HFS	1.3, 2.2
		MUS	1.4, 2.1
		EAT	2.2, 3.2, 4.1, 4.2
		SPC	2.2, 3.2
		DIG	1.2, 2.3
		SUR	2.3, 3.3
3	be able to estimate values for physical quantities and use their estimate to solve problems	HFS	3.3
		EAT	2.2, 5.4
		SUR	2.2
4	understand the limitations of physical measurement and apply these limitations to practical situations	Practical skills	4
		Maths notes	7
		EAT	1.1, 2.2, 4.1, 4.2
		SPC	2.2, 4.2
		DIG	1.2, 2.3
		SUR	2.3

Statement from examination specification		Chapter	Section(s)
5	be able to communicate information and ideas in appropriate ways using appropriate terminology	HFS	5.3
		MUS	2.2, 3.2
		EAT	5.2, 5.3
		SPC	4.2, 5.2
		DIG	1.4, 2.1
		SUR	2.2, 3.4, 5.1
6	*understand applications and implications of science and evaluate their associated benefits and risks	SUR	1.2, 2.1, 3.4
7	understand the role of the scientific community in validating new knowledge and ensuring integrity	DIG	4.2, 4.3
8	understand the ways in which society uses science to inform decision making.	SPC	3.1
		SUR	1.2, 3.4

* All the chapters discuss applications and implications of physics. These references indicate where risk and benefit are discussed.

HIGHER, FASTER, STRONGER

Why a chapter called *Higher, Faster, Stronger?*

'Unthinkable' they said; 'Surely no-one will ever run a mile in under four minutes.' Not only were the commentators proved wrong in 1954, but in the 60 years since then, 16 seconds have been lopped off the world record mile. More impressive still, a full six minutes have been hacked off the women's 5000 metres record. Off the track, the story is the same. Before the authorities stepped in and changed the design of the javelin, javelin throws were beginning to endanger the crowd at the other end of the stadium.

What's going on? Are we becoming a more powerful species? The place to search for an explanation of this record-breaking frenzy is in the laboratory. With physiology, psychology and physics, science has revolutionised sport, giving us a better understanding of how to train winners using physical and mental processes (Figure 1.1a, b, c).

The emergence of the new scientific discipline of sports science helped to build today's champions. Using tools such as computer-linked video, researchers can now analyse the movements involved in sporting activity in minute detail. This allows trainers to correct even tiny errors in an athlete's performance. Advances in the science of materials have brought equally dramatic changes, with almost every conceivable property of an athlete's clothing and footwear optimised for performance. With so much resting on winning, measurement technology now enables races to be decided on differences of just a few milliseconds.

Higher, Faster, Stronger is (loosely) the Olympic motto. In this chapter, you will see how many basic physics concepts can be applied to sports ranging from sprinting to bungee jumping in order to help athletes go 'higher, faster, stronger'.

Figure 1.1a Highest

Figure 1.1b Fastest

Figure 1.1c Strongest

OVERVIEW OF PHYSICS PRINCIPLES AND TECHNIQUES

In this chapter, you will study the physics of motion, force and energy. You may be familiar with some of the ideas from GCSE. Here, you will deepen your understanding of these concepts by applying them to solve real problems. Many of the concepts, such as force and energy, are fundamental to the whole of physics, and you will meet them in almost every part of the course.

You will have many opportunities for practical work, investigations and computer datalogging. You will learn how to extract additional information from a set of measurements, and you will also use computer software to analyse various sporting activities, just as sports science researchers do.

In later chapters you will do further work on:

● vectors in *Probing the Heart of Matter*

● graphs in *Digging Up the Past*, *The Medium is the Message* and *Probing the Heart of Matter*

● kinematics and dynamics in *Good Enough to Eat* and *Transport on Track*

● kinetic energy and work in *Transport on Track*, *Probing the Heart of Matter* and *Reach for the Stars*

● properties of materials in *Good Enough to Eat*, *Spare Part Surgery* and *Build or Bust*?

1 Running

1.1 Biomechanics

'Super Saturday' became 'Golden Saturday' at the London 2012 Olympics when Team GB bagged three gold medals within the space of an unforgettable hour at the athletics stadium. Jessica Ennis claimed gold in the heptathlon and Mo Farah did likewise in the 10 000 m. Sandwiched between the two was a gold medal in the men's long jump for Greg Rutherford, who jumped 8.31 m to gain Britain's first gold medal in the event since 1964.

To be a good jumper, Greg Rutherford had to train to be a very fast sprinter. He also had to develop very careful timing in his jumping technique. The science of biomechanics is devoted to trying to help sportsmen and women get the best possible result by helping them improve their technique. Biomechanics focuses on the forces on a human body and sports equipment, and on the effects of these forces.

You can use transducers to measure external forces, such as those exerted by a cyclist on a pedal, and then convert the forces into electrical signals. Internal forces exerted by the muscles and applied to the bones and joints in the human body are harder to measure directly (transducers would have to be implanted). However, they can be calculated indirectly by a technique known as inverse dynamics, for which you need the mass of each part of the human body and the accelerated motion. You can also use position–time data from video to calculate accelerations of each segment of the body.

We will look at some examples of inverse dynamics later on in this part of the chapter. First, we will see how to record and analyse motion.

Figure 1.2 Team GB Olympic gold medal winner Greg Rutherford

1.2 Describing motion

The performance of an athlete in a running event is usually recorded simply as the time taken to complete the distance. Table 1.1 lists some times for the men's and women's 10 000 metre world record. It has been suggested that women will soon be running faster than men.

By studying physics, you are following in the footsteps of one of the world's best athletes. Durham physics graduate Jonathan Edwards became world record holder in the triple jump in the summer of 1995 at the World Athletics Championships in Gothenburg, Sweden. He leapt his way to into the record books by jumping in excess of 18 m. In the space of a couple of months he became an MBE and BBC Sports Personality of the Year for 1995. He also won the silver medal in the Olympics in Atlanta the following year.

Year	Time/minutes women	Time/minutes men
1970	35.50	27.65
1975	34.02	27.50
1980	31.75	27.37
1985	30.98	27.22
1990	30.22	27.13
1995	29.52	26.72
2000	29.52	26.38
2005	29.52	26.30
2010	29.32	26.18

Table 1.1 World record times for the 10 000 m event

⚙️ **ACTIVITY 1 RECORD TIMES**

Plot the data from Table 1.1 on a single set of axes. Choose a sensible scale for your graph and label it clearly.

Continue (extrapolate) each graph forward in time and discuss (with reasons) whether you think women will one day beat the men in the 10 000 m event.

Speed

Data such as those in Table 1.1 allow us to calculate the average speed of an athlete:

average speed = distance travelled ÷ time taken   (1)

Expressed in the symbols that are normally used, Equation 1 becomes:

$$v = \frac{\Delta s}{\Delta t}$$ (1a)

The symbol Δ is the Greek capital letter delta, which is used to mean 'change in' or 'difference in', so if s represents the athlete's position then Δs means 'change in position', i.e. the distance travelled. Δt represents the time interval. Notice that Δ is *not* a number multiplying s or t.

In the right direction

An orienteer runs from post A 300 m, then 500 m, then 400 m, finally reaching post B. How far is she from the first post A? Figure 1.3 shows some possibilities. You do not know how far she is from A, because the directions were not specified. An orienteer would use a compass to get her bearings and find out which direction to travel in. She would need to specify the distance to be travelled in a given direction.

When we mean 'distance in a specified direction' we use the word **displacement**. Similarly, speed in a specified direction is called **velocity**. Physical quantities where *direction is as important as size* are called **vector quantities**. (The size of a vector is often called its **magnitude**.) A quantity where there is no question of a direction being involved is called a **scalar**. A good example of a scalar quantity is *temperature*; for instance, 5 °C south-east hardly makes sense. When measuring vector quantities you need to pay attention to how you direct the measuring instrument: as a rather trivial example, you can hardly measure an object's weight with a horizontal spring balance. Yet if a patient's temperature is being taken, it does not matter in which direction the thermometer is pointing out of their mouth.

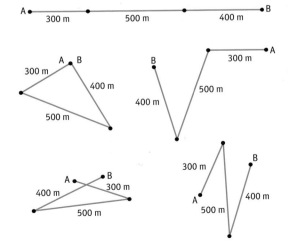

Figure 1.3 Some possible locations of post B if directions are not specified

STUDY NOTE

To review your knowledge and understanding of speed, see HFS Additional Sheet 1.

MATHS REFERENCE

The symbol Δ

See Maths note 0.2

STUDY NOTE

To review your knowledge and understanding of displacement and velocity vectors, see HFS Additional Sheet 2.

Acceleration

STUDY NOTE

In Part 1 of this chapter we will be concerned only with motion in one dimension (back and forth along a straight line), and we will use positive and negative signs to denote the direction.

In Part 2 of this chapter you will see how to deal with vectors in two dimensions and use notation that distinguishes vectors from scalar quantities.

STUDY NOTE

To review your knowledge and understanding of acceleration, see HFS Additional Sheet 3.

When we say that something is moving, we are not giving much information away. Is an athlete travelling at constant speed? Is she changing direction? Is she speeding up or slowing down? When we consider acceleration, we are interested in how the velocity changes:

$$\text{change in velocity} = \text{final velocity} - \text{initial velocity} \tag{2}$$

Conventionally, u represents the initial velocity and v the final velocity (it may help to think of u coming before v in the alphabet), and Δv represents the change in velocity. We can write Equation 2 as:

$$\Delta v = v - u \tag{2a}$$

This leads to a definition of **acceleration**:

$$\text{acceleration} = \text{change in velocity} \div \text{time taken} \tag{3}$$

In symbols:

$$a = \frac{\Delta u}{\Delta t} \qquad \text{or} \qquad a = \frac{(v-u)}{\Delta t} \tag{3a}$$

Another useful version of Equation 3 is:

$$v = u + a\Delta t \tag{3b}$$

Notice that we use change of velocity and not change in speed. Acceleration is a vector of quantity, having both magnitude and direction. Equation 3 can only be used in situations with **uniform acceleration**, as in Table 1.2, which shows motion with an acceleration of $2\,\text{m s}^{-2}$, i.e. the velocity is increasing by $2\,\text{m s}^{-1}$ every second.

An important example of uniform acceleration is that of an object in **free fall**, i.e. moving only under the influence of gravity. In the initial part of a parachute jump or a bungee jump, you are in free fall, accelerating vertically downwards with the **acceleration due to gravity**, symbolised by g, which (close to the Earth's surface) is always $9.81\,\text{m s}^{-2}$.

Time	Velocity
0 s	$1.5\,\text{m s}^{-1}$
1 s	$1.5\,\text{m s}^{-1} + 2\,\text{m s}^{-1} = 3.5\,\text{m s}^{-1}$
2 s	$3.5\,\text{m s}^{-1} + 2\,\text{m s}^{-1} = 5.5\,\text{m s}^{-1}$
3 s	$5.5\,\text{m s}^{-1} + 2\,\text{m s}^{-1} = 7.5\,\text{m s}^{-1}$

Table 1.2 Changing velocity

If an object accelerates uniformly, its average speed is given by:

$$\text{average speed} = \frac{1}{2}(u + v) \tag{4}$$

From Equation 1 this gives us:

$$s = \frac{1}{2}(u + v)t \tag{5}$$

⚙ **ACTIVITY 3 FREE FALL**
Carry out some simple activities to illustrate the constant acceleration of objects falling under gravity.

QUESTIONS

Q 1 A jogger who is initially running at $2.0\,\text{m s}^{-1}$ accelerates uniformly at a rate of $1.5\,\text{m s}^{-2}$ for $3.0\,\text{s}$. Calculate his final velocity.

Q 2 How fast will a bungee jumper be moving after he has been in free fall for $2.5\,\text{s}$?

Q 3 A squash ball travelling at $9.0\,\text{m s}^{-1}$ horizontally to the right is hit by a racket that stops it in $0.003\,\text{s}$. Calculate the acceleration.

Q 4 A tennis ball moving to the right at a velocity of $5.0\,\text{m s}^{-1}$ is struck by a tennis racket and accelerated to the left, leaving the tennis racket at a speed of $25\,\text{m s}^{-1}$ to the left. If the contact time is $0.012\,\text{s}$, calculate the average acceleration.

> **MATHS REFERENCE**
> Index notation and powers of 10
> See Maths note 1.1
> Index notation and units
> See Maths note 2.2

1.3 Motion graphs

Graphs are often used to represent motion. Not only do they give a visual record, they also enable us to extract additional information about the motion. Figure 1.4 shows two **displacement–time graphs**. In Figure 1.4(a), the velocity is constant: the graph is a straight line, and dividing any given displacement by Δt gives the same answer for the velocity – the velocity is equal to the **gradient** of the displacement–time graph.

> **MATHS REFERENCE**
> Gradient of a linear graph
> See Maths note 5.3

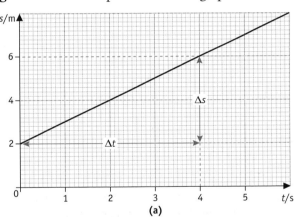
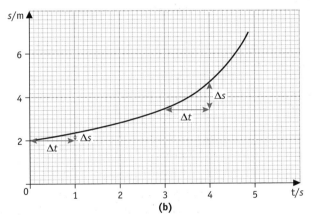

Figure 1.4 Displacement–time graphs for motion with (a) uniform velocity (b) non-uniform velocity

In Figure 1.4(b) you can tell that the velocity is non-uniform because the graph does not show equal displacements in equal time intervals; in other words, the graph is not straight.

A calculation of $\dfrac{\Delta s}{\Delta t}$ gives the average velocity in a given time interval Δt.

Figure 1.5 shows three **velocity–time graphs**. In Figure 1.5(a) the velocity does not change – the acceleration is zero. Figure 1.5(b) is a plot of the data in Table 1.2: the acceleration is uniform (the velocity changes by equal amounts in equal time intervals) so the graph is a straight line, and dividing any given change in velocity Δv by the corresponding time interval Δt gives the same answer – the acceleration is the gradient of the velocity–time graph. In Figure 1.5(c), the graph is not straight because the acceleration is not uniform – the velocity does not change by equal amounts in equal time intervals.

In everyday language, 'accelerate' simply means 'get faster' and 'decelerate' means 'get slower'. In physics we tend always to use the term 'accelerate' with appropriate signs to indicate its direction. A negative acceleration is *not* necessarily a slowing down – if something that is already moving in the negative direction experiences acceleration in the same direction, it will get faster.

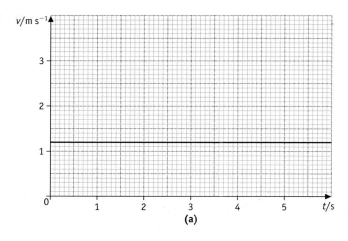

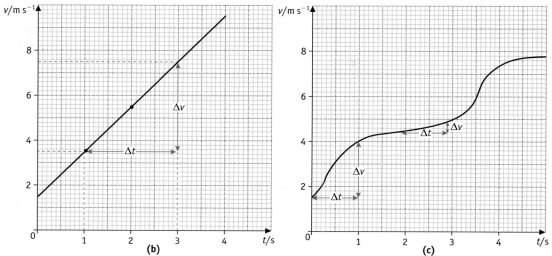

Figure 1.5 Velocity–time graphs for motion with (a) zero acceleration, (b) uniform (non-zero) acceleration and (c) non-uniform acceleration

QUESTIONS

Q 5 Find the velocity of the motion shown in Figure 1.4(a) by (a) using the values of Δs and Δt shown and (b) drawing another triangle on a copy of Figure 1.4(a) that has a different Δs and Δt.

Q 6 How would you interpret (a) a displacement–time graph that sloped more steeply than Figure 1.4(a) and (b) a displacement–time graph that sloped down from left to right?

Q 7 Calculate the acceleration of the motion shown in Figure 1.5(b).

Q 8 How would you show a negative acceleration on a velocity–time graph?

Small changes

Athletes such as sprinters, hurdlers, triple jumpers and so on improve their technique by observing their motion on a video playback frame by frame or in a strobe photograph. This allows them to study their motion in detail and then work with a coach to develop ways of improving their technique. In Activities 4 and 5 you will do something similar, analysing motion in some detail.

In most real-life examples of motion, the velocity is not uniform. Usually there is some acceleration from rest, and often the velocity changes before the final deceleration to rest. Acceleration, too, is not usually uniform. It can change because of wind resistance or changing muscle effort, or running on a slope. However, it is still possible to use Equation 2 if you split the motion into time intervals where the velocity is *nearly* uniform (as in Figure 1.4(b)). Likewise, acceleration can be calculated using Equation 3 for a small time interval where it is *nearly* uniform, as in Figure 1.5(c).

⚙ **ACTIVITY 4 NON-UNIFORM MOTION**

Use ticker tape, a stop-frame video or a camcorder to record your own motion when sprinting from a crouched start. Plot a graph of your displacement against time.

Calculate your velocity in each small interval between dots or between frames, and then also calculate your acceleration in each small time interval.

PRACTICAL SKILLS REFERENCE

Carrying out practical work

See Practical skills notes 3.1–3.2

Analysis and interpretation of data

See Practical skills note 4.1

If you have many very small time intervals, you need to perform lots of calculations. This can be very boring and so a computer program is usually used. The *Tracker* video analysis and modeling tool website includes a collection of mechanics videos and analysis software for free download. You can also use the *Tracker* software to analyse your own videos.

⚙ **ACTIVITY 5 PRODUCING GRAPHS OF MOTION**

Use *Tracker* or similar software to produce graphs showing the displacement, velocity and acceleration for one or more of the following (see Figure 1.6): sprint start, squash, soccer, tennis. Alternatively, use a motion sensor to generate graphs of your own motion. With *Logger Pro* you can synchronise the motion sensor data to your video clip to get a closer analysis of how your body moves. Keep a copy of your graphs for use in later activities.

STUDY NOTE

For further information about *Tracker*, see HFS Additional Sheet 4.

(a)

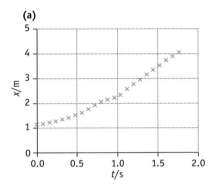

(b)

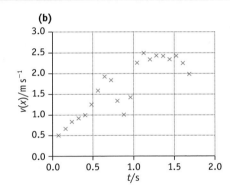

(c)

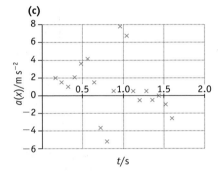

Figure 1.6 The motion of a sprinter shown as graphs of (a) displacement–time, (b) velocity–time and (c) acceleration–time

In Activity 4 you found the **instantaneous velocity** by dividing a small change in displacement by a small change in time. If you are working directly form a curved displacement–time graph, it is difficult to read values that are very close together. It is better to draw a **tangent** (a straight line touching the curve) at the required point, as shown in Figure 1.7, and then to work out its gradient. Likewise, you can find the **instantaneous acceleration** by drawing a tangent to a velocity–time graph and working out its gradient.

⚙ **ACTIVITY 6 TANGENTS AND GRADIENTS**

By drawing tangents on a displacement–time graph from Activity 5, find the velocity at two different times. Compare your answers with the velocities at those times calculated by *Tracker* or similar software (if used). Similarly, find the acceleration at two times by drawing tangents on a velocity–time graph.

STUDY NOTE

If a curve is described by a mathematical equation, then its gradient at any point can be found using calculus. See HFS Additional Sheet 5.

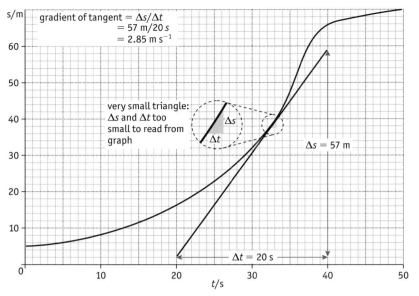

Figure 1.7 Working out instantaneous velocity from a displacement–time graph

Going the distance

You have seen how to use a record of displacement to deduce an athlete's velocity, and how to use velocity data, in turn, to find acceleration. But can the same thing be done in reverse? Can a record of velocity be used to deduce displacement?

In Figure 1.8(a) the displacement in the first 4 s is:

$$1.5 \, \text{m s}^{-1} \times 4.0 \, \text{s} = 6.0 \, \text{m}$$

This displacement is equal to the area of the shaded portion of the graph. In Figure 1.8(b) the velocity is not uniform, but if we choose a time interval small enough that the velocity v is *nearly* uniform, then the displacement in that small time interval Δt is given by:

$$\Delta s = v \Delta t$$

This is equal to the area of the narrow shaded strip. The total displacement in a longer time interval can be found by adding up all the areas of the narrow strips (each with a different height). In other words, displacement can be found from the **area under a velocity–time graph**.

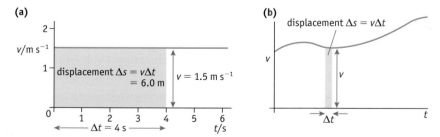

Figure 1.8 Working out displacement from a velocity–time graph (a) with **uniform velocity** and (b) with non-uniform velocity

Uniform acceleration

If the acceleration is uniform, then the velocity–time graph is a straight line, as in Figure 1.9, and the displacement can be found by adding together the areas of the rectangle and the triangle as shown.

Expressing the areas of the rectangle and triangle in symbols leads to another useful equation for uniformly accelerated motion, which lets us calculate displacement directly without going via a graph:

$$\Delta s = u \Delta t + \frac{1}{2} a (\Delta t)^2 \tag{6}$$

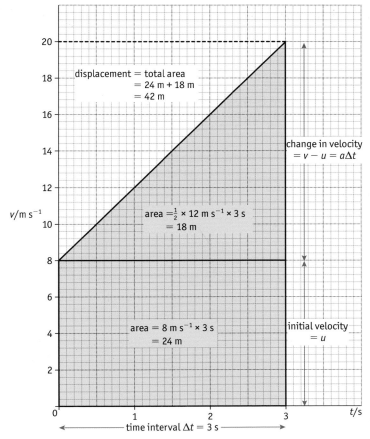

Figure 1.9 The area under a straight velocity–time graph

Usually you will see Equation 6 written using just t (not Δt) to represent the overall time taken and s to represent the overall displacement:

$$s = ut + \frac{1}{2}at^2 \qquad (6a)$$

Alternatively, use Equations 3b and 5:

$$s = \frac{1}{2}(u + v)t \qquad \text{(Equation 5)}$$

$$s = \frac{1}{2}u + \frac{1}{2}vt$$

$$= \frac{1}{2}u + \frac{1}{2}(u + at)t$$

$$= ut + \frac{1}{2}at^2 \qquad \text{(Equation 6a)}$$

Equations 3b and 6a can be combined to produce another useful relationship that relates change of velocity directly to the displacement:

$$v^2 = u^2 + 2as \qquad (7)$$

You can derive Equation 7 by squaring Equation 3b (and dropping the Δ):

$$v^2 = (u + at)^2 = u^2 + 2aut + a^2t^2$$

and by multiplying Equation 6 by $2a$:

$$2as = 2aut + a^2t^2$$

Comparing the right-hand sides leads to Equation 7.

STUDY NOTE

For more about using the area under this graph, see HFS Additional Sheet 6.

MATHS REFERENCE

Algebra and elimination

See Maths note 3.4

PRACTICAL SKILLS REFERENCE

Scientific questions and information research

See Practical skills note 1.1

Carrying out practical work

See Practical skills notes 3.1–3.2

Analysis and interpretation of data

See Practical skills note 4.1

Conclusion and evaluation

See Practical skills notes 5.1–5.2

STUDY NOTE

If a curve is described by a mathematical equation, then the area under any part can be found using calculus. See HFS Additional Sheet 7.

⚙ **ACTIVITY 7 FINDING *g* BY TIMING FREE FALL**

Carry out some explorations of freely falling objects that show how the time of fall is related to the distance fallen. Use your results to find the acceleration due to gravity.

Non-uniform acceleration

If the velocity–time graph is curved, then the area can be found by counting squares on the graph paper or by using a computer program to work out and add together the areas of many very narrow strips.

When you are counting squares, the vertical axis must start at zero, otherwise the height of each strip does not represent the velocity. Also, be careful to use the scales of the graph and not the actual sizes of the squares.

QUESTIONS

Q 9 A sprinter runs at a uniform speed of $8.00 \, \mathrm{m\,s^{-1}}$ as she approaches the finish, then puts on a spurt to overtake her rival and accelerates at $0.70 \, \mathrm{m\,s^{-2}}$ for 3 s before crossing the line. What is her final velocity, and what distance does she cover in the final three seconds of her sprint?

Q 10 Figure 1.10 shows velocity–time graphs for two athletes in a race. After 30 seconds, who is ahead and by approximately how much?

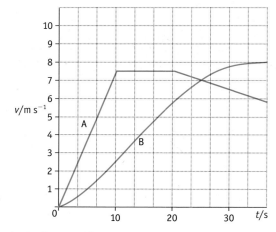

Figure 1.10 Velocity–time graphs for Question 10

1.4 Force and acceleration: Newton's laws of motion

Newton's first and second laws of motion

You have seen how to calculate acceleration from measurements of velocity or displacement. Sports scientists often find it useful to go one stage further and use so-called inverse dynamics to work out the forces that provide the accelerations, using the relationship

$$F = ma \tag{8}$$

where m is the mass of the accelerated object and F the net force acting on it. Like acceleration, force is a vector, and when dealing with one-dimensional motion we can use positive and negative signs to indicate the direction of a force. It is sometimes useful to combine Equations 3a and 8 to give:

$$F = ma = \frac{m\Delta v}{\Delta t} \tag{8a}$$

Equation 8 expresses **Newton's second law of motion**.

STUDY NOTE

To review your knowledge and understanding of force and acceleration, see HFS Additional Sheet 8.

Newton's first law of motion states that an object moves at constant velocity or remains at rest unless an unbalanced force acts on it, while the second law relates to the size of the unbalanced force to the change that it causes.

QUESTIONS

Q 11   When starting a race, a sprinter of mass 65 kg accelerates forwards at $2.0\,\mathrm{m\,s^{-2}}$ (Figure 1.11). What must be the net forward force acting on her body?

Q 12   A tennis ball of mass 120 g approaches a racket at $5.0\,\mathrm{m\,s^{-1}}$ and is hit back in the opposite direction at $25\,\mathrm{m\,s^{-1}}$ (Figure 1.12). If the contact time with the racket is 0.015 s, what is the average force exerted on the ball by the racket?

Figure 1.11 A sprint start

Figure 1.12 A tennis ball in contact with a racket

⚙ ACTIVITY 8   INVERSE DYNAMICS
Using your results from Activity 5, estimate the net force acting to accelerate the person or object you studied. You might need to estimate the mass of the sprinter or the squash, tennis or soccer ball.

⚙ ACTIVITY 9   MEASURING FORCES DIRECTLY
Use a force sensor with graphing software or bathroom scales calibrated in newtons to measure the forces involved in various activities such as jumping, throwing and catching.

In Activity 9 you probably took it for granted that the bathroom scales or force sensor register a non-zero vertical force even when you are standing still. But how does this tie in with Newton's first and second laws of motion, and Equation 8? The explanation involves some careful thinking about forces – and another of Newton's laws of motion.

Weight and gravitational field

The relationship between force, mass and acceleration (Equation 8) gives us another way of looking at free fall. Close to the Earth's surface, *any* object in free fall has an acceleration of $9.81\,\mathrm{m\,s^{-2}}$. The gravitational force responsible for the acceleration must, therefore, depend on the object's mass: an object of mass 1 kg must experience a force of 9.81 N, a 2 kg object must experience a force of $2 \times 9.81\,\mathrm{N}$, and so on. We can express this by saying that, close to its surface, the Earth's **gravitational field strength**, symbolised by g, is $9.81\,\mathrm{N\,kg^{-1}}$.

We call the gravitational force acting on an object its **weight**. This can be confusing because in everyday language we use the word 'weight' to mean the same thing as mass. Weight in measured in newtons and is a vector (it acts downwards). The weight W of an object of mass m is given by a special case of Equation 8:

$$W = mg \tag{9}$$

QUESTION

Q 13 Estimate your own weight.

If gravity was the only force acting then a downward acceleration would result, so if you are standing still your weight must be balanced by an upward force. How does this come about?

Pairs of forces: Newton's third law of motion

The sprinter in Question 11 exerts a 'backwards' force on the starting block, but he accelerates because the block (and the Earth to which it is attached) exerts a 'forwards' force on him. This is an example of **Newton's third law of motion**, which can be stated as 'all forces involve the interaction between two objects' or 'all forces come in pairs'. The two forces are always:

- between two different objects

- equal in size

- opposite in direction

- of the same type (e.g. both electrostatic or both gravitational).

In the example of the sprinter, he pushes backwards on the starting-block-plus-Earth with a force of 130 N (Figure 1.13), and the block pushes him forwards also with a force of 130 N (Figure 1.13). A force of 130 N on a 65 kg person gives him a significant acceleration, but the same size force acting on the block-plus-Earth produces such a minute acceleration that it is not detectable.

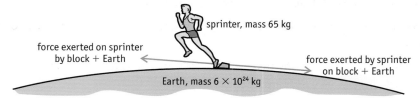

sprinter, mass 65 kg

force exerted on sprinter by block + Earth

force exerted by sprinter on block + Earth

Earth, mass 6×10^{24} kg

Figure 1.13 Forces involved in the interaction between sprinter and starting block

Consider another example: when a bungee jumper is in free fall, there is a pair of gravitational forces acting between him and the Earth. The downward force on the bungee jumper (his weight) produces an acceleration of $9.81 \, \text{m s}^{-2}$, but an upward force of the same size acting on the Earth produces no noticeable effect (Figure 1.14).

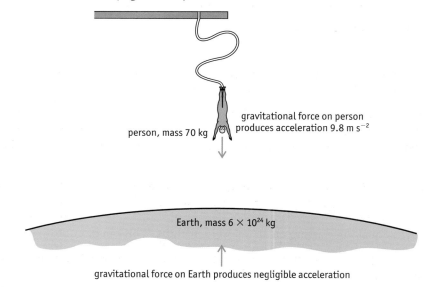

person, mass 70 kg

gravitational force on person produces acceleration $9.8 \, \text{m s}^{-2}$

Earth, mass 6×10^{24} kg

gravitational force on Earth produces negligible acceleration

Figure 1.14 Forces involved in the interaction between bungee jumper and Earth

If you stand on the floor, there is still a pair of gravitational forces acting between you and the Earth. But now you exert a downward force on the floor (equal to your weight) and the compressed material in the floor exerts an equal force upwards on you – you and the floor are interacting according to Newton's third law. In Activity 9, you recorded the force exerted by the scales (or a force sensor): you and the scales interact via a pair of forces, and in turn the scales and the floor also interact. If you are at rest, the force registered is equal to your own weight. However, if you jump off the scales you do so by pushing downwards with additional force, and the scales in turn exert an upward force upon you to produce an upward acceleration.

The forces involved in the interactions between athletes and their surroundings are not only important in producing the required accelerations. They are also responsible for injuries – if you hit something with a force, you also experience a force of the same size exerted by the object.

QUESTIONS

Q 14 In line with Newton's third law, identify the pairs of forces that involve a javelin thrower and say what type of force they are.

Q 15 A squash player hits a ball of mass 0.024 kg with her racket. The ball is decelerated at 12 200 m s^{-2}. Calculate the size and direction of the force exerted on the ball, and write down the size and direction of the force exerted by the ball on the racket.

Q 16 **(a)** What are the pairs of 'Newton's third law' forces involved when a (not very good) diver **(i)** is in free fall and then **(ii)** splashes into the water?

   (b) Explain why splashing awkwardly into the water is painful, whereas a smooth dive is not.

   (c) In Figure 1.14, what is the magnitude of the acceleration of the Earth?

1.5 Momentum

In contact sports such as rugby (Figure 1.15), tackling an opponent can be quite a challenge. When an opponent runs at you, how much **momentum** they have is important. The more mass they have, and the faster they are running, the greater their momentum and the more difficult they will be to stop.

Momentum, usually given the symbol p, is defined as:

momentum = mass × velocity

$$p = mv \qquad (10)$$

The SI units of momentum are kg m s^{-1}, as mass is in kg and velocity in m s^{-1}. For example, when a 90 kg rugby player runs at 7 m s^{-1}, his momentum is 630 kg m s^{-1}.

Momentum associated with an object's velocity (i.e. its motion in a straight line) should properly be called **linear momentum** to distinguish it from *angular* momentum, which is associated with rotational motion. However, if there is no scope for confusion it is usually just referred to as 'momentum'.

Momentum is a *vector*. A vector (velocity) multiplied by a scalar (mass) is a vector. The *direction* of momentum is important. So, 630 kg m s^{-1} of rugby opponent on a collision course with you is a very different prospect to 630 kg m s^{-1} of a rugby opponent heading directly away from you.

At this stage in your course you only need to consider momentum in one dimension – that is, left or right, up or down, north-east or south-west, etc. If we define one direction as positive, anything travelling in the opposite direction has negative momentum.

Figure 1.15 Tackle him?

MATHS REFERENCE

Manipulating units

See Maths note 2.2

STUDY NOTE

In the chapter probing the *Heart of Matter* you will consider momentum in more than one dimension.

QUESTIONS

Q 17 Jay has a mass of 60 kg and a speed of $6.5\,\text{m s}^{-1}$. Kay has a mass of 65 kg and runs at a constant speed covering a distance of 180 m in 30 s. Who has the greater momentum?

Q 18 Calculate the momentum of a 600 g javelin travelling at $20\,\text{m s}^{-1}$.

Q 19 What is the total momentum of Jay and Kay (from Question 17) if they are **(a)** running in the same direction as each other and **(b)** running towards each other?

Momentum conservation

Why do we need to introduce another quantity (momentum) to describe and analyse motion, in addition to mass, acceleration and so on? The usefulness of momentum becomes clear when we study what happens in collisions. Two ice hockey players crashing together, a tennis ball being served and a karate chop breaking blocks are all examples of collisions (Figure 1.16).

Figure 1.16 Sporting collisions

⚙ ACTIVITY 10 CONTACT SPORTS

Use air track vehicles or trolleys to represent colliding participants in a contact sport. Observe some collisions and compare the total momentum before and after. Include situations in which one vehicle is initially at rest as well as those where both vehicles initially move towards one another. Include collisions in which the two vehicles become coupled together as well as those in which they bounce off one another. Notice what happens to the velocities after impact. Try altering the mass of one or both vehicles.

In Activity 10 you should have found that even though the momentum of each of the colliding objects changes in a collision, the *total* momentum of both objects added together (with appropriate plus and minus signs) is the same after the collision as it was beforehand. This illustrates the **law of conservation of (linear) momentum**:

total momentum before a collision = total momentum after a collision (11)

We express this in symbols as:

$$m_1 u_1 + m_2 u_2 = m_1 v_1 + m_2 v_2 \qquad (11a)$$

This important law of motion applies to *all* interactions between objects *so long as no external forces act on them*. It is directly related to Newton's second and third laws of motion. To see why, think about the situation in Figure 1.17.

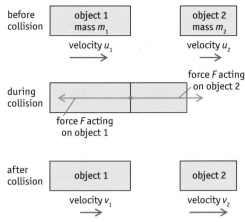

Figure 1.17 Collision between two objects

Suppose the objects are in contact with one another for a time Δt. During that time they each exert a force on the other. Newton's third law describes this situation. The forces must be the same size (F) and act in opposite directions: in the *negative* direction on object 1 and the positive direction on object 2. Newton's second law (Equation 8) relates each object's change of velocity to the force acting on it.

object 2: $m_2(v_2 - u_2) = F\Delta t$

object 1: $m_1(v_1 - u_1) = -F\Delta t$

Comparing these two equations:

$$m_1(v_1 - u_1) = -m_2(v_2 - u_2)$$

Multiplying out the brackets and rearranging produces Equation 11:

$$m_1 u_1 + m_2 u_2 = m_1 v_1 + m_2 v_2 \qquad \text{(Equation 11a)}$$

For analysing what happens when two (or more) objects interact, momentum conservation is a very useful approach.

> **STUDY NOTE**
>
> Note that u_1, u_2, v_1 and v_2 can take *any* value. Any or all of them could be positive, negative or zero.

WORKED EXAMPLE

Q Ellie (mass 50 kg) ice skates into Laura (mass 40 kg). Before the collision, Ellie was travelling at $4\,\text{m s}^{-1}$ and Laura was at rest. After the collision, they move off together at the same velocity as each other. By considering momentum, determine their velocity, v, after the collision.

A Total momentum before = $(50\,\text{kg} \times 4\,\text{m s}^{-1}) + (40\,\text{kg} \times 0\,\text{m s}^{-1})$

$p = 200\,\text{kg m s}^{-1} + 0$

$= 200\,\text{kg m s}^{-1}$

By the law of conservation of momentum:

momentum after = $p = 200\,\text{kg m s}^{-1}$

After the collision a total mass of $m = 90\,\text{kg}$ is moving at velocity v:

$p = mv$

$v = \dfrac{p}{m} = \dfrac{200\,\text{kg m s}^{-1}}{90\,\text{kg}}$

$= 2.2\,\text{m s}^{-1}$

This will be in the same direction as Ellie's initial velocity.

QUESTION

Q 20 Suppose that Ellie and Laura (from the example above) are both travelling towards each other at $4\,\text{m s}^{-1}$. If they move off together after the collision, calculate their velocity. Hint: remember that velocity is a vector and a negative velocity indicates travel in the opposite direction.

1.6 Summing up Part 1

In this part of the chapter you have explored some key ideas about forces and motion and seen how graphs can be used to display and analyse motion. You will use all these ideas again later in this chapter and elsewhere in your study of physics. Activity 11 is intended to help you review your work so far, and Question 21 shows that ideas about motion are relevant to situations other than sport.

> **⚙ ACTIVITY 11 SUMMING UP PART 1**
>
> Spend a few minutes checking through Part 1. Make sure you understand the meanings of all the key terms printed in bold. Then use at least five of those terms to describe the forces involved in sprinting and to explain how the 'cushion' in the sole of a running shoe helps prevent damage to the sprinter's feet.

> **FURTHER INVESTIGATION**
>
> In practice, many falling objects do not fall freely — they are affected by air resistance as well as by gravity. If you have an opportunity, you could investigate some of the records of falling objects (and people) from the *Tracker* website to see to what extent air resistance affects their motion.
>
> A shuttlecock is designed to be affected by air resistance. You could investigate how the shape and weight distribution of a cone-shaped object affect its motion in the air.

QUESTION

Q 21 An instrument called a dynamometer is used to test the performance of trains. It can measure and record, among other things, a train's speed, acceleration and distance travelled, together with the time at which the measurements were taken. Figure 1.18 shows a record for a train of mass 200 000 kg until it reached its maximum speed of 35 m s^{-1}.

(a) Between what times was the train's acceleration uniform?

(b) What was the magnitude of this uniform acceleration?

(c) What was the magnitude of the instantaneous acceleration at $t = 80$ s?

(d) Calculate the size of the net force that produced the uniform acceleration.

(e) How far had the train travelled during the interval from $t = 0$ s to $t = 40$ s?

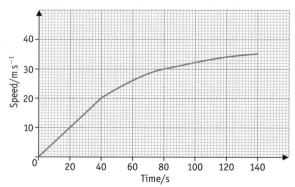

Figure 1.18 Dynamometer record for Question 21

2 Climbing and balancing

I put the gear between my teeth as I shift my left foot for more purchase. The other leg is out to the right, just balancing against the face, and my left hand is firmly wedged in a crack. The rope dangles like a deadweight beneath me. The waves crash below and I think of my partner, anchored to the bottom of the cliff. I slot the gear into the crack just below my hand, twist it into place and attach the quick-draw. One good, strong yank downwards. It's solid, should take my fall. My hand is starting to hurt now, aching from being clenched and sore from the friction. I pick the rope up. 35 metres is heavy and my toes are slipping, but it's only an arm's length higher to the krab. Into the clip and I'm safe. I find another hold with my free hand and shift my feet. 'Take in!' The rope tugs at my harness as it goes taut. Slowly, I let it take my weight – the gear is good for now. My arms hang down by my sides and I stretch my fingers out. It feels good. Over my shoulder the view across the sea is stunning. A final flex and I'm back to it. Hand wedged into position again, foot in place. My other hand reaches up to the next hold and I lever myself up, finding a good niche for my foot and another ledge for my fingers. The balancing act begins again.

Climbing on The Promontory, Baggy Point, North Devon.

In the passage above, a climber is describing a climb on the sea cliffs of the North Devon coast. The sport of rock climbing is quite a contrast to athletics. However complicated or contorted the move in rock climbing, all the forces must somehow combine to produce **equilibrium** (i.e. a net force of zero) almost all of the time, unlike athletics where forces and accelerations can be deliberately large. The only occasion when a rock climber is not in equilibrium is when there might be an acceleration in transferring position – or of course when falling.

In this part of the chapter we are going to explore the equilibrium of forces and also look at some of the physical properties of materials that help to make the sport of rock climbing safe.

2.1 Hanging on

The climber in Figure 1.19(a) is clearly in equilibrium – there are no horizontal forces acting and the upward vertical force exerted by the rock face balances his weight vertically downwards. The climber in Figure 1.19(b) is also in equilibrium, though the situation is a little more complicated – there are four points of contact with the rock, which together with his weight produce five forces all acting in different directions. Figure 1.19(c) shows yet another situation (a so-called *Tyrolean traverse*) where forces are acting in different directions.

⚙ ACTIVITY 12 FORCES IN DIFFERENT DIRECTIONS

Can you see any similarities between the equilibrium situations of Figures 1.19(b) and (c)? (Try to wipe the 'physical context' from the pictures and think just about the directions of forces acting on the climbers.)

Use the arrangement shown in Figure 1.20 to explore the effect of pulling ropes in different directions while still trying to maintain equilibrium.

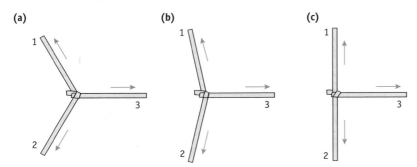

Figure 1.20 Diagram for Activity 12

Figure 1.19 Rock climbers in equilibrium

It should be clear from Activity 12 that when forces combine with each other, we don't just have to think about how large each one is but also in which direction it is acting. In Activity 14 you will extend the qualitative ideas of Activity 12 by taking measurements of tension in, and angle of, a rope. Before you do that, what sort of behaviour might you expect? We can get a clue from considering what is probably the simplest vector quantity of all – displacement.

Combining displacement vectors

You will be familiar with displacement vectors if you have ever done orienteering or any navigation across open country. It is simply an instruction to move from one point to another, and it must contain the *two* pieces of information: how far and which way (unlike the situation in Figure 1.3).

Figure 1.21(a) shows two displacement vectors: d_1 is 5 km north (call this direction 0°) and d_2 is 3 km in a direction 40° clockwise from north. Let us start from point O and carry out the displacement d_1 first then d_2. This is shown in Figure 1.21(b) and takes us to point P. Alternatively, we could do d_2 first then d_1, as in Figure 1.21(c).

Whichever way we combine the vectors, the net effect is exactly the same: the vector from O to P is the same in both diagrams and is the *single* vector that replaces the two separate ones. Careful measurement on Figure 1.21(d) shows that it is 7.5 km in a direction 15° from N. This single vector is called the **resultant** vector of d_1 and d_2: if we denote it by R we write:

$$R = d_1 + d_2 \tag{12}$$

STUDY NOTE

In printed texts vectors are usually in **bold** type. When writing them yourself it is usual to underline them with a wavy line. The magnitude (size) of a vector is a scalar quantity, so is shown in the same way as any other scalar, i.e. in *italic*, non-bold type.

STUDY NOTE

Note that the '+' sign in Equation 8 is not the same as an ordinary arithmetic (scalar) addition. However, we borrow the sign to show that we are combining the vectors, and we describe the procedure as vector addition. It is obviously not true that $R = d_1 + d_2$ (scalars, *magnitude only*).

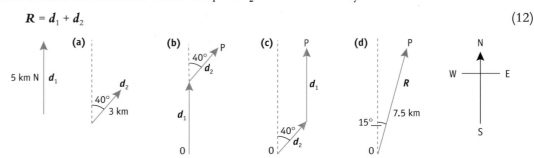

Figure 1.21 Combining displacement vectors (1 cm = 2.5 km)

If we need to combine more than two vectors then we just continue the process of joining them 'head-to-tail', ending up with a **vector polygon** as in Figure 1.22. The resultant is always found by joining the starting point O to finishing point P.

Zero resultant

We can rewrite Equation 12 as:

$$d_1 + d_2 - R = 0 \tag{12a}$$

We can interpret this as the combination of the vector $-R$ with the sum $(d_1 + d_2)$, giving a resultant of zero. If in Figure 1.21(b) or (c) we added the vector $-R$ at point P (the minus sign simply means reverse the direction), then it is clear that we end up back at O and the resultant is zero.

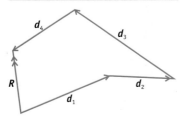

Figure 1.22 A vector polygon

⚙ ACTIVITY 13 VECTOR POLYGON

Draw on graph paper a vector polygon similar to Figure 1.22. It need not be an exact match. Draw up a table of two columns headed 'Magnitude' and 'Direction', and with the help of a ruler and protractor enter the information for each of the vectors.

Now combine the vectors in a variety of different orders. You will get quite different polygons but you ought to find that the resultant is the same in each case.

Combining force vectors by drawing

Figure 1.23 shows three forces W, T_1 and T_2 that are in equilibrium and so their resultant is zero. Do they combine like displacement vectors? Activity 14 provides the answer.

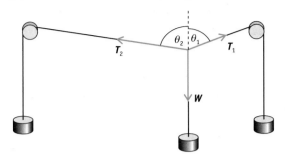

Figure 1.23 Three force vectors in equilibrium

⚙ ACTIVITY 14 FORCES IN EQUILIBRIUM

Use the apparatus shown in Figure 1.24 to investigate whether force vectors combine like displacement vectors. For each equilibrium arrangement, construct a vector addition diagram and see if it is closed – do we end up back where we started? The critical step is to choose a scale so that each force is represented by a line of length proportional to its magnitude, e.g. 2 cm to 1 N.

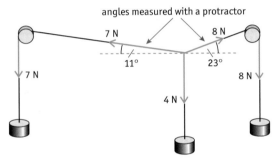

Figure 1.24 Apparatus for Activity 14

Careful measurements show that forces do indeed behave as displacement vectors when they combine. This means that when any number of forces is in equilibrium, the vectors form a closed polygon. This can be expressed in symbols:

$$\Sigma F = 0 \tag{13}$$

The symbol Σ (Greek sigma) means 'the sum of all'. When applied to vectors, the sum must take account of their directions as well as the magnitudes.

A common special case is when there are just three forces: here the polygon is a triangle usually called the **triangle of forces**.

> **MATHS REFERENCE**
> The symbol Σ
> See Maths note 0.3

QUESTION

Q 22 Figure 1.25 shows a simplified end-on view of a cable car (looking along the length of the cable). It is being blown by high wind, which can produce a sideways force of up to 5000 N. The total weight of the car is 2.5×10^4 N. Assume that it is in equilibrium (i.e. not swinging). T is the force exerted on the car by the support arm, which is fixed rigidly to the car but can rotate on the cable.

Draw a triangle of forces for this arrangement. Choose a suitable scale, working on graph paper for convenience, and start with a vector whose details you know. (Does it matter which?) As accurately as you can, measure the values of T and θ.

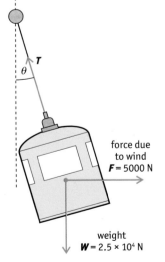

Figure 1.25 Forces acting on a cable car

It is always true that if three **coplanar** non-parallel forces (coplanar means acting in the same plane) are in equilibrium, their lines of action pass through the same point.

STUDY NOTE

For more on centres of gravity see Section 2.3

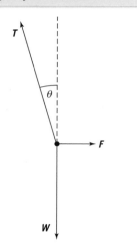

Figure 1.26 Free-body diagram for a cable car

Free-body diagram

What you have just been drawing in Activity 15 are **free-body diagrams**.

We often need to know whether an object is in equilibrium or whether there is a resultant force acting on it. To help analyse the situation it is often useful to draw a diagram of the object by itself, representing it by a dot, and then mark on the size and direction of all of the forces acting on it. The object can be represented by a dot because this marks its **centre of gravity** – the point through which all of its weight may be considered to act. (For a person with their legs in line with their torso and their arms at their sides, the centre of gravity is approximately at the belly button.) Figure 1.26 is a free-body diagram for the cable car shown in Figure 1.25.

QUESTION

 Draw free-body diagrams for:

(a) a plane flying at constant velocity in still air

(b) a skier being dragged at constant velocity uphill on a ski-tow

(c) a friction-free puck sliding on ice at constant velocity

(d) a ball that has just been thrown in the air (neglecting the very small amount of air resistance).

Combining force vectors by calculation

STUDY NOTE

Note the use of **bold** or *italic* font. *F* is the magnitude of the vector **F**, and so on.

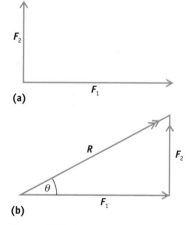

Figure 1.27 Two forces at right angles

Since most force situations of interest will involve different directions, it is obviously important, not least from considerations of strength and safety, to be able to deal accurately with them (just think about buildings, bridges or aircraft). Is there any way of doing this apart from scale drawing?

As an introduction, consider the case when two force vectors are acting at a point at right angles to each other (Figure 1.27(a)). The vector addition diagram, including the resultant **R**, is obviously a right-angled triangle as in Figure 1.27(b). (Remember that **R** *replaces* **F**$_1$ and **F**$_2$ and is equivalent to the other two acting together – we are *not* introducing a third extra force.) From Pythagoras we can say:

$$R^2 = F_1{}^2 + F_2{}^2 \tag{14}$$

or

$$R = \sqrt{(F_1{}^2 + F_2{}^2)} \tag{14a}$$

and also:

$$\tan\theta = \frac{F_2}{F_1} \tag{15}$$

or

$$\theta = \tan^{-1}\frac{F_2}{F_1} \tag{15a}$$

So in this special case we can find the magnitude and direction of **R** by calculation alone.

MATHS REFERENCE

Sine, cosine and tangent of an angle

See Maths note 6.2

QUESTION

Q 24 Figure 1.28 shows a climber supported by a rope and 'walking' down a vertical rock face. Sketch the triangle of forces acting on the climber when she is momentarily at rest and then calculate the magnitudes of the horizontal force exerted by the rock and the tension in the rope.

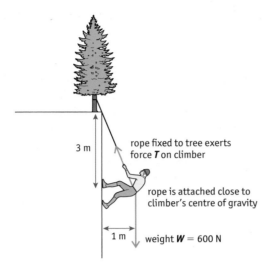

3 m

rope fixed to tree exerts force **T** on climber

rope is attached close to climber's centre of gravity

1 m

weight **W** = 600 N

Figure 1.28 Diagram for Question 24

Resolving a force into perpendicular components

So what about two vectors that are not at right angles, as in Figure 1.21 and Activity 15? The trick is to take each force in turn and resolve it (split it up) into two perpendicular **components** (parts). For example, the vector d_2 in Figure 1.21 can be thought of as the resultant of two displacements – one due north (d_N) and one due east (d_E) (Figure 1.29). These two components form a right-angled triangle with d_2 as the hypotenuse, from which we can see that the magnitudes of the components are given by:

$$d_N = d_2\cos40°$$

and:

$$d_E = d_2\sin40°$$

The overall displacement $d_1 + d_2$ can then be treated as the sum of two northerly displacements plus an easterly displacement, which together make two sides of a right-angled triangle, so the magnitude and direction of the resultant can be calculated.

This example illustrates a general rule. Any vector P making an angle θ with a particular direction can be resolved into two components, one parallel to the chosen direction and one perpendicular to it:

magnitude of parallel component = $P\cos\theta$ (16a)

magnitude of perpendicular component = $P\sin\theta$ (16b)

We now have another way of looking at equilibrium of forces. In any direction you choose, all the components of forces in that direction must combine to produce a resultant of zero. Activity 16 illustrates this.

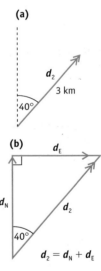

(a)

d_2

3 km

40°

(b)

d_E

d_N

d_2

40°

$d_2 = d_N + d_E$

Figure 1.29 Resolving a displacement vector into perpendicular components

⚙ ACTIVITY 16 COMPONENTS OF FORCE VECTORS

Return to your data for Activity 14. Using your values of tensions, weight and directions, draw up a table of the horizontal and vertical components of each force.

By adding separately the horizontal and vertical components, show to what extent the condition for equilibrium is satisfied experimentally.

Tyrolean traverse

The Tyrolean traverse (Figure 1.19(c)) is a technique for crossing a deep chasm suspended on a rope. In the pioneering days of mountaineering the rope was thrown across a chasm and lassoed onto a suitable spike. Figure 1.30 shows a close-up of how it might work in practice. In Question 25 and Activity 17 you are going to use what you have learned about forces to explore the Tyrolean traverse in a bit more detail. Question 26 applies the same ideas to a more complicated situation where the two ends are not on a level.

Figure 1.30 Tyrolean traverse

Suppose for convenience the two parts of the rope each make an angle of 15° with the horizontal and the climber has a weight of 600 N. How can we find the tension in the rope? A free-body diagram (Figure 1.31) helps. From the symmetry, the tension in the two halves must be the same. (Warning! – this is only true when the two angles are the same.) If we resolve vertically:

$$T\cos75° + T\cos75° = 600\,\text{N}$$

$$(\text{or } T\sin15° + T\sin15° = 600\,\text{N})$$

$$2T\cos75° = 600\,\text{N}$$

$$0.52T = 600\,\text{N}$$

$$T = 1160\,\text{N}$$

i.e. the tension is nearly twice the climber's weight.

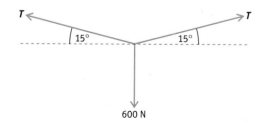

Figure 1.31 Free-body diagram for a person on a Tyrolean traverse

QUESTION

 Q 25 **(a)** Repeat the calculation in the text for progressively smaller angles with the horizontal. (Hint: call the angle with the horizontal θ and produce a formula for T in terms of θ.) What is your general conclusion?

(b) If the rope is designed to take a maximum tension of 15 kN, what is the smallest angle the rope must be allowed to make with the horizontal for this particular weight of climber?

⚙ ACTIVITY 17 MODEL OF TYROLEAN TRAVERSE

Set up the apparatus as in Figure 1.32(a) so that the tensions in both sides are *equal* and much bigger that *W*. Gently pull the load across the traverse from one side to the other by lowering one of the side masses. Investigate how the sag *y* varies with distance *x* from the centre (Figure 1.32(b)).

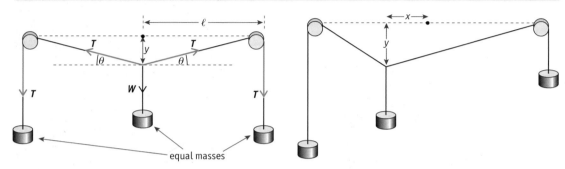

Figure 1.32 (a) The starting arrangement for Activity 17. (b) Moving the load

QUESTION

 Q 26 A cable car is being pulled up a mountain in calm conditions. The cable above it is at an angle of 24° with the horizontal and the cable down to the valley station is at 23°. The weight of the car is 1.0×10^5 N.

(a) Draw a free-body diagram and a triangle of forces for the cable car.

(b) By resolving horizontally and vertically, form a pair of simultaneous equations containing the tension in each part of the cable. Solve these to find the tensions.

(c) Why is it impossible for the two angles to be the same? (Note: this question becomes much more manageable if you first draw a diagram and then write down your working carefully step by step.)

Out of equilibrium

So far we have dealt only with situations where forces combine to produce a zero resultant. Yet if a climber is pushing on a foothold to give himself an upward acceleration, or if a rope snaps and allows him to fall, then the resultant force is not zero but produces acceleration as described by Equation 8. This can be written as:

$$\Sigma F = ma \tag{8b}$$

The direction of the acceleration vector is the same as the direction of the resultant force.

QUESTION

 Q 27 A skydiver falling vertically experiences a net vertical force of 500 N. A sideways gust of wind exerts a force of 100 N.

(a) What are the magnitude and direction of the resultant force on the skydiver?

(b) If the diver plus kit has a total mass of 100 kg, what is the acceleration?

WORKED EXAMPLE

Q A rock climber of mass 71 kg (including kit) pushes down against a foothold with a force of 900 N at 10° to the vertical. Draw a free-body diagram showing forces on the climber and use a vector addition diagram to find the resultant force acting on her. (There is no tension in her climbing rope.) What is her acceleration?

A She experiences a force in the opposite direction to the one she exerts on the foothold. Figure 1.33(a) shows the two forces acting on her.

From the vector diagram in Figure 1.33(b), the resultant force is approximately 250 N at 40° to the vertical.

The magnitude of the acceleration is $a = 250\,\text{N}/71\,\text{kg} = 3.5\,\text{m s}^{-2}$. She accelerates in the same direction as the resultant force, i.e. 40° to the vertical.

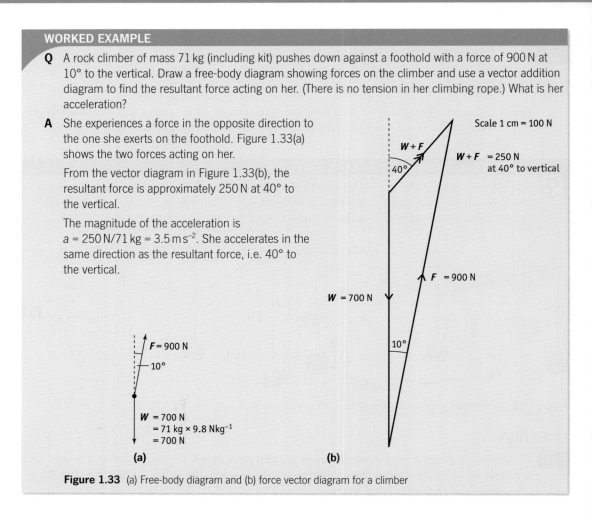

Figure 1.33 (a) Free-body diagram and (b) force vector diagram for a climber

2.2 On the ropes

Climbing ropes obviously have to be **strong** (a large tension is needed to break them). Hanging from a horizontally supported rope can produce tensions several times the hanging weight, and if you fall while climbing the safety rope must be able to exert large decelerating forces on your body.

Climbing ropes are also **elastic** – they stretch when put under tension and return (not always completely) to the original length when the load is removed. A useful term to compare different samples is **stiffness**: one rope is stiffer than another if the extension is smaller for the same force. (The opposite of stiffness is **compliance**.)

⚙ ACTIVITY 18 TENSION AND EXTENSION

Test a variety of fibres that might be used to make climbing ropes (Figure 1.34). Find out how the extension of a fibre varies with tension and find the breaking strength of each sample.

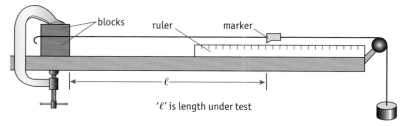

Figure 1.34 Diagram for Activity 18

Hooke's law

In Activity 18 you might have found that some of your samples had a constant stiffness for a range of loads. Samples that behave in this way are said to obey **Hooke's law**. For such a sample:

tension $\propto$ extension

or

$$F = kx \qquad (18)$$

where F is the net applied force and x is the resulting extension. The constant k is defined as the stiffness of the sample, and the SI units of stiffness are $N\,m^{-1}$. In graphical terms, for Hooke's law to hold, the force–extension graph has to be linear *and pass through the origin*. You will probably find that your results show that Hooke's law is not very closely followed. A point where the graph starts to deviate significantly from Hooke's law is called the **limit of proportionality**.

MATHS REFERENCE

Graphs and proportionality
See Maths note 5.1

STUDY NOTE

There are some materials (notably metals) that follow Hooke's law quite well for small extensions and then suddenly deviate from it. You will study this behaviour in the chapter *Spare Part Surgery*.

QUESTIONS

Q 28 A certain rope extends by 0.020 m when supporting a load of 800 N and by 0.012 m when supporting a load of 600 N. Does the rope obey Hooke's law? Calculate the stiffness of the rope under each of the loads.

Q 29 Suppose a 2 m length of climbing rope obeys Hooke's law and has a stiffness of $6\,kN\,m^{-1}$.

(a) If the rope supports the weight of a 650 N climber, by how much does the rope extend?

(b) If 4 m of the same rope supports the same climber, what would the extension be?

Drop tests

The skill in designing climbing ropes for different tasks is to get the right combination of stiffness and strength. Climbing ropes are subjected to a standard drop test for safety certification: a mass of 80 kg attached to 5 m of the rope is dropped freely and the force exerted on the rope is measured as it brings the mass to rest.

2.3 Balancing

In Section 2.1 you drew free-body diagrams in which a person or an object was represented as a single point (its centre of gravity) and all forces acted through that point. However, it is not always possible to represent things quite so simply. Forces often act through different points in an extended object, and even if the resultant force is zero there can be a **turning effect** that causes the object to rotate. If the object is 'pinned down' at one point then that point acts as a pivot and the object rotates about it.

Rock climbers must take care that their weight and the other forces acting on their body do not give rise to a turning effect otherwise they would fall. Yet in sports such as gymnastics and athletics, turning effects are important as athletes use them to control the motion of their bodies and the equipment they use (see Figure 1.35).

The turning effect or **moment**, M, of a force, F, about any point is defined as:

$$M = Fx \qquad (19)$$

where x is the *perpendicular* distance between the force's **line of action** and that point (Figure 1.36). With force in newtons (N) and distance in metres (m), moment has the SI unit newton-metre (N m).

Think about what Equation 19 means. For example, it is easier to hold a heavy object close to your body rather than with your arm outstretched. The mass (and weight) is unchanged, the only difference being the distance from your shoulder. The turning effect (moment) of the force is greater when the distance is greater.

Figure 1.35 Gymnast Dorina Boczogo on a balance beam

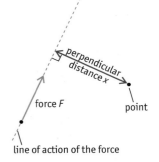

Figure 1.36 Moment of a force

WORKED EXAMPLE

Q The shot-put is an athletics event in which a small heavy sphere is thrown. A shot weighs 71 N. Calculate the moment of the weight of the shot about your shoulder if you hold it level with your shoulder at distance 20 cm.

A Moment = 71 N × 0.20 m = 14.2 N m

QUESTION

 (a) Estimate the turning effect due to the same 71 N shot-put if it is held level with your shoulder but this time at arm's length.

(b) Explain what happens to the moment of the force due to the weight of the shot-put if it is still held at arm's length but level with your hip. A diagram may help your explanation.

Moments and equilibrium

If the moments of all the forces acting on an object add up to zero then there will be no change in the object's rotational motion – it will either be at rest or rotating at a constant rate. The size of the moment(s) attempting to turn the object clockwise is exactly matched by the size of the moment(s) attempting to turn the body in the opposite, anticlockwise, direction.

For an extended object to be in equlibrium, there are therefore *two* requirements:

● all the forces acting on it must have a resultant force of zero

and

● the moments of all the forces must have an overall turning effect of zero.

To apply the second condition, you need to choose one convenient point and add up the moments of all the forces trying to turn the object clockwise about that point and then add all the moments trying to turn it anticlockwise. For equilibrium, these two sums should give the same number; this is known as the **principle of moments**:

sum of clockwise moments = sum of anticlockwise moments

WORKED EXAMPLE

Q Two circus performers are practising a routine on a teeterboard (Figure 1.37). Suppose that:

the beam weighs 500 N and is supported at its mid point (its centre of gravity);

one performer weighs 900 N and the line of action of his weight is 1.35 m measured horizontally from the support;

the second performer, standing on the opposite side of the support, weighs 850 N.

When the beam is in equilibrium (a) what is the upward force exerted by the support and (b) what is the horizontal distance between the support and the second performer's centre of gravity?

A (a) Resultant of vertical forces must be zero.

Downwards: sum of weights = 500 N + 900 N + 850 N
= 2250 N

So the support must exert an upward force of 2250 N.

(b) Applying the principle of moments about the point of support, and using subscripts 1 and 2 for the two performers:

$W_2 x_2$ (clockwise) = $W_1 x_1$ (anticlockwise)

$$x_2 = \frac{W_1 x_1}{W_2}$$

$$= \frac{W900\,\text{N} \times 1.35\,\text{m}}{850\,\text{N}} = 1.43\,\text{m}$$

Figure 1.37 Circus performers on a teeterboard

STUDY NOTE

Part (b) of the worked example could be tackled by considering the moments about *any* convenient point. (See Question 31.)

Moments and centre of gravity

Earlier in this chapter (Section 2.1) we defined centre of gravity as the point through which an object's weight appears to act. This means that a single upward force, exactly equal to the object's weight and applied at its centre of gravity, will keep the object in equilibrium. Applying the same upward force at a position to either side of the centre of gravity would make it rotate.

You will also come across the term **centre of mass**. If we apply a force to an object's centre of mass, the force's effect on the object's motion is the same as if the entire mass were concentrated at that point – that is, only its linear motion is affected. A force whose line of action does not go through the centre of mass affects the object's rotational motion. Unless the object is in a very non-uniform gravitational field, the centre of mass and centre of gravity are exactly the same, so the terms can be used interchangeably.

If an object is supported in equilibrium by a single force acting through its centre of gravity then the moments about that point (due to all the weights of all the different bits of the object) must add up to zero. This gives us a way to find the centre of gravity of an extended object. For simple symmetrical shapes, it can be found just by observation: identify the middle of the object. If a less simple object can be described by mathematical equations, its centre of gravity can be found mathematically (using calculus). For more complex and irregular shaped objects, the centre of gravity can be found experimentally.

If you suspend an object (or a model of the object) from a single point, it will come to rest with its centre of gravity directly below the suspension point – in this way you can identify a line that passes through the centre of gravity. Suspending the object from a different point identifies another line that also passes through the centre. Repeat this using several different suspension points, and the centre of gravity is where all the lines intersect.

Gymnastics in the balance

The balance beam is a gymnastics event that uses a beam just 10 cm wide. To remain in equilibrium on the beam (i.e. not tipping over to the left or right), the gymnast must be balanced. When symmetrical over the beam (see Figure 1.39), it is fairly obvious that the clockwise and anticlockwise moments about the beam are balanced.

However, when the positioning is not symmetrical over the balance beam, a gymnast such as Dorina Boczogo (see Figure 1.35) must ensure that the moment produced by her weight on one side of the beam balances the moment due to her weight on the other side of the beam. This does *not* mean that she has to have equal weight on each side of the beam. Activity 20 illustrates how gymnasts can control their balance by adjusting the position of their centre of gravity.

Figure 1.38 A wobble board or balance board

Figure 1.39 Clockwise moment = anticlockwise moment

QUESTIONS

Q 31 Demonstrate that part (b) of the Worked example on page 28 gives the same answer if you consider the moments about the point 1.40 m from the support where the first performer is standing in Figure 1.37.

Q 32 Look at the gymnast in Figure 1.35 and explain how she is able to remain in equilibrium even though she isn't symmetrical above the beam.

2.4 Summing up Part 2

In this part of the chapter you have studied two areas of physics, both of which you will revisit shortly. In Section 2.1 you have seen how to resolve and combine displacement and force vectors in two dimensions – you will meet these ideas again in Parts 3 and 5 of this chapter. You have also begun to study elastic properties of materials, which you will meet again in Part 4 of this chapter and later in this course. Finally, in Section 2.3 you have extended your knowledge of equilibrium to include extended objects, using ideas about moments and centre of gravity.

☼ ACTIVITY 21 SUMMING UP PART 2

Check through Part 2 and make sure you know the meaning of all the terms printed in bold. Then discuss the following questions in a small group.

- Make a sketch of the climber shown in Figure 1.30 performing a Tyrolean traverse. Add arrows to show the vertical forces acting on the climber: his weight (acting at his centre of gravity) and the upward forces exerted by the rope on each of his hands, and on his legs where they cross the line.
- By considering the principle of moments, discuss the likely relative sizes of the three upward forces.
- What can you say (qualitatively) about the stiffness of a rope suitable for a Tyrolean traverse?
- When setting up a Tyrolean traverse, should you aim to get the rope nearly horizontal or to let it sag?
- Consider the design of a rope for rock climbing. What are the consequences for the climber of making the rope either very stiff or very compliant?
- A climbing rope catalogue states that the standard drop test produces an extension of 7.5% of the original length. What extension(s) does this correspond to for your samples in Activity 18? Would any sample have broken already in trying to reach this extension?
- What can you say about the motion of a falling climber from the instant the rope starts to go under tension?
- Suppose you had rope samples of widely varying stiffness and you subjected them to the standard drop test. Sketch a sequence of graphs (on the same axes of force against time) to show the effect of decreasing stiffness. (Qualitative only – no calculation.)

MATHS REFERENCE

Fractions and percentages
See Maths notes 3.1

FURTHER INVESTIGATION

For ropes with widely varying stiffness, use a force sensor to study how the tension in the rope varies with time during a drop test and how this variation itself depends upon the stiffness.

The behaviour of many natural fibres is affected by their water content. Investigate how the force–extension graph and the breaking strength of some natural fibres depend on water content.

Activity 17 used a simple model of a Tyrolean traverse. Investigate, and analyse theoretically, a less simple model in which the rope extends. Investigate how the sag varies with load when the load is in the middle and when a fixed load is moved from the middle to one end.

3 Working out work

3.1 Energy return shoes

If you were to walk in to a sports shop to look for a new pair of trainers, you would be confronted with an incredible choice. You can attach space-age technology to your feet, packed with gels, fluids and air bags. Companies spend millions on research each year, with engineers putting new designs and materials through their paces with the help of computer-linked sensors in mechanical testing laboratories. The most significant innovation has been the advances in cushioning. A runner hits the ground with a force up to three times his or her body weight, so athletes have welcomed materials that lessen the impact and the chances of injury.

Cushioning aside, how do you choose between all the varieties of trainer? Sales people will often try to blind you with science and technological jargon. In this section we will examine one particular claim – that some shoes can supply you with extra energy, so you can jump

> **ACTIVITY 22 SELLING SCIENCE**
>
> Read the advertisement in Figure 1.40 for the 'Rebound!' trainer, one of the original energy return shoes. Discuss in a group the following questions.
>
> ● How did the article use science to try to persuade the reader?
> ● What scientific claims did the manufacturers make?
> ● Were the claims supported by any evidence?

Rebound!

The revolutionary *Rebound!* trainer incorporates unique Springback technology, designed to reduce impact injury and to enhance both speed and endurance.

Hit the ground running

Each time your foot hits the ground as you run, you feel a force of up to 4 times your body weight. The repeated impact increases fatigue and can lead to injury. The Springback shock absorption system cushions your foot and spreads the impact to reduce jarring. Try running in *Rebound!* and you'll soon notice the difference.

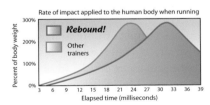

A spring in your step

Our technologists have created a unique Springback system that combines comfort with resilience. A foam matrix incorporates specially designed air sacs that cushion your foot and deform to absorb the impact when subjected to a force. Embedded in the matrix is a system of springs that use compression forces to store energy during foot strike and return it as your foot leaves contact with the ground. This energy return is what makes the *Rebound!* different. In a conventional rubber sole, up to 95% of kinetic energy is wasted. But the *Rebound!* can return as much as 50%, giving you extra lift-off at every step.

Further and faster

Tests in our laboratories show that the *Rebound!* can knock precious seconds off a sprint and has the potential to reduce fatigue and pain in long-distance events.
Athletes and coaches tell us that *Rebound!* trainers really do make a difference.
Marathon Mark says 'I noticed a difference almost immediately, my legs felt like they had more energy and that lasted all through my first training run wearing *Rebound!* My calf muscles love *Rebound!* and I'm definitely not going back to any other shoe.'
Sprinter Susie says 'The *Rebound!* really supports my feet and I feel lighter and faster. I couldn't believe the difference'.

Designed for you

Every runner is different so the Springback system is available in four different specifications to match your body weight, pace and foot-strike parameters. Our trained staff will help you choose the right specification for your needs. And you can choose from three stylish *Rebound!* designs to put fashion at your feet.

Figure 1.40 The Rebound! trainer

Figure 1.41 Two examples illustrating kinetic energy

STUDY NOTE

In Section 2.3 you saw that the moment of a force also has SI units of N m. However, the SI unit for moment is not equivalent to the joule. The moment of a force and work done by a force are not at all the same sort of quantity. Work, or energy, is a scalar and has no direction associated with it. The moment of a force is not a scalar; its direction (clockwise or anticlockwise) is important.

higher and run further. These 'energy return' shoes are supposed to store energy like a spring in the cushioning material of the sole when your foot hits the ground, and return it as you move off.

How well does science imitate nature? Do 'energy return' shoes justify the hype? We will try to find out if there is any truth in the claims, using ideas about energy.

Energy

In your GCSE work you probably learned that there is gravitational potential energy, electrical energy, chemical energy – you may know several others. They are all measured in the same units, joules (J), but do you know what makes, say, gravitational energy different from chemical energy? When energy seems to come in so many varieties, things can start to become confusing. You may be relieved to know that, basically, there are only two 'types' of energy – **kinetic energy** and **potential energy**. All the others are really either kinetic or potential or a combination of the two.

Kinetic energy is the energy an object has because of its movement. Figure 1.41 shows two examples of kinetic energy: the sprinter clearly has kinetic energy but, at a molecular level, so does a hot drink because its molecules are in rapid motion.

Potential energy is the energy a body has due to its position or the arrangement of its parts. Look at the examples of potential energy in Figure 1.42.

Figure 1.42 Three examples illustrating potential energy

Gravitational energy, due to being raised up, is such a common example of potential energy that you can be forgiven for thinking it is the only one. However, 'chemical energy' in the drink is really potential energy, due to the arrangement of atoms in its molecules giving them the 'potential' (the possibility) of taking part in a chemical reaction. The 'elastic energy' stored in the sole of the running shoe is also potential energy because it is due to the rearrangement of molecules as the material is compressed.

You will also have met the idea of **energy conservation**: in any process, energy can be transferred but cannot be created or destroyed. While bearing in mind that all energy is kinetic or potential, it is still sometimes useful to use other terms to 'label' the stages in an energy transfer process in order to keep track of what is happening.

STUDY NOTE

To read more on people's ideas about energy, see HFS Additional Sheet 10.

ACTIVITY 23 TALKING ENERGY

Describe the energy transfers that are shown in Figure 1.43.

Can you think of a way of communicating with a friend that does not involve an energy transfer?

Figure 1.43 The stages of a foot strike

The claim for energy return shoes is that they store significant amounts of the runner's kinetic energy and return it as kinetic energy to make you, for example, run faster or jump higher. To investigate this claim further, we need to be able to measure energy.

Work

We measure the energy an object has by the **work** it can do. 'Work' in physics has a more precise meaning than in everyday life: work is done when a force moves something. So a body has energy if it can do work, i.e. move something else with a force. Look back at Figures 1.41 and 1.42 and convince yourself that all these examples show situations where work can be done. Work is defined as follows:

work = force × displacement *in direction of force*   (20)

When work is done, energy is transferred, which gives us a useful way of measuring energy:

work done = energy transferred   (20a)

In symbols:

$$\Delta E = \Delta W = F\Delta s \qquad (20b)$$

In SI units, work and energy have units of joules, J. $1\,J = 1\,N\,m$.

For example, at the start of a race, an athlete pushes against a starting block and moves her body (her centre of gravity) through 0.80 m, exerting a constant force of 250 N.

work done = 250 N × 0.80 m = 200 J

Efficiency

In addition to the 200 J of 'useful' energy transfer, some energy will be 'wasted' in heating – rowing makes you hot! – so rather more than 200 J will have been transferred from her muscles altogether. The **efficiency** of any energy transfer process is defined as:

$$\text{efficiency} = \frac{\text{energy usefully transferred}}{\text{total energy transferred}} \qquad (21)$$

Efficiency is often expressed as a percentage. For example, if the athlete's muscles are 20% efficient, then 20% (one-fifth) of the energy transferred increases her kinetic energy while the remaining 80% is wasted in making her hot. So, to increase her kinetic energy by 200 J she must have transferred 1000 J altogether, with 800 J being 'wasted' in heating her muscles.

STUDY NOTE

In Section 2.3 you saw that the moment of a force also has SI units of N m. However, the SI unit for moment is not equivalent to the joule. The moment of a force and work done by a force are not at all the same sort of quantity. Work, or energy, is a scalar and has no direction associated with it. The moment of a force is not a scalar; its direction (clockwise or anticlockwise) is important.

MATHS REFERENCE

Derived units

See Maths note 2.3

MATHS REFERENCE

Fractions and percentages

See Maths note 3.1

Calculating energy return

Using the concept of work to measure energy, it is possible to test the claims about energy return shoes. For an adult male runner, Figure 1.44 shows the pattern of compressions in the sole of an 'energy return' shoe. As a rough approximation, the average force on the shoe during a running step is about 2.5 times body weight (about 2000 N for a person of mass 80 kg). From such pictures, we can estimate the average compression to be about 5 mm (0.005 m). So:

$$\text{work done} = 2000\,\text{N} \times 0.005\,\text{m} = 10\,\text{J}$$

This figure agrees well with what researchers have found. They have also found that only about 6 J of this may be recovered (the rest is 'wasted' in heating the shoe and the surroundings). Could 6 J enable a basketball player to jump much higher? Can it give you extra speed while you're running? To answer these questions, we need some more formulae.

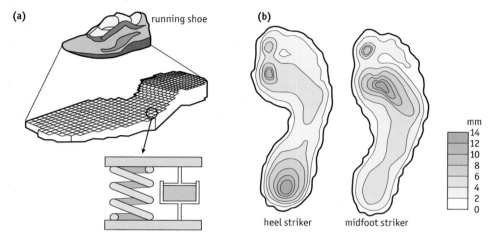

Figure 1.44 Computer-generated pictures showing (a) a model of how the sole of a shoe is compressed during impact and (b) peak deflections of a sole caused by two types of runner

Kinetic and potential energy

As an object falls, it loses gravitational potential energy. If an object of mass m falls through a height Δh then the force acting is just the object's weight, and so:

$$\text{loss of gravitational potential energy} = \text{weight} \times \text{loss of height} \tag{22}$$

If the object is moved upwards then the process is reversed and it regains its gravitational energy. Using ΔE_{grav} to represent change in gravitational potential energy, and Equation 9 to express the object's weight, we get:

$$\Delta E_{grav} = mg\Delta h \tag{22a}$$

What about running? How can we calculate kinetic energy? From your earlier work you are probably familiar with the formula for **kinetic energy** E_k of an object of mass m at speed v:

$$E_k = \frac{1}{2}mv^2 \tag{23}$$

This equation can be derived using others that you have used in Part 1 of this unit. Suppose a force of magnitude F accelerates an object of mass m from rest so that it reaches a speed v after moving through a distance Δs. Putting $u = 0$ in Equation 7 we can write:

$$v^2 = 2a\Delta s$$

$$\text{so } a\Delta s = \frac{1}{2}v^2$$

We can also use Equations 8 and 20a to write:

$$\Delta E_k = F\Delta s = ma\Delta s = \frac{1}{2}mv^2$$

ACTIVITY 24 GRAVITATIONAL ENERGY IN A JUMP

Measure the height through which you can jump and then calculate the change in your gravitational potential energy.

What difference would an additional 6 J from 'energy return' trainers make to the height of your jump?

ACTIVITY 25 KINETIC ENERGY IN RUNNING

Measure your kinetic energy when running. Try to devise a way to measure your speed as accurately as possible.

What difference would 6 J from 'energy return' trainers make to your speed?

In Activities 24 and 25, it is likely that you found that the energy returned was too small to give you much extra speed or height, so it looks as if the effect of energy return shoes is minimal. However, published research with real athletes has found that running in a shoe with a gas-inflated cushioning system reduces the oxygen consumption by 2% compared to a regular foam-cushioned shoe (although the researchers suggested that this could have been due to factors other than energy return).

Nature has already endowed us with an energy return mechanism which, it turns out, is rather more efficient. When your heel strikes the ground, about 70 J of energy is stored and returned by the muscle in the lower leg, and another 70 J by the Achilles tendon. Energy return training shoes owe a lot more to marketing than to science.

QUESTIONS

 Q 33 Suppose an athlete has an efficiency of 25%. How much energy is transferred from her muscles when she does 200 J of work?

 Q 34 Calculate the kinetic energy of a jet boat of mass 200 kg that can tear across the water at 160 km h^{-1} (44 m s^{-1}).

 Q 35 Which do you think has more kinetic energy (don't calculate it), a speed skier at 150 mph or a small car travelling at 50 mph? Use the following typical figures to check whether your guess was right:

     mass of car: 600 kg   mass of skier: 80 kg

     speed of car: 22 m s^{-1} speed of skier: 66 m s^{-1}

 Q 36 Acapulco, Mexico, is the home of high diving championships, where divers jump from a ravine 35 m above the sea.

(a) Calculate the loss in gravitational potential energy, and so the gain in kinetic energy, of a diver of mass 65 kg, and then calculate the diver's speed on hitting the sea.

(b) Explain whether or not a more massive diver would hit the sea at the same speed. (Assume the diver falls freely, i.e. gravity is the only force acting, and use $g = 9.81$ N kg^{-1} = 9.81 m s^{-2}.)

3.2 Speed skiing

Speed skiing (Figure 1.45) is the fastest non-motorised sport on Earth. The world record is close to 156 miles per hour – about the top speed of a sports car. Wearing only a rubber suit, and with feet strapped into two 2.4 m long boards, the speed skier hurtles down a steep 'waterfall' of ice.

The speed skier has a huge amount of kinetic energy, which in a collision could easily break every bone in the body and prove fatal. Because of this the ski authorities limit the speed that the skiers can reach in competitions by specifying a maximum length of the acceleration zone (see Figure 1.46). They can calculate the maximum allowable distance using Equations 20 and 22. But can you see a problem? Equation 20 says that we must use the displacement in the direction of the force, but the skier's motion is not parallel to the vertical force of gravity.

Figure 1.45 Speed skier

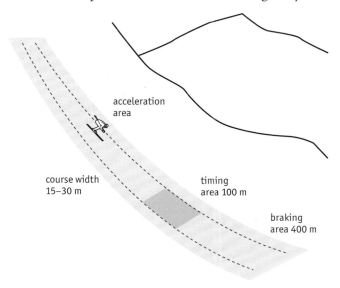

Figure 1.46 The RTS speed skiing course at Willamette Pass, Oregon, is one of three sanctioned courses in the USA and ten in the world. One section has a 52° slope.

MATHS REFERENCE

Sine, cosine and tangent
See Maths note 6.2

From Figure 1.47 you can see that, while the skier travels a distance Δs along the slope, the displacement in the direction of the force is the change in vertical height Δh. Using the trigonometric rules for a right-angled triangle:

$$\Delta h = \Delta s \cos\theta$$

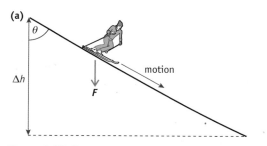

Figure 1.47 Skiing down a slope

In other words, Δh is the vertical component of the skier's displacement vector. It is the component of the displacement parallel to the direction of the force, as described by Equation 16 in Part 2 of this chapter. We can modify Equation 20 to take account of the angle θ between force and displacement:

$$\Delta E = \Delta W = F\Delta s \cos\theta \qquad \text{(Equation 20c)}$$

You can also arrive at this more general version of Equation 20 by considering the component of the force that acts along the slope, $F\cos\theta$, and by multiplying by the overall displacement Δs.

QUESTION

 Q 37 Calculate the maximum length of an acceleration zone at 50° to the horizontal if skiers are not to exceed 66 m s⁻¹ (about 150 mph). (Hint: look at your answers to Questions 35 and 36.)

3.3 Pumping iron

It is not just strong men and weightlifters who pump iron. These days, gyms are full of people who build 'resistance training' into their workouts (Figure 1.48). Even if you don't play sport competitively, lifting weights can benefit your health. Stronger muscles are less prone to injury, and it is believed that building muscle can help you 'burn' your food more quickly.

Power

Weight training simply means increasing the resistance to a muscle's movement. Making the muscles work harder stimulates their growth. However, for most athletes strength is not the main objective but **power**. Loosely speaking, power is 'fast strength'. Whether it's in the legs, back, arms or shoulders, power is important for almost every sport.

If you look in a sports training manual, you might see power defined as:

$$\text{power} = \text{force} \times \text{velocity} \tag{24}$$

However, if you consult a physics textbook you will find it is defined as 'the rate of doing work' or 'the rate of energy transfer':

$$\text{power} = \frac{\text{work done or energy transferred}}{\text{time taken}} \tag{25}$$

$$P = \frac{\Delta W}{\Delta t}$$

$$\text{or } P = \frac{\Delta e}{\Delta t} \tag{25a}$$

The SI units of power are W or J s⁻¹; 1 W = 1 J s⁻¹.

Using Equations 20 and 25:

$$P = \frac{F\Delta s}{\Delta t} = F\frac{\Delta s}{\Delta t}$$

From Equation 1, $\frac{\Delta s}{\Delta t} = v$ and so we have:

$$P = Fv \tag{24a}$$

So the two meanings are equivalent – they are both useful in different circumstances. (Remember, though: just as Δs is the displacement in the direction of the force, so v is the component of velocity in the direction of the force.)

Figure 1.48 Pumping iron

WORKED EXAMPLES

Q A woman training on a stepping machine 'climbs' 150 m in 2 minutes. If her mass is 60 kg, calculate her power.

A Using Equations 9, 20 and 25:

work done against gravity = $F\Delta s = mg\Delta s$

$$\begin{aligned}\text{power} &= \frac{mg\Delta s}{\Delta t} \\ &= \frac{(60\,\text{kg} \times 9.8\,\text{N kg}^{-1} \times 150\,\text{m})}{120\,\text{s}} \\ &= 736\,\text{W}\end{aligned}$$

Q A Formula 1 racing car travelling at its top speed of 95 m s⁻¹ has an engine power of 15 kW. Calculate the thrust of the engine (i.e. the force it produces on the car).

A Rearranging Equation 24:

$$F = \frac{P}{v} = \frac{1.5 \times 10^4\,\text{W}}{95\,\text{m s}^{-1}} = 158\,\text{N}$$

In the second example, you might wonder why the engine needs to provide a thrust if the car is not accelerating. The thrust from the engine is balanced by an equal, opposite force from air resistance and friction with the road, and the car moves at constant velocity.

QUESTIONS

Q 38 An athlete is working out by doing 'bench presses'. Each lift raises 60 kg through a distance of 60 cm. If he wanted to generate 150 W of power, how quick would each lift have to be?

Q 38 A sprinter of mass 60 kg accelerates to her top speed of 10 m s^{-1} in 3 s. Calculate her average power while accelerating.

Measuring power

In any physical activity, the output power that you measure (as in Activity 25) is less than the overall input power from muscles, because the process is never 100% efficient and you have not measured the energy wasted in heating. Table 1.3 below lists some typical input powers for various human activities. You might like to compare them with your output power measured in Activity 25 and shown in Figure 1.49.

Activity	Input power/W kg^{-1}
Resting, lying down	1.2
Sitting	1.2
Standing	1.2
Eating	1.2
Dressing/undressing	2.3
Showering	4.1
Typing at a computer	2.3
Walking (5.5 km h^{-1})	6.4
Cycling (15 km h^{-1})	5.8
Jogging (8 km h^{-1})	9.4
Fast running (6 min mile)	18
Swimming (fast crawl)	18
Playing musical instrument	2.9
Playing cricket	4.7
Playing table tennis	5.3
Playing tennis	7.1
Skiing	9.4
Dancing (energetically)	7.6
Playing football	11
Gymnastics	12

Table 1.3 Some activities and their input power demands

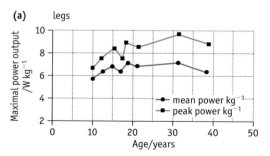 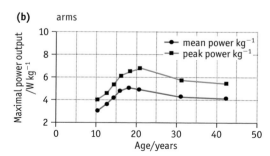

Figure 1.49 Graphs of maximum power output per kg of body mass against age

Use videos (for example, from YouTube) and software such as *Tracker* to estimate the output power of a weightlifter, space shuttle or other moving object.

Use the data in Table 1.3 to estimate how much energy you need to take in (from food) in a typical day.

A Fuse bar supplies about 1000 kJ. Use Table 1.3 to estimate how many Fuse bars you would 'burn off' during a sporting activity.

In a discussion or by exchanging notes, compare your results with someone else's.

QUESTIONS

Q 40 A sports car can generate a maximum 60 kW of power. If it has a mass of 800 kg, what is the minimum time in which the car could accelerate from rest to 30 m s^{-1}?

Q 41 Your 'basal metabolic rate' – the amount of power you generate while resting (pumping blood, breathing and keeping warm) – is about 90 W. Calculate the amount of energy you need per day for simply existing.

Q 42 A 'kinetic' watch needs no battery. A tiny weight is set in motion by the slightest movements of your arm and, according to the manufacturer, enough energy to drive the watch for two weeks is stored electrically. If the power needed to drive the watch is 0.1 mW (1×10^{-4} W), estimate the amount of energy stored in the watch.

3.4 Summing up Part 3

In this part of the chapter you have seen how you can measure using the concept of work. You have applied the theory of conservation of energy and formulae for kinetic and gravitational potential energy to model different sporting situations. Finally, you have explored the relationship between power and energy.

A good way to reinforce the new ideas you have learned is to produce a 'concept map'. First, make a list (spread out on a large sheet of paper) of all the terms printed in bold in this part of the chapter plus any others that you think important. Then draw lines between all related terms. Finally, label each line with a phrase or equation describing the link.

Alternatively, you could download 'freemind' software, which allows you to produce an interactive revision map. You can use visual aids and colour to help highlight areas, and paste in hyperlinks to websites and animations on the Internet.

4 Stretching and springing

In this part of the chapter you are going to look at two sports that rely on elastic materials: bungee jumping (Figures 1.50 and 1.51) and pole vaulting. In doing so, you will revisit and use ideas from Parts 1 to 3 of this chapter.

Figure 1.50 The popular sport of bungee jumping

Figure 1.51 One of the authors doing research for this chapter

4.1 Bungee jumping

Standing on a platform built from the side of a sheer cliff face, I looked down. Forty-five metres below me the blue waters lay in wait, glistening in the sun. I had never been so terrified in my life. There was no way my brain was going to let me jump — it was as though an invisible force held me back.

'Stretch your arms out wide' came the voice from behind me, 'and whatever you do, don't grab the rope as you go down.' I tightened my shoelaces once more. 'Are you sure the rope won't slip off my ankles?' I asked.

The two technicians went through the equipment checklist a second time.

'Harnesses.' 'Checked.'

'Static sleeve.' 'Checked.'

'Hey, Bob. This carabiner's a bit loose. Do you think that matters?'

'No. It's been like that for ages.'

Bungee technicians took great pleasure in scaring first-timers.

'Okay, you're on for a jump!'

There was no turning back. Gingerly I stepped forward until my toes were right at the end of the platform. The countdown began. 'Five … four … three …' The voice of fear in my head was replaced by another:

'How can you face your friends if you wimp out?' I jumped.

For the next three and a half seconds I was weightless – like an astronaut in orbit, but at a fraction of the cost. And what a rush it was! It's hard to describe because it was like being in another world – with no sound and nothing supporting me. My body felt utterly vulnerable, powerless to prevent itself smashing into the water surface at over 100 kilometres an hour.

Panic was beginning to swamp my consciousness, but just then came the reassuring tug on my ankles from the cord above. I knew bungee ropes could stretch four times their natural length, but it seemed to extend forever. I could feel the tension building up and had to close my eyes. And then I felt the splash of water on my face as my head dipped briefly under, before I was pulled up again. Suddenly I was an enormous yo-yo, reaching fully half way back to the top. Gradually the bounces grew smaller and smaller until I came to rest above the waiting jet boat. The sense of relief was overwhelming.

Bungee jumping is not a new sport. For hundreds of years, men of the island of Pentecost, in the South Pacific, have leaped from wooden towers with jungle vines attached to their ankles (Figure 1.52). For them it's a test of their courage – the closer they swoop to the ground, the greater their bravery. Inevitably there have been deaths, one of which happened while Queen Elizabeth II and the Royal Family were watching the ceremony. So how has bungee jumping evolved into a relatively safe activity?

It has a lot to do with two guys from New Zealand. One is a daredevil businessman called A. J. Hackett, and the other, Henry van Asch, is a physicist. Back in the mid-1980s they planned some outrageous stunts to bring bungee jumping to the world's attention, including a leap from the Eiffel Tower. A policeman arrested Hackett after the jump (presumably once he'd stopped bouncing). A. J. Hackett Bungee became the world's first professional bungee operation in Queenstown, New Zealand. Since then, bungee jumping has become established worldwide.

Figure 1.52 The origins of bungee jumping

Analysing a bungee jump

In Activity 29 you are going to put yourself into the position of a bungee designer: given a piece of bungee rope, how do you choose the length to stop someone just short of the ground? Make it too long and they're history; too short and you'll remove a lot of the excitement. Before you do, you will see how you can apply the physics of this chapter to working out the correct length of a bungee rope.

One approach to solving many problems involving motion is to use forces. The forces on a bungee jumper are shown in Figure 1.53. Because the tension in the rope varies with extension, the force on the jumper is not constant, which makes it difficult to apply the equations of motion.

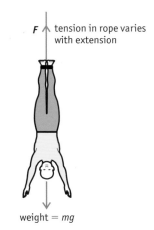

F tension in rope varies with extension

weight = mg

Figure 1.53 The forces on a bungee jumper

Another approach is to use energy conservation. Figure 1.54 shows the energy transfers at different stages during a jump. As the jumper falls, he loses gravitational potential energy. At first, during free fall, he gains kinetic energy. Then the rope begins to stretch, reducing the jumper's kinetic energy. Energy is transferred to the rope as it stretches, so the rope now has potential energy that we will call **elastic energy** (and symbolise E_{el}). When the jumper comes momentarily to rest at the bottom of the first 'bounce', his kinetic energy is again zero; he has lost gravitational potential energy and the rope has gained elastic potential energy. Energy conservation tells us that the gravitational energy lost ($mg\Delta h$) must be equal to the elastic energy gained by the rope.

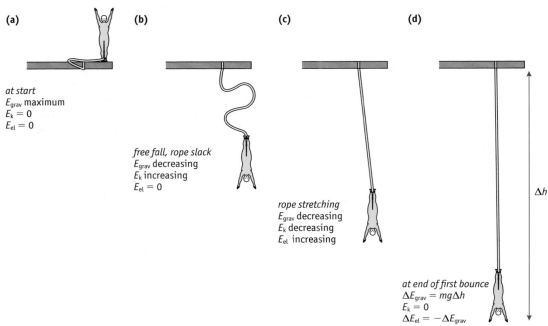

(a)

at start
E_{grav} maximum
$E_k = 0$
$E_{el} = 0$

(b)

free fall, rope slack
E_{grav} decreasing
E_k increasing
$E_{el} = 0$

(c)

rope stretching
E_{grav} decreasing
E_k decreasing
E_{el} increasing

(d)

Δh

at end of first bounce
$\Delta E_{grav} = mg\Delta h$
$E_k = 0$
$\Delta E_{el} = -\Delta E_{grav}$

Figure 1.54 Energy in a bungee jump

STUDY NOTE

Notice that this is very similar to finding the distance travelled from a velocity–time graph. (See Section 1.3.)

Measuring elastic energy

You will remember we used the definition of work to derive formulae for gravitational and kinetic energy. Force–extension graphs give us a way to find the work done in stretching a bungee rope. Figure 1.55 shows a typical force–extension graph. The force varies, so we cannot simply multiply force by distance to find the work done in stretching the sample. However, for a small increase in extension, Δx, the stretching force F is very nearly constant, so the work done is equal to the area of the strip:

$$\Delta W = F \times \Delta x$$

The total work done in stretching the sample can be found by adding up all the areas of the narrow strips (each with a different height). In other words, the elastic energy stored can be found from the **area under a force–extension graph**.

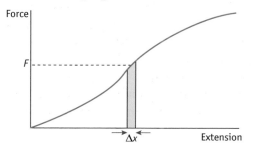

Figure 1.55 A force–extension graph

For a material that obeys Hooke's law, the force–extension graph is a straight line (Figure 1.56) and there is a simple formula for E_{el}:

$$E_{el} = \frac{1}{2}Fx \qquad (26)$$

where F is the force needed to produce an extension x. Using Equation 18 we can write an expression involving the stiffness k, which is constant for a sample that obeys Hooke's law:

$$E_{el} = \frac{1}{2}kx^2 \qquad (27)$$

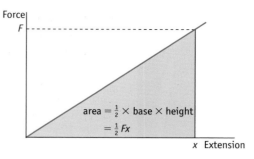

Figure 1.56 A force–extension graph for a material that obeys Hooke's law

However, with a rubber bungee cord, which does not obey Hooke's law, the graph is curved. We therefore estimate the area by counting squares of graph paper under the curve. In Figure 1.57, the values for force and extension are marked on the graph. On the scale shown, the area of each square represents $10\,\text{N} \times 0.1\,\text{m} = 1\,\text{J}$. You can estimate the area by counting only the squares where at least half the area is under the curve, giving 25 squares, i.e. the elastic energy stored is 25 J.

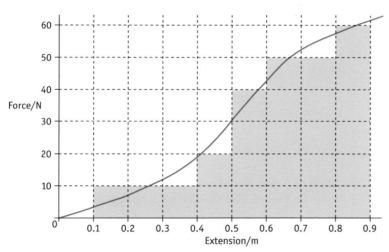

Figure 1.57 Estimating E_{el} by counting squares

⚙ ACTIVITY 29 BUNGEE CHALLENGE

Set up a model bungee jump using a piece of elastic. By calculating elastic energy from a force–extension graph, you can work out the height from which a given object can 'jump' with a given piece of elastic so that it will just miss the floor.

QUESTIONS

Q 43 In a bow and arrow, the wire stretches by 60 cm when the bow is pulled back. If the stiffness of the wire is $0.4\,\text{N m}^{-1}$, how much elastic energy is stored?

Q 44 In most bungee jumps, several cords are used, just in case one of them fails. *The number of cords depends on the jumper's body weight.* Explain the sentence in italics.

Q 45 In one of the earliest helicopter bungee jumps, a 75 kg man jumped from a helicopter with a rope 250 m long. His cord stretched to 610 m (2000 feet). Calculate **(a)** the gravitational potential energy lost as he fell, **(b)** the stiffness of the cord assuming it obeyed Hooke's law and **(c)** the extension of the cord when he finally came to rest.

4.2 Pole vaulting

Pole-vaulters are truly the astronauts of the stadium (Figure 1.58). In the 1960s there was a sudden rise in the pole-vault record heights (Figure 1.59), the result of fibreglass poles replacing bamboo and aluminium poles. Fibreglass totally changed the event, allowing the pole to bend nearly into a half circle during the swing.

Can we expect the pole-vault record to keep on increasing, or is there a limit? Answer Questions 45 and 46 to help you decide.

Figure 1.58 The French pole-vaulter Renaud Lavillenie

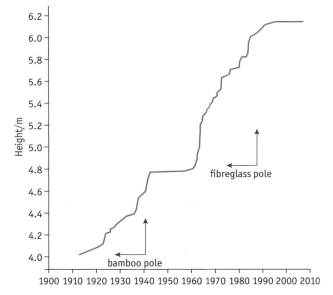

Figure 1.59 Pole-vault records

QUESTIONS

Q 46 Write down the labels that you would need to add to Figure 1.60 so that it shows the energy in a pole vault (as Figure 1.54 showed for a bungee jump).

Q 47 **(a)** If a pole vaulter can sprint at $10\,\mathrm{m\,s^{-1}}$ (Usain Bolt ran at a mean speed of $10.44\,\mathrm{m\,s^{-1}}$ when setting the 100 metres world record of $9.58\,\mathrm{s}$ in 2009), through what height can he raise his entire centre of gravity if all his kinetic energy is used to supply additional gravitational potential energy?

(b) Assuming that the vaulter's centre of gravity is 1 m above the ground when running, estimate the height of the vault.

(c) Say what, in practice, might **(i)** prevent the vaulter from clearing this height and **(ii)** enable him to exceed this height.

(d) Say whether you think the graph in Figure 1.59 will keep on rising. (Use $g = 9.81\,\mathrm{N\,kg^{-1}} = 9.81\,\mathrm{m\,s^{-2}}$.)

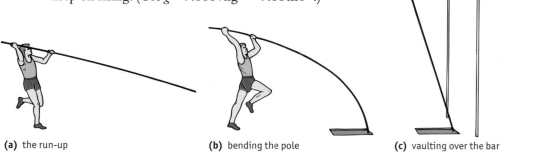

(a) the run-up   **(b)** bending the pole   **(c)** vaulting over the bar

Figure 1.60 Stages in a pole vault

4.3 Summing up Part 4

In this part of the chapter you have seen how to apply the idea of energy conservation and how to measure elastic energy using a force–extension graph. In doing so, you have used and extended ideas from earlier in the chapter. Questions 47 to 50 give you further practice in using ideas about energy.

QUESTIONS

Use $g = 9.81\,\mathrm{N\,kg^{-1}} = 9.81\,\mathrm{m\,s^{-2}}$ in these questions.

Q 48 An overhead electricity cable between two pylons stretches 50 cm under its own weight. How much elastic energy does it store? (Assume the cable obeys Hooke's law and has $k = 10^7\,\mathrm{N\,m^{-1}}$.)

Q 49 Itaipu, one of the world's biggest hydroelectric power stations, lies near one of the world's natural wonders – the Iguaçu Falls in South America. It supplies a large fraction of Brazil's and Paraguay's energy needs. When the flow of water is $10\,000\,\mathrm{m^3\,s^{-1}}$ the power station generates 12 GW of power (one gigawatt, $1\,\mathrm{GW} = 10^9\,\mathrm{W}$).

(a) Calculate the mass of water flowing per second. (Density of water = $1000\,\mathrm{kg\,m^{-3}}$)

(b) Estimate the height through which the water drops. What assumption did you make? Will this lead to an underestimate or an overestimate of the height?

Q 50 **(a)** A swimmer moving at constant speed through the water uses a force to do work but does not increase her kinetic energy. How can this be?

(b) Figure 1.61 is a graph of the energy cost of swimming a kilometre for aquatic animals. For humans, a typical energy cost while swimming is $80\,\mathrm{kJ\,min^{-1}}$ and it takes many minutes to swim a kilometre. Approximately where on the graph would the 'human' data point lie? Comment on this.

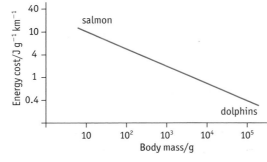

Figure 1.61 The energy cost of swimming

Q 51 Here is an energy puzzle. A rock climber slips vertically, gradually stretching her rope until it supports her, i.e. the tension in the rope is equal to her weight ($F = mg$). She falls through a height Δh and her rope is stretched by the same amount. She has lost gravitational potential energy $\Delta E_{grav} = mg\Delta h$. But the elastic energy stored in the rope (which obeys Hooke's law) is $\Delta E_{el} = \dfrac{1}{2}Fx = \dfrac{1}{2}mg\Delta h$. What has happened to the missing energy?

5 Jumping and throwing

Many events in the Olympics involve launching objects into the air. The jumping events involve throwing your own body as a **projectile** and the throwing events involve launching another object.

The four Olympic throwing events are discus, shot, javelin and hammer. Despite the varying masses and shapes of all these objects thrown, there are two main aspects that all throwers have to master: a speed-building phase and a throwing position angle.

The main components of long jump are horizontal speed and vertical lift. International long jumpers should be fast enough to earn a place in their national relay squad. Jesse Owens and Carl Lewis were the world's fastest sprinters in their time and were also the best long jumpers. Heike Drechsler was one of the world's best ever women long jumpers, holding joint world records for the 200 m and has a personal best of 10.91 s for the 100 m sprint in 1986. Coaching for the long jump involves coaching for sprinting. The long jump also involves achieving sufficient height to stay in the air for a long time. The longer the time in the air and the greater the horizontal speed, the greater the horizontal distance travelled.

5.1 Ski jumping

The Winter Olympic sport of ski jumping is similar to the long jump – the aim is to leave the ramp at high speed in order to travel as far as possible before landing. In this section, you will explore the relationship between the launch speed and the length of the 'jump' and so reach some general conclusions about projectiles that move freely under gravity.

> **⚙ ACTIVITY 30 SKI JUMP**
> Use the arrangement shown in Figure 1.62 to see how the launch height h_1, and the height of the vertical drop h_2 affect the horizontal distance travelled.

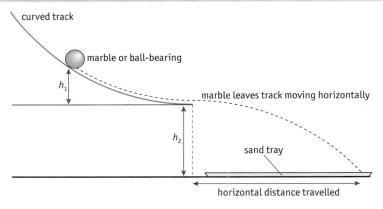

Figure 1.62 A model ski jump

Activity 30 shows that increasing the launch height and the vertical drop both increase the length of the jump. How can these results be explained more precisely? Activity 31 provides a clue.

> **⚙ ACTIVITY 31 PROJECTILE MOTION**
> Release two squash balls side by side at the same time. Do they hit the floor at the same time? Repeat, but this time launch one squash ball horizontally. Do they hit the floor at the same time?

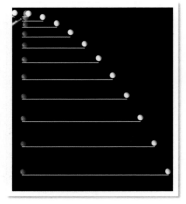

Figure 1.63 Strobe photographs of projectiles

Figure 1.63 shows strobe photographs of two balls moving as in Activity 31. Notice that they both hit the floor at the same time. It does not matter that one of them has got a horizontal velocity as well as a vertical acceleration. Notice too, that the sideways-moving ball covers equal horizontal distances in equal time intervals – its horizontal velocity remains constant and is unaffected by its vertical motion. The vertical and horizontal components of the motion are *independent of each other*, so we can treat them quite separately.

Projectile motion

The displacement, velocity and acceleration of the projectile (the ball or the skier) are all vectors. We can treat the horizontal components of these vectors completely separately from the vertical components. We will use subscripts x and y to indicate horizontal and vertical components of velocity and acceleration.

If the ball, or skier, leaves the ramp horizontally, the initial velocity vector has no vertical component: $u_y = 0$. In the vertical direction, the force of gravity provides a uniform acceleration so the vertical component of velocity increases. The vertical motion is described by Equations 3b and 6a with $a_y = g = 9.81\,\mathrm{m\,s^{-2}}$, taking downwards as positive:

$$v_y = gt$$

and

$$y = \frac{1}{2}gt^2 \tag{28}$$

In the horizontal direction there is no component of the gravitational force, so there is no acceleration: $a_x = 0$. The horizontal velocity remains equal to its initial value u_x and the same as Equation 6a with $a = 0$:

$$x = u_x t \tag{29}$$

The horizontal and vertical components combine to give a projectile a **trajectory** (path through the air) that has the shape of a **parabola**. Activity 32 illustrates this.

ACTIVITY 32 PARABOLIC TRAJECTORY

Use Equations 28 and 29 to complete Table 1.4 and plot the trajectory of a ball thrown sideways at $2\,\mathrm{m\,s^{-1}}$.

Time t/s	Vertical displacement y/m	Horizontal displacement x/m
1		
2		
3		
4		
5		

Table 1.4 Table for Activity 32

The following example shows how analysis of projectile motion can be useful in police forensic work.

WORKED EXAMPLE

Q A car ran off a mountain road and landed 80 m from the foot of a cliff face having fallen 100 m. Was the driver going too fast? The speed limit was 30 mph (about $13\,\mathrm{m\,s^{-1}}$).

A If air resistance is ignored, the horizontal component of the velocity will not change as the car leaves the road and travels through the air. The horizontal velocity can be estimated if the horizontal distance travelled (80 m) is divided by the time that the car is in the air.

Dealing with vertical motion first to find t:

displacement vertically, $y = 100\,\mathrm{m}$
initial velocity, $u_y = 0\,\mathrm{m\,s^{-1}}$
acceleration downwards due to gravity, $g \approx 10\,\mathrm{m\,s^{-2}}$

Using Equation 28: $y = \frac{1}{2}gt^2$, so:

$$t = \sqrt{\left(\frac{2y}{g}\right)} = \sqrt{\left(\frac{2 \times 100\,\mathrm{m}}{10\,\mathrm{m\,s^{-2}}}\right)} = 4.47\,\mathrm{s}$$

Now the horizontal velocity can be found using Equation 29:

$$u_x = \frac{x}{t} = \frac{80\,\mathrm{m}}{4.47\,\mathrm{s}} = 17.897\,\mathrm{m\,s^{-1}} \approx 18\,\mathrm{m\,s^{-1}}$$

So the driver was well over the speed limit and this probably contributed to the crash.

5.2 Throwing

In throwing events such as the discus and shot, and in games such as football or golf, the projectile is not launched horizontally. But what launch angle gives the maximum range?

A top British shot-putter (ranked third in the UK at the time with a distance of 17.90 m) took part in biomechanical tests to find the limiting factors in his performance. The digitised information from a video of his throwing was analysed by computer. Data on height of release h, projection speed V, and projection angle θ (see Figure 1.64) were all recorded. By calculating the effect of changing the angle and launch speed, he found that he needed to increase the speed and alter the launch angle. By changing his technique, he increased his personal best by 0.4 m.

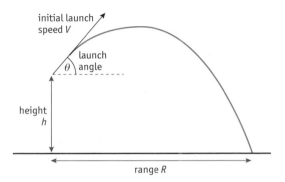

Figure 1.64 Measurements on a shot-putt trajectory

The range of a projectile

You can analyse the motion of a shot by resolving the initial velocity into horizontal and vertical components:

$$u_x = V \cos \theta$$

and:

$$u_y = V \sin \theta \tag{30}$$

and then treating the horizontal and vertical motions independently.

For a projectile launched from ground level ($h = 0$), you can find the time of flight by considering the vertical component of its motion and using Equation 6a:

$$s = ut + \frac{1}{2}at^2$$

With $s = 0$ (the projectile falls back to the ground), $u = u_y = V \sin \theta$ and $a = -g$, we have:

$$0 = V \sin \theta t - \frac{gt^2}{2}$$

so:

$$\frac{gt^2}{2} = Vt \sin \theta$$

$$t = \frac{2V \sin \theta}{g} \tag{31}$$

The **range** R (i.e. the horizontal displacement x) can then be found using Equation 29:

$$R = x = u_x t$$

$$= \frac{V \cos \theta \times 2V \sin \theta}{g}$$

$$= \frac{2V^2 \sin \theta \cos \theta}{g} \tag{32}$$

In this simple situation, the range is greatest for $\theta = 45°$.

However, real life is less straightforward – for a start, h is rarely zero. Also, air resistance significantly affects the motion of many projectiles, so the launch angle varies according to the object in question.

The angle of release in a hammer throw is close to 45° because it is launched from near the ground and because air resistance has little effect on its motion. The shot-put requires an angle less than 45° because it is launched from a position higher than where it lands. Because of their shape, a discus and javelin 'float' on the air: the angle of release depends on release speed and headwind but is always less that 45°. The effects of 'spin' and air resistance make the trajectories of cricket and golf balls even more complicated – again, their best launch angle is less than 45°.

Using a computer model

In Activity 33, you use a computer to calculate the range of a projectile launched from above the ground. The main advantage of the computer is that it can perform routine calculations very quickly. You, as the scientist, just need to tell it the correct calculations to perform. Once you get an equation of the physics correct and set up a working computer program based on correct physical equation, you can design problems that may be very difficult or expensive to run for real. If the results do not match up with what happens in a real-world experiment, this tells you that the equation inserted in the program is probably wrong. Refinements can then be made until the computer simulation is closer to reality. Effectively, you can perform a computer experiment and obtain results quickly, cheaply and safely. Engineers design aircraft, cars, buildings and bridges in this way.

ACTIVITY 33 RANGE OF A PROJECTILE

By carrying out some algebra, derive an equation for the range of a projectile launched from above the ground. Ignore air resistance. Use a spreadsheet to calculate the range for various launch speeds and angles.

5.3 Summing up Part 5

In this part of the chapter you have revisited ideas about vectors and about uniformly accelerated motion and used them to study projectiles. Questions 52–54 and Activities 34 and 35 use these ideas in a variety of sporting and non-sporting situations, both real and imaginary!

QUESTIONS

Q 52 A skier slides down the slope shown in Figure 1.65, leaving the ramp at X horizontally at $20\,\mathrm{m\,s^{-1}}$.

(a) She drops through 20 m before hitting the mountainside at Y. Calculate the time this takes.

(b) Using the time from (a), calculate the horizontal displacement R.

(c) Explain how each of the following actions affects the distance R:
   (i) the skier pushes herself off horizontally when leaving X
   (ii) the skier tries to jump upwards at X before leaving the ramp.

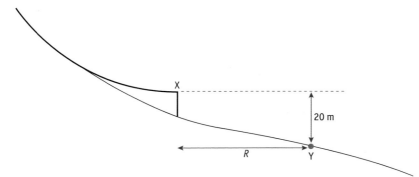

Figure 1.65 Ski-jump diagram for Question 52

Q 53 A cartoon character (such as 'Roadrunner', for instance) is sometimes shown running off the edge of a cliff (Figure 1.66). It is only when he looks down and realises that there is no ground at his feet that he stops moving forwards and starts to drop vertically.

(a) Explain what *should* happen to the horizontal component of his velocity and the vertical component of his velocity as soon as he runs off the edge of the cliff.

(b) Sketch the cartoon trajectory of his motion and also the correct physical parabolic trajectory.

Figure 1.66 A cartoon character runs over the edge of a cliff

Q 54 Figure 1.67 is from a 16th-century book and shows the supposed trajectory of a cannon ball.

(a) What evidence have you seen that shows that such a trajectory is incorrect?

(b) Sketch a more realistic path for the cannon ball (ignoring air resistance).

(c) If the cannon ball is launched from ground level at a speed of $50\,\mathrm{m\,s^{-1}}$, calculate its range for launch angles of 30°, 45° and 60°.

Figure 1.67 The supposed trajectory of a cannon ball, drawn in 1561

⚙ ACTIVITY 34 WHAT HAPPENS NEXT?

A James Bond-type superhero has just spotted a wicked villain climbing over the balcony of a building opposite, intent on some dastardly deed (Figure 1.68). He takes aim and fires. Just as he does so, the villain notices what's happening and lets go, hoping to drop to the ground and escape. What happens next? Does the villain escape the bullet? Use your knowledge of projectile motion to complete the story.

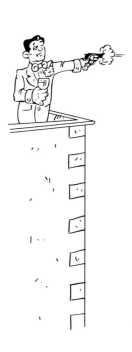

Figure 1.68 What happens next?

⚙ ACTIVITY 35 FORCE TO KICK A FOOTBALL

By carrying out and analysing measurements of mass, distance and time (Figure 1.69), calculate the size of the force used to kick a football.

PRACTICAL SKILLS REFERENCE

Carrying out practical work

See Practical skills notes 3.1–3.2

Analysis and interpretation of data

See Practical skills note 4.1

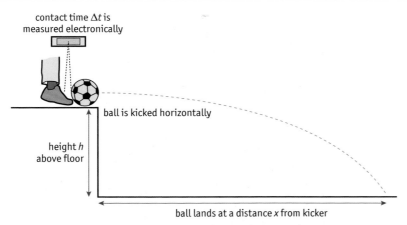

contact time Δt is measured electronically

ball is kicked horizontally

height h above floor

ball lands at a distance x from kicker

Figure 1.69 Apparatus for Activity 35

FURTHER INVESTIGATION

Use computer models and experimental measurements to investigate the effect of air resistance on the range of projectiles with various shapes.

6 Last lap

6.1 Summing up the chapter

In this chapter you have studied some aspects of motion, balanced and unbalanced forces, moments and energy. This concluding session is intended to help you to look back over the whole chapter and consolidate your knowledge and understanding.

> ### ⚙ ACTIVITY 36 SPORTS CONSULTANT
>
> Look back through the chapter and make sure you know the meanings of the key terms printed in bold.
>
> Use what you have learned in this chapter to write a brief guide for a coach or sports teacher to help them integrate physics into their training. Choose any sport you like that involves one or more of the concepts you have studied in the chapter. Here are a few possibilities: high jump, skiing, paragliding, sailing.
>
> Include explanations of the relevant physics principles, and how to apply them to the sport. Write in an appropriate style for your readers.

Throughout this chapter, you have seen how graphs can be just as useful as equations in calculating physical quantities. You have used the gradient of a graph and the area under a graph.

> ### ⚙ ACTIVITY 37 USING GRAPHS
>
> Summarise in a table all the different quantities you know how to find using gradients and areas of graphs along with the graph they are measured from.

6.2 Questions on the whole chapter

Q 55 A fielder throws a cricket ball of mass 160 g towards the stumps. The wicket keeper catches the ball, which is travelling at $15 \, \text{m s}^{-1}$. In bringing the ball to rest, his hands move 0.4 m backwards. What is the average stopping force applied to the ball?

Q 56 In 1976, basketball player Darrell Griffith's standing vertical jump measured 1.20 m. Estimate the speed at which he left the ground.

Q 57 A karate expert sets up a block of wood, mass 500 g, to break with his fist. The energy needed to smash the block is 40 J. Estimate the minimum speed of the karate expert's fist to break it, assuming that all its kinetic energy is transferred to the block.

Q 58 A snooker cue of mass 450 g strikes a cue ball 'head on' at $0.95 \, \text{m s}^{-1}$. The ball has mass 160 g. Immediately after striking the cue ball, the cue's velocity is reduced to $0.4 \, \text{m s}^{-1}$.

(a) Show that the initial total momentum is about $0.4 \, \text{kg m s}^{-1}$.

(b) Calculate the velocity of the cue ball.

Q 59 Ingrid, Agnetha and Novalie are identical triplets who love playing on their see-saw. They each weigh 300 N and the see-saw is 2 m long with the pivot in the middle. If Ingrid sits at the very end on one side of the see saw, where can Agnetha and Novalie sit so that the see-saw balances? (Agnetha and Novalie can't sit in the same place!) It may help to sketch a diagram as part of your answer, indicating the distances from the pivot that each girl sits.

Q 60 A ski-lift can carry 100 people at a time up a slope at 20° to the horizontal, at $3 \, \text{m s}^{-1}$. Estimate the minimum power of the ski-lift motor.

Q 61 When an aeroplane lands on an aircraft carrier, it can be stopped by a huge steel 'arresting wire' that is stretched across the deck. A plane of mass 20 t lands at $50\,\mathrm{m\,s^{-1}}$ and the wire has a stiffness $k = 3.3 \times 10^8\,\mathrm{N\,m^{-1}}$. ($1\,\mathrm{t} = 1 \times 10^3\,\mathrm{kg}$). Find:

(a) the kinetic energy of the plane landing

(b) the amount the arresting wire stretches (assuming the wire obeys Hooke's law).

Q 62 A car skidded off the road and hit a low stone wall. Glass from the windscreen was found 4.0 m in front of the car windscreen in the field.

(a) If the height of the middle of the windscreen was 1.2 m, estimate the speed of the car as it hit the wall.

(b) Why is this value likely to be lower than the actual speed of the car when it had been on the road?

6.3 Achievements

Now you have studied this chapter you should be able to achieve the outcomes listed in Table 1.5.

	TABLE 1.5 ACHIEVEMENTS FOR THE CHAPTER HIGHER, FASTER, STRONGER	
	Statement from Examination Specification	*Section(s) in this chapter*
1	know and understand the distinction between base and derived quantities and their SI units	1.2, 1.4, 1.5, 2.3, 3.1
2	demonstrate their knowledge of practical skills and techniques for both familiar and unfamiliar experiments	1.3, 1.4, 1.5, 2.1, 2.2, 2.3
3	be able to estimate values for physical quantities and use their estimate to solve problems	1.4, 3.1, 3.3, 4.3
5	be able to communicate information and ideas in appropriate ways using appropriate terminology	3.1, 3.3, 3.4, 5.3
9	be able to use the equations for uniformly accelerated motion in one dimension: $$s = \frac{(u+v)t}{2}$$ $$v = u + at$$ $$s = ut + \tfrac{1}{2}at^2$$ $$v^2 = u^2 + 2as$$	1.2, 1.3
10	be able to draw and interpret displacement/time, velocity/time and acceleration/time graphs	1.3
11	know the physical quantities derived from the slopes and areas of displacement/time, velocity/time and acceleration/time graphs, including cases of non-uniform acceleration, and understand how to use the quantities	1.3
12	understand scalar and vector quantities, and know examples of each type of quantity and recognise vector notation	1.2, 2.1
13	be able to resolve a vector into two components at right angles to each other by drawing and by calculation	2.1
14	be able to find the resultant of two coplanar vectors at any angle to each other by drawing, and at right angles to each other by calculation	2.1
15	understand how to make use of the independence of vertical and horizontal motion of a projectile moving freely under gravity	5.1, 5.2
16	be able to draw and interpret free-body force diagrams to represent forces on a particle or on an extended but rigid body	2.1, 2.3
17	be able to use the equation $\sum F = ma$, and understand how to use this equation in situations where m is constant (Newton's second law of motion), including Newton's first law of motion where $a = 0$, objects at rest or travelling at constant velocity (Use of the term terminal velocity is expected)	1.4, 2.1

continued

TABLE 1.5 ACHIEVEMENTS FOR THE CHAPTER HIGHER, FASTER, STRONGER *continued*

Statement from Examination Specification	*Section(s) in this chapter*
18 be able to use the equations for gravitational field strength $g = \dfrac{F}{m}$ and weight $W = mg$	1.4
19 CORE PRACTICAL 1: Determine the acceleration of a freely falling object	1.3
20 know and understand Newton's third law of motion and know the properties of pairs of forces in an interaction between two bodies	1.4
21 understand that momentum is defined as $p = mv$	1.5
22 know the principle of conservation of linear momentum, understand how to relate this to Newton's laws of motion and understand how to apply this to problems in one dimension	1.5
23 be able to use the equation for the moment of a force, moment of force = Fx where x is the perpendicular distance between the line of action of the force and the axis of rotation	2.3
24 use the concept of centre of gravity of an extended body and apply the principle of moments to an extended body in equilibrium	2.3
25 be able to use the equation for work $\Delta W = F\Delta s$ including calculations when the force is not along the line of motion	3.1, 3.2
26 be able to use the equation $E_k = \frac{1}{2}mv^2$ for the kinetic energy of a body	3.1
27 be able to use the equation $\Delta E_{grav} = mg\Delta h$ for the difference in gravitational potential energy near the Earth's surface	3.1, 4.1, 4.2
28 know, and understand how to apply, the principle of conservation of energy including use of work done, gravitational potential energy and kinetic energy	3.1, 4.1, 4.2
29 be able to use the equations relating power, time and energy transferred or work done: $P = \dfrac{E}{t}$ and $P = \dfrac{W}{t}$	3.3
30 be able to use the equation: efficiency = $\dfrac{\text{[useful energy (or power) output]}}{\text{[total energy (or power) input]}}$	3.2

Answers

Q 1 $v = u + a\Delta t$

$= 2.0\,\mathrm{m\,s^{-1}} + 1.5\,\mathrm{m\,s^{-2}} \times 3.0\,\mathrm{s}$

$= 2.0\,\mathrm{m\,s^{-1}} + 4.5\,\mathrm{m\,s^{-1}} = 6.5\,\mathrm{m\,s^{-1}}$

Q 2 $v = u + a\Delta t$

Assuming he is falling from rest:

$u = 0\,\mathrm{m\,s^{-1}}$

Taking downwards as positive, $a = g = +9.8\,\mathrm{m\,s^{-2}}$,

$\Delta t = 2.5\,\mathrm{s}$, so

$v = +9.8\,\mathrm{m\,s^{-2}} \times 2.5\,\mathrm{s}$

$= +24.5\,\mathrm{m\,s^{-1}}$

Q 3 $a = \dfrac{(v - u)}{\Delta t}$

$= \dfrac{(0\,\mathrm{m\,s^{-1}} - 9.0\,\mathrm{m\,s^{-1}})}{0.003\,\mathrm{s}}$

$= \dfrac{-9.0\,\mathrm{m\,s^{-1}}}{0.003\,\mathrm{s}}$

$= -3000\,\mathrm{m\,s^{-2}}$

Q 4 $a = \dfrac{(v - u)}{\Delta t}$

$v = -25\,\mathrm{m\,s^{-1}}$, $u = 5.0\,\mathrm{m\,s^{-1}}$, $\Delta t = 0.012\,\mathrm{s}$

$a = \dfrac{(-25.0\,\mathrm{m\,s^{-1}} - 5.0\,\mathrm{m\,s^{-1}})}{0.012\,\mathrm{s}}$

$= -2500\,\mathrm{m\,s^{-2}}$

Note that the velocity directions are carefully given positive and negative signs; positive for rightwards velocity and negative for leftwards.

Q 5 **(a)** $\Delta s = 4.0\,\mathrm{m}$ (s has increased from 2.0 m to 6.0 m) and

$\Delta t = 4.0\,\mathrm{s}$ so $v = 4.0\,\mathrm{m}/4.0\,\mathrm{s} = 1.0\,\mathrm{m\,s^{-1}}$

(b) If you draw any other triangle on this graph you should get the same velocity.

Q 6 **(a)** The velocity would be more than $1.0\,\mathrm{m\,s^{-1}}$ – displacement increases by more than 1.0 m in each second.

(b) The velocity would be negative, i.e. the motion is in the negative direction so the displacement in the positive direction decreases with time – or (if the graph goes below the horizontal axis) the displacement becomes larger in the negative direction.

Q 7 Using the triangle shown in Figure 1.5(b):

$\Delta v = 7.5\,\mathrm{m\,s^{-1}} - 3.5\,\mathrm{m\,s^{-1}} = 4.0\,\mathrm{m\,s^{-1}}$ and

$\Delta t = 3.0\,\mathrm{s} - 1.0\,\mathrm{s} = 2.0\,\mathrm{s}$

$a = \dfrac{4.0\,\mathrm{m\,s^{-1}}}{2.0\,\mathrm{s}} = 2.0\,\mathrm{m\,s^{-2}}.$

Using any other triangle would give the same answer.

Q 8 The graph would slope downwards from left to right, showing that the velocity in the positive direction is decreasing, or (if the graph goes below the horizontal axis) that the velocity is increasing in the negative direction.

Q 9 Using Equation 3b:

final velocity:

$v = u + a\Delta t = 8.00\,\mathrm{m\,s^{-1}} + 0.70\,\mathrm{m\,s^{-2}} \times 3.00\,\mathrm{s}$

$= 8.0\,\mathrm{m\,s^{-1}} + 2.1\,\mathrm{m\,s^{-1}} = 10.1\,\mathrm{m\,s^{-1}}$

displacement:

$s = ut + \dfrac{1}{2}at^2$

$= 8.00\,\mathrm{m\,s^{-1}} \times 3.00\,\mathrm{s} + \dfrac{1}{2} \times 0.70\,\mathrm{m\,s^{-2}} \times (3.00\,\mathrm{s})^2$

$= 24.0\,\mathrm{m} + 3.15\,\mathrm{m} = 27.15\,\mathrm{m}$

Q 10 A is ahead (there is a larger area under A's graph).

A's total displacement can be found by adding together the areas (1–4) of the triangles and rectangles as shown in Figure 1.70:

displacement = 37.5 m + 75 m + 5 m + 65 m

$= 182.5\,\mathrm{m}$

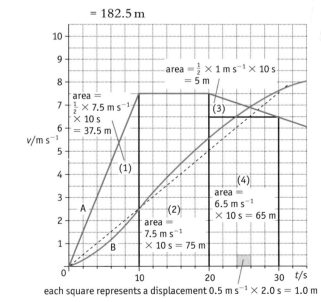

Figure 1.70 Graph for the answer to Question 10

Alternatively, use Equation 4 – but remember to treat each 10 s interval separately, since the acceleration is different in each case.

HIGHER, FASTER, STRONGER

B's total displacement can be found by counting the squares under the curved line. Each large square represents a displacement of 1.0 m (see Figure 1.70). Alternatively (and quicker), notice that B's graph can be approximated to a straight line giving a triangle of 'height' 7.5 m s^{-1} and 'base' 30 s, which represents a displacement of approximately:

$$\frac{1}{2} \times 7.5\,\text{m s}^{-1} \times 30\,\text{s} = 112.5\,\text{m}$$

This puts A about 70 m ahead of B after 30 s.

(You could refine this by estimating the number of graph-paper squares above and below the curved line, and adding and subtracting them from 112.5 m. Using this approach, B's actual displacement is about 5 m greater than 112.5 m — say 118 m altogether.)

Q 11 Using Equation 8:

net force $F = ma$

$$= 65\,\text{kg} \times 2.0\,\text{m s}^{-2}$$
$$= 130\,\text{kg m s}^{-2} = 130\,\text{N}$$

Q 12 Using Equation 8a:

$$F = \frac{(m\Delta u)}{\Delta t}$$

Taking the initial direction of motion as positive:

$u = +5.0\,\text{m s}^{-1}$, $v = -25.0\,\text{m s}^{-1}$

$\Delta v = v - u = -25.0\,\text{m s}^{-1} - 5.0\,\text{m s}^{-1} = -30.0\,\text{m s}^{-1}$

(notice the negative sign) so

$$F = \frac{0.120\,\text{kg} \times (-30.0\,\text{m s}^{-1})}{0.015\,\text{s}}$$
$$= -240\,\text{N}$$

The negative sign shows that the force was acting in the opposite direction to the initial motion — which it would need to be in order to stop and reverse the motion of the ball.

Q 13 The answer will depend on your mass — but whatever the numbers, you should give your answer in newtons and say that it acts downwards. As you are asked for an estimate, you can use an approximate value for $g \approx 10\,\text{N kg}^{-1}$. For example, suppose $m = 64\,\text{kg}$. Taking downwards as positive, $g \approx +10\,\text{N kg}^{-1}$, $W = mg \approx 64\,\text{kg} \times 10\,\text{N kg}^{-1} = 640\,\text{N}$ acting downwards.

Q 14 There are three 'Newton's third law' pairs of forces:

- contact force of person on the ground and ground on the person
- contact force of person on the javelin and javelin on the person
- gravitational force of person on the Earth and the Earth on the person.

Q 15 Taking the initial direction of the ball's motion as positive: $a = -12\,200\,\text{m s}^{-2}$

$F = ma$

$$= 0.024\,\text{kg} \times (-12\,200\,\text{m s}^{-2})$$
$$= -292.8\,\text{N} \; (\approx 300\,\text{N})$$

The ball exerts a force of equal size on the racket, in the same direction as its initial motion.

Q 16 (a) (i) There is a pair of gravitational forces attracting the diver and earth towards each other (as in Figure 1.14).
 (ii) In addition to the gravitational forces, as the diver enters the water there is a pair of forces involving the diver and the water — the diver exerts a downward force on the water and the water exerts an upward force that decelerates the diver.

(b) In an awkward splash landing, the diver comes to rest rapidly, experiencing a large change of velocity in a short time, i.e. a large acceleration, so a large, painful, force must be exerted on the diver by the water. If the diver enters the water smoothly, the change of velocity is much more gradual, i.e. the acceleration (and hence the force exerted by the water) is smaller.

(c) The two forces in the diagram are a third-law-force pair, so they are equal in size:

$$F_{\text{Earth}} = -F_{\text{diver}}$$

Using $F = ma$:

$$m_{\text{Earth}}a_{\text{Earth}} = -m_{\text{diver}}a_{\text{diver}}$$

$$a_{\text{Earth}} = \frac{-m_{\text{diver}}a_{\text{diver}}}{m_{\text{Earth}}}$$

Acceleration of Earth:

$$a_{\text{Earth}} = \frac{(70\,\text{kg} \times 9.8\,\text{m s}^{-1})}{6 \times 10^{24}\,\text{kg}}$$
$$= 1.1 \times 10^{-22}\,\text{m s}^{-2}$$

Q 17 Jay's momentum $p_J = 60\,\text{kg} \times 6.5\,\text{m s}^{-1} = 390\,\text{kg m s}^{-1}$

Kay's momentum $p_K = 65\,\text{kg} \times \left(\frac{180\,\text{m}}{30\,\text{s}}\right)$

$$= 65\,\text{kg} \times 6\,\text{m s}^{-1} = 390\,\text{kg m s}^{-1}$$

They have identical momentum.

Q 18 Momentum $p = 0.600\,\text{kg} \times 20\,\text{m s}^{-1} = 12\,\text{kg m}^{-1}$

Q 19 (a) $p = p_J + p_K = 390\,\text{kg m s}^{-1} + 390\,\text{kg m s}^{-1} = 780\,\text{kg m s}^{-1}$

(b) Now p_K is negative: $p = p_J + p_K = 390\,\text{kg m s}^{-1} + -390\,\text{kg m s}^{-1} = 0\,\text{kg m s}^{-1}$.

Q 20   Taking Ellie's original direction as positive:

Ellie's initial momentum = $m_E u_E$ = 50 kg × 4 m s^{-1}

$\qquad$ = 200 kg m s^{-1}

Laura's initial momentum = $m_L u_L$ = 40 kg × −4 m s^{-1}

$\qquad$ = −160 kg m s^{-1}

Total initial momentum, p = 200 kg m s^{-1} + (−160 kg m s^{-1})

$\qquad$ = 40 kg m s^{-1}

Total momentum after collision p = 40 kg m s^{-1}

After collision $v = \dfrac{p}{m} = \dfrac{40\,\text{kg m s}^{-1}}{90\,\text{kg}}$ = 0.44 m s^{-1}

As this is a positive velocity, they will be moving in the same direction as Ellie was initially.

Note: you could define Laura's initial direction as positive. The combined momentum is then negative, which shows that motion after the collision is in the opposite direction to Laura's initial motion.

Q 21   (a) Acceleration was uniform from 0 s to 40 s.

(b) Magnitude of uniform acceleration:

$a = \dfrac{\Delta v}{\Delta t}$

$\quad = \dfrac{20\,\text{m s}^{-1}}{40\,\text{s}}$

$\quad = 0.5\,\text{m s}^{-2}$

(c) Magnitude of the instantaneous acceleration at t = 80 s is found from slope of graph at t = 80 s.

$a = \dfrac{\Delta v}{\Delta t}$

$\quad = \dfrac{20\,\text{m s}^{-1}}{130\,\text{s}}$

$\quad = 0.15\,\text{m s}^{-2}.$

(Your answer may differ by up to about ± 0.03 m s^{-2}, depending on exactly how you drew your tangent line.)

(d) Net force:

$F = ma$

$\quad = 200\,000\,\text{kg} \times 0.5\,\text{m s}^{-2}$

$\quad = 100\,000\,\text{N}$

(e) Using area under section of graph between 0 s and 40 s:

displacement = $\dfrac{1}{2}$ × 20 m s^{-1} × 40 s

$\qquad = 400\,\text{m}$

(Or you could use Equation 4 with u = 0 m s^{-1}, a = 0.5 m s^{-2}, t = 40 s, which gives the same answer.)

Q 22   The three forces W (the weight acting vertically), H (the wind acting horizontally) and T (the force exerted by the support arm at an angle θ to the vertical) are in equilibrium so must form a triangle (Figure 1.71). Measurement on Figure 1.71 shows that $T \approx 25\,500$ N and $\theta \approx 11°$.

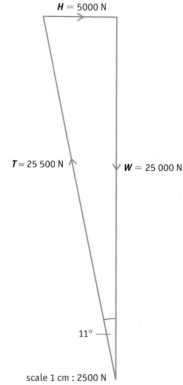

Figure 1.71 Vector diagram for the answer to Question 22

Q 23   (a) The plane has constant velocity (which means no acceleration) therefore the forces must be in equilibrium: ΣF = 0. See Figure 1.72(a).

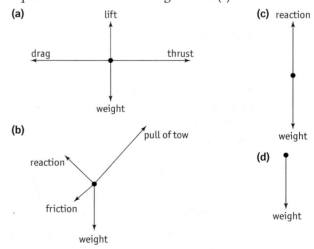

Figure 1.72 The answers to Question 23: (a) a plane with constant velocity, (b) a skier being towed up a slope, (c) a friction-free ice puck with constant velocity, (d) a ball after being thrown into the air

(b) As the skier is moving at constant velocity, the net force is zero ΣF = 0.

(c) The only forces are vertical: the weight of the puck and the upward reaction (contact force) exerted by the ice.

(d) The only force acting on the ball is gravity. (A common misconception is to also draw the force from the hand that has just released it.)

Q 24 See Figure 1.73. From Figure 1.28, $\tan\theta = \dfrac{1}{3}$

Horizontal force:

$F = W\tan\theta$

$\quad = 600\,\text{N} \times \dfrac{1}{3}$

$\quad = 200\,\text{N}$

By Pythagoras:

$T^2 = F^2 + W^2$

$\quad = (200\,\text{N})^2 + (600\,\text{N})^2$

$\quad = 4.00 \times 10^5\,\text{N}^2$

so $T = 632\,\text{N}$

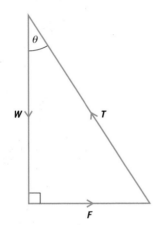

Figure 1.73 Vector diagram for the answer to Question 24

Q 25 **(a)** $T = \dfrac{W}{2\sin\theta}$, where W is the climber's weight (600 N).

As θ becomes small, then $\sin\theta$

approaches zero and T becomes very large.

(b) Rearranging the expression from (a):

$\sin\theta = \dfrac{W}{2T} = \dfrac{600\,\text{N}}{(2 \times 15 \times 10^3\,\text{N})}$

$\quad = 2 \times 10^{-2}$

$\theta = \sin^{-1}(2 \times 10^{-2}) = 1.1°$

Q 26 **(a)** Figure 1.74 shows a free-body diagram and a force vector diagram for the problem.

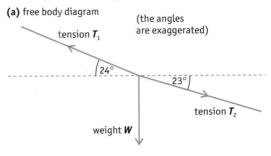

Figure 1.74 Diagrams for the answer to Question 26

(b) The horizontal components of $\boldsymbol{T}_1$ and $\boldsymbol{T}_2$ must be equal and opposite:

$T_1 \cos24° = T_2 \cos23°$ (i)

And the vertical component of $\boldsymbol{T}_1$ acting upwards must equal W and the vertical component of $\boldsymbol{T}_2$ acting downwards:

$T_1 \sin24° = W + T_2 \sin23°$ (ii)

Rearranging (i) gives:

$T_2 = T_1\left(\dfrac{\cos24°}{\cos23°}\right)$ (iii)

Substituting (iii) in (ii) gives:

$T_1 \sin24° = W + T_1\left(\dfrac{\cos24°}{\cos23°}\right)\sin23°$

Rearranging:

$T_1\left(\sin24° - \left(\dfrac{\cos24°}{\cos23°}\right)\sin23°\right) = W$

$T_1 = W \div \left(\sin24° - \left(\dfrac{\cos24°}{\cos23°}\right)\sin23°\right)$

$\quad = 5.27 \times 10^6\,\text{N}$

Substituting this value back into (i) gives:

$T_2 = T_1\left(\dfrac{\cos24°}{\cos23°}\right) = 5.23 \times 10^6\,\text{N}$

(c) If T_1 and T_2 both acted along the same direction, then it would be impossible to draw the closed vector triangle in Figure 1.74. It is the difference in the vertical components of T_1 and T_2 that supports the weight of the cable car.

Q 27 (a) See Figure 1.75. By Pythagoras:

$R^2 = (500\,\text{N})^2 + (100\,\text{N})^2 = 2.60 \times 10^5\,\text{N}^2$

so $R = 510\,\text{N}$

$\tan\theta = \dfrac{100}{500} = 0.2$, so $\theta = 11.3°$

(b) $R = \Sigma F = ma$

$a = \dfrac{R}{m} = \dfrac{510\,\text{N}}{100\,\text{kg}} = 5.1\,\text{m s}^{-2}$

The direction of acceleration is that of the resultant force, i.e. at 11.3° to the vertical.

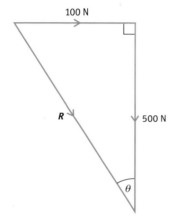

Figure 1.75 Diagram for the answer to Question 27

Q 28 The rope does *not* obey Hooke's law. The load in the second test is three-quarters that in the first (600 N/800 N = 0.75), but it does not produce three-quarters the extension (0.012 m/0.020 m = 0.60).

In the first case:

$\text{stiffness} = \dfrac{800\,\text{N}}{0.020\,\text{m}}$

$= 4.00 \times 10^4\,\text{N m}^{-1}$

$= 40.0\,\text{kN m}^{-1}$

In the second case:

$\text{stiffness} = \dfrac{600\,\text{N}}{0.012\,\text{m}}$

$= 50.0\,\text{kN m}^{-1}$

Q 29 (a) From Equation 18, extension $x = \dfrac{F}{k}$

$x = \dfrac{650\,\text{N}}{(6 \times 10^3\,\text{N m}^{-1})} = 1.1 \approx 10^{-1}\,\text{m}\ (= 11\,\text{cm})$

(b) Imagine that the 4 m rope is two 2 m ropes joined end to end. Each rope would be subject to the same force (650 N), so each would extend by 11 cm, giving a total extension of 22 cm.

Q 30 (a) If your arm is about 60 cm long, then
$M \approx 71\,\text{N} \times 0.60\,\text{m} \approx 40\,\text{N m}$
(The answer is approximate as the distance is a rough estimate.)

(b) The turning effect will be smaller because of the smaller perpendicular distance between your shoulder and the weight's line of action (Figure 1.76).

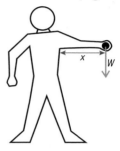

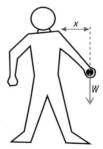

Figure 1.76 Diagram for the answer to Question 30(b)

Q 31 See Figure 1.77.

$2250\,\text{N} \times 1.35\,\text{m}$ (clockwise) $= 500\,\text{N} \times 1.35\,\text{m} + 850\,\text{N}$ $(x_2 + 1.35\,\text{m})$ (anticlockwise)

$x_2 + 1.35\,\text{m} = \dfrac{1750\,\text{N} \times 1.35\,\text{m}}{850\,\text{N}} = 2.88\,\text{m}$

$x_2 = 1.43\,\text{m}$

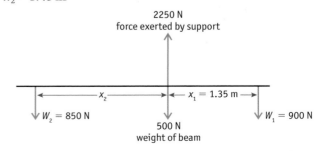

Figure 1.77 Diagram for the answer to Question 31

Q 32 Her left arm and both legs are extended at one side of the beam, the opposite side to her torso. Although the torso has a greater weight than the arm and legs, the line of action of its weight is closer to the support point (her right hand). The weight of the arm and legs is smaller, but the line of action is further from the support, so the moment due to the extended arm and legs can balance the moment due to the torso.

Q 33 200 J is 25% of the total energy, so:

total energy = 4 × 200 J = 800 J

Q 34 $E_k = \dfrac{1}{2}mv^2$

$= \dfrac{1}{2} \times 200\,\text{kg} \times (44\,\text{m s}^{-1})^2$

$= 1.94 \times 10^5\,\text{J}$

Q 35 The skier has slightly more kinetic energy than the car (if you guessed 'the same' you were not far out).

Car: $E_k = \dfrac{1}{2} \times 600\,\text{kg} \times (22\,\text{m s}^{-1})^2 = 1.45 \times 10^5\,\text{J}$

Skier: $E_k = \dfrac{1}{2} \times 80\,\text{kg} \times (66\,\text{m s}^{-1})^2 = 1.74 \times 10^5\,\text{J}$

Q 36 (a) $\Delta E_{\text{grav}} = mg\Delta h$

$= 65\,\text{kg} \times 9.81\,\text{N kg}^{-1} \times 35\,\text{m}$

$= 2.23 \times 10^4\,\text{J}$

$E_k = 2.23 \times 10^4\,\text{J}$

Rearranging Equation 23, $v^2 = \dfrac{2E_k}{m}$

so $v = \sqrt{\left(\dfrac{2E_k}{m}\right)}$

$= \sqrt{\left(\dfrac{2 \times 2.23 \times 10^4\,\text{J}}{65\,\text{kg}}\right)}$

$= 26\,\text{m s}^{-1}$

(b) The mass makes no difference to the speed. This can be shown algebraically:

$v = \sqrt{\left(\dfrac{2E_k}{m}\right)} = \sqrt{\left(\dfrac{2\Delta E_{\text{grav}}}{m}\right)}$

$= \sqrt{\left(\dfrac{2mg\Delta h}{m}\right)} = \sqrt{(2g\Delta h)}$

An alternative argument is to say that all free-falling objects have the same acceleration so will fall at the same rate and so reach the same speed.

Q 37 Angle between slope and *vertical* is $\theta = 40°$

Refer back to Question 35: kinetic energy of 80 kg skier moving at 66 m s⁻¹ is $1.74 \times 10^5\,\text{J}$

$\Delta W = F\Delta s \cos\theta$

so $\Delta s = \dfrac{\Delta W}{(F \cos\theta)}$

$\Delta W = 1.74 \times 10^5\,\text{J}$

F = downward gravitational force on skier

$= 80\,\text{kg} \times 9.81\,\text{N kg}^{-1}$

so $\Delta s = \dfrac{1.74 \times 10^5\,\text{J}}{(80\,\text{kg} \times 9.81\,\text{N kg}^{-1} \times \cos 40°)}$

$= 290\,\text{m}$

Alternatively, start with some algebra to eliminate mass as in Question 36:

$\dfrac{1}{2}mv^2 = mg\Delta h = mg\Delta s \cos\theta$

so $\Delta s = \dfrac{v^2}{(2g \cos\theta)}$

$= \dfrac{(66\,\text{m s}^{-1})^2}{(2 \times 9.8\,\text{m s}^{-1} \cos 40°)}$

$= 290\,\text{m}$

Q 38 Combining Equations 22 and 25:

$P = \dfrac{mg\Delta h}{\Delta t}$

so $t = \dfrac{mg\Delta h}{P}$

$= \dfrac{60\,\text{kg} \times 9.81\,\text{N kg}^{-1} \times 0.60\,\text{m}}{150\,\text{W}}$

$= 2.4\,\text{s}$

Q 39 $\text{Power} = \dfrac{\text{gain in kinetic energy}}{\text{time taken}}$

$= \dfrac{\dfrac{1}{2}mv^2}{\Delta t}$

$= \dfrac{\dfrac{1}{2} \times 60\,\text{kg} \times (10\,\text{m s}^{-1})^2}{3\,\text{s}}$

$= 1000\,\text{W}$

Q 40   Car must gain kinetic energy $\frac{1}{2}mv^2$.

Power $P = \dfrac{\Delta E}{\Delta t}$

So $\Delta t = \dfrac{\Delta E}{P} = \dfrac{\frac{1}{2}mv^2}{P}$

$= \dfrac{\frac{1}{2} \times 800\,\text{kg} \times (30\,\text{m s}^{-1})^2}{60 \times 10^3\,\text{W}}$

$= 6.0\,\text{s}$

Q 41   1 day $= 24 \times 60 \times 60\,\text{s} = 8.64 \times 10^4\,\text{s}$

so energy $= 90\,\text{W} \times 8.64 \times 10^4\,\text{s}$

$= 7.8 \times 10^6\,\text{J}$

Q 42   2 weeks $= 14 \times 8.64 \times 10^4\,\text{s}$

so energy $= 14 \times 8.64 \times 10^4\,\text{s} \times 10^{-4}\,\text{W} = 121\,\text{J}$

Q 43 $E_{el} = \frac{1}{2}kx^2 = \frac{1}{2} \times 0.4\,\text{N m}^{-1} \times (0.6\,\text{m})^2 = 7.2 \times 10^{-2}\,\text{J}$

Q 44   Each cord contributes just part of the force that acts on the jumper. For example, if a 600 N jumper is supported at rest by six cords, then a 700 N jumper will stretch a seven-cord rope by the same amount – each cord provides a force of 100 N.

Q 45   **(a)** $\Delta h = 610\,\text{m}$

$\Delta E_{grav} = mg\Delta h = 75\,\text{kg} \times 9.8\,\text{N kg}^{-1} \times 610\,\text{m}$

$= 4.5 \times 10^5\,\text{J}$

(b) Extension of cord, $x = 610\,\text{m} - 250\,\text{m} = 360\,\text{m}$

$E_{el} = \frac{1}{2}kx^2$

so $k = \dfrac{2E_{el}}{x^2} = 6.9\,\text{N m}^{-1}$

(c) Now the cord must just support his weight, i.e. upward force exerted by cord is $F = kx = mg$

so $x = \dfrac{mg}{k} = \dfrac{75\,\text{kg} \times 9.81\,\text{N kg}^{-1}}{6.9\,\text{N m}^{-1}}$

$= 107\,\text{m}$

Q 46   See Figure 1.78.

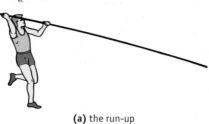

E_k maximum
E_{grav} minimum
E_{el} $= 0$

(a) the run-up

E_k decreasing
E_{grav} minimum
E_{el} increasing

(b) bending the pole

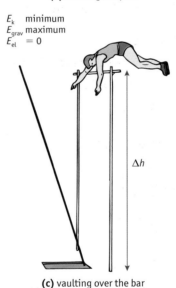

E_k minimum
E_{grav} maximum
E_{el} $= 0$

Δh

(c) vaulting over the bar

Figure 1.78 The answer to Question 46

Q 47   **(a)** Initial $E_k = \frac{1}{2}mv^2$. Increase in gravitational energy, $\Delta E_{grav} = mg\Delta h$. If all E_k becomes E_{grav}, then:

$mg\Delta h = \frac{1}{2}mv^2$

$\Delta h = \dfrac{v^2}{2g} = \dfrac{(10.0\,\text{m s}^{-1})^2}{2 \times 9.81\,\text{m s}^{-2}} = 5.1\,\text{m}$

(b) If his centre of gravity just clears the bar, then the height will be 6.1 m.

(c) (i) The energy conversion via bending the pole will not be 100% efficient so not all the initial E_k will become E_{grav}. Also, the vaulter still has some E_k at the top of the vault – he is moving over the bar.

(ii) The vaulter is not simply catapulted over, but can push himself further upwards using the pole.

(d) Probably not. Improvements in materials are unlikely to make much difference as the process must already be close to 100% efficient. Athletes may be able to increase the speed of the run-up (although probably not by much) and refine their vaulting technique, but these will probably make only a slight difference to the height of the vault. (In 2014, the world record of 6.15 m set in 1993 was broken by a leap of 6.16 m.)

Q 48 $E_{el} = \dfrac{1}{2}kx^2 = \dfrac{1}{2} \times 10^7\,\text{N m}^{-1} \times (0.5\,\text{m})^2$

$\qquad\quad = 1.25 \times 10^6\,\text{J}$

Q 49 **(a)** The mass flow rate is $10\,000\,\text{m}^3\,\text{s}^{-1} \times 1000\,\text{kg m}^{-3} = 10^7\,\text{kg s}^{-1}$

(b) Assume that all gravitational energy lost by the falling water is eventually transferred electrically, i.e. that the overall process is 100% efficient. In 1 second, falling water must transfer $\Delta E = 12 \times 10^9\,\text{J}$. This is achieved by a mass $m = 10^7\,\text{kg}$ falling through a height Δh where $\Delta E = mg\Delta h$, so

$$\Delta h = \frac{\Delta E}{mg} = \frac{12 \times 10^9\,\text{J}}{(10^7\,\text{kg} \times 9.81\,\text{N kg}^{-1})}$$

$$= 122\,\text{m}$$

In practice the efficiency will be (much) less than 100%, so the water will have to fall through a (much) greater height in order to generate the same amount of electrical power.

Q 50 **(a)** She is opposed by an equal force due to the water so she does not accelerate. She transfers energy by heating the water and herself, rather than increasing her kinetic energy.

(b) The data point for humans would lie slightly to the left of the 'dolphin' point at 10^5 g (100 kg). A human of mass 80 kg would expend about $1\,\text{kJ kg}^{-1}\,\text{min}^{-1}$, which is equivalent to $1\,\text{J g}^{-1}\,\text{min}^{-1}$. Swimming 1 km would take many minutes, so a human swimmer would expend many $\text{J g}^{-1}\,\text{km}^{-1}$, putting the data point well above the plotted line. Humans transfer considerably more energy while swimming than would an aquatic animal of similar body mass. This is because our bodies are a less suitable shape (less streamlined) so we experience a much greater opposing force than if we had evolved for swimming.

Q 51 Some of the energy must have been transferred elsewhere. If she slipped 'gradually' by sliding against a rock face, then friction between her body and the rock would have given rise to heating, which would account for the apparently 'missing' energy. If she fell and 'bounced' before coming to rest (as in a bungee jump) she would initially have some kinetic energy, then heating of the air, air resistance and internal heating in the rope would account for the 'missing' energy.

Q 52 **(a)** Her initial vertical velocity is zero. Using Equation 26:

$$y = \frac{1}{2}gt^2 \text{ so}$$

$$t = \sqrt{\left(\frac{2y}{g}\right)} = \sqrt{\left(\frac{2 \times 20\,\text{m}}{9.81\,\text{m s}^{-2}}\right)} = 2.0\,\text{s}$$

(b) Using Equation 29:

$$x = u_x t = 20\,\text{m s}^{-1} \times 2.0\,\text{s} = 40\,\text{m}$$

(c) (i) This would increase u_x, so she would travel further in the time she is in the air.

(ii) If she is initially moving upwards, she would take longer to reach the ground so would travel further.

Q 53 **(a)** The horizontal velocity remains constant and the vertical velocity increases steadily with a uniform acceleration.

(b) See Figure 1.79.

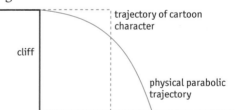

Figure 1.79 The answer to Question 53(b)

(a) You might have seen: long-exposure photographs of projectiles, or stop-frame video or film. Also, if you sketch a parabola on a whiteboard, you can throw a small projectile so that it follows the same path – you cannot do this if you sketch the path shown in Figure 1.67.

(b) See Figure 1.80.

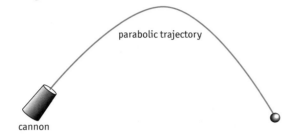

Figure 1.80 The answer to Question 54(b)

(c) $\theta = 30°$:

$$\text{range} = \frac{1\ 2 \times (50\,\text{m}\,\text{s}^{-1})^2 \sin30° \cos30°}{9.8\,\text{m}\,\text{s}^{-2}}$$

$$= 221\,\text{m}$$

$\theta = 45°$:

$$\text{range} = \frac{2 \times (50\,\text{m}\,\text{s}^{-1})^2 \sin45° \cos45°}{9.8\,\text{m}\,\text{s}^{-2}}$$

$$= 255\,\text{m}$$

$\theta = 60°$:

range = 221 m (same as $\theta = 30°$ because $\sin30° = \cos60°$ and $\cos60° = \sin30°$)

THE SOUND OF MUSIC

Why a chapter called *The Sound of Music?*

From the womb to the grave, music affects all of our lives. Whether we are performing it, actively listening to it or just allowing it to drift over us in the background, music forms an important part of the soundscape accompanying us throughout life. Many have wondered: 'What is music', and how it is different from 'noise'?

Since ancient times, humans have been interested in the science of musical sound. From Roman architects trying to control echoes in amphitheatres, to the study of pitch and harmonic sound, scientists have explored how sound travels, its speed, loudness and quality. Musical instruments have developed from simple origins to the complex and high quality orchestral instruments we know today. New technology has further revolutionised music making, allowing the widespread distribution of recorded music, now digital of course, and the development of synthesised sound.

Figure 2.1a Mixer desk

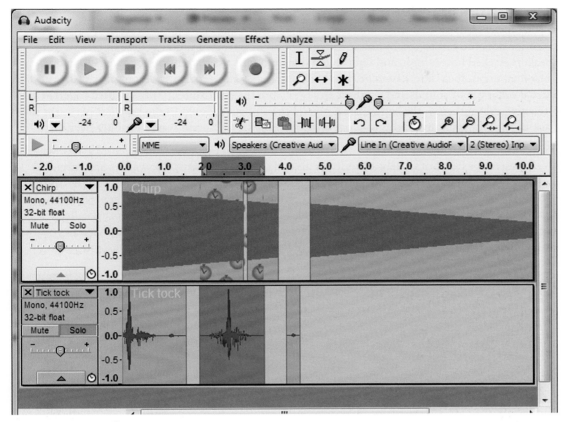

Figure 2.1b *Audacity®* screenshot

OVERVIEW OF PHYSICS PRINCIPLES AND TECHNIQUES

In this chapter you will build on ideas from GCSE about vibrations and waves, looking particularly at how these can be represented graphically. In Part 1 you will see how waves combine by a process called superposition, and how the waves produced by musical instruments are related to their physical properties. You will use computer software to explore and synthesise complex sounds.

Part 2 concentrates on the compact disc and DVD. You will discover how a disc stores sound and how the player retrieves it, and how wave properties of the laser light are exploited in order to recover the information. You will also see that, while a wave picture allows us to explain many properties of light, we need to introduce a different idea (that of photons) to explain how a laser works.

In the course of this chapter you will also be using and developing some key mathematical and ICT skills and techniques. Several activities are concerned with the generation and interpretation of graphs – the understanding of exactly what these graphs mean is crucial to the chapter. You will also use software, both as a data source and to analyse your own data.

In later chapters you will do further work on:

● travelling waves – in *Technology in Space*, *Reach for the Stars* and *Build or Bust?*

● the behaviour of light – in *Good Enough to Eat*

● superposition, interference and standing waves – in *Digging Up the Past* and *Build or Bust?*

● refraction and reflection – in *Build or Bust?*

● photons and energy levels – in *Technology in Space* and *Probing the Heart of Matter*

1 Making sounds

1.1 Synthetic sounds

A person steps out on to a stage. Six steel wires are struck sharply. They vibrate only millimetres to either side, too fast to see. Simultaneously, a flood of distorted sound volleys outwards from speakers stacked house-high, and ten thousand people shift their attention forwards. A second person emerges, flicks a few switches and begins to finger a pattern on to rectangular plastic keys. A virtual orchestra of sounds and rhythms emerges from the electronics, skilfully fused together into a recognisable anthem – the band has begun and the audience, down to the very last person at the back of the vast stadium, begins to move to the pulsing of the sound waves washing over them.

This familiar scenario of a modern concert would have been inconceivable a century ago, when an orchestra consisted of dozens of individuals and their instruments. Nowadays an individual can be a whole orchestra: musical sounds can be recorded and replayed, time after time. And, most astonishing of all, a simple keyboard or computer can be programmed to reproduce the sounds of any instrument, or in fact any sound, at the press of a button by a process called synthesising. A typical electronic keyboard may contain the 'voices' of several hundred instruments and synthesised effects as well as pre-programmed percussive and instrumental accompaniments.

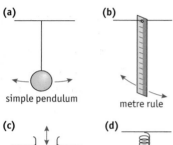

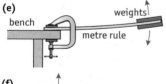
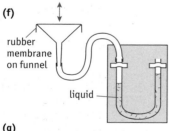

(a) simple pendulum

(b) metre rule

(c) weight in boiling tube — water

(d) a loaded spring

(e) bench, weights, metre rule

(f) rubber membrane on funnel, liquid

(g) marble on curtain track

Figure 2.2 Oscillators

> **ACTIVITY 1 SYNTHETIC SOUND – HOW REALISTIC IS IT?**
>
> Listen carefully to two extracts of the same piece of music, one with musicians playing real instruments and one computer-synthesised version of the same piece.
>
> Listen to synthesised versions of common sounds from children's interactive books or a smartphone mixing app, such as GarageBand®.
>
> Comment on the quality and realism of the synthesised sounds.

Getting from a real sound to a computer-synthesised version requires an understanding of the physical nature of sound. This is your aim in the first part of this chapter.

1.2 Oscillations

All sources of sound involve vibrations:

- A guitar string vibrates to produce a sound.
- The skin of a drum and a table top both vibrate when struck. (Can you suggest why the vibrations of the table top are smaller and die away faster?)
- Your vocal chords vibrate as you make sounds. Feel the vibration with your fingertips placed on the front of your neck as you hum a note.
- The prongs of a tuning fork vibrate. (You can see this if you touch the surface of water with a humming tuning fork.)

A motion that repeats itself over and over again, at regular time intervals, is called a **periodic oscillation**. Behaviour of this type is remarkably common (Figure 2.2). Oscillating periodic motion is often referred to as **harmonic motion** because of its relation to sound.

Describing and representing oscillations

The sequence of events that form one 'unit' of a periodic motion is called a **cycle**. In one cycle, the oscillating object moves to and fro, returning to its original position and direction, whereupon the cycle begins again. The time it takes for the system to complete one cycle is called its **time period**. The **frequency** of an oscillation is defined as the number of cycles executed per unit time. One cycle per second is called one hertz (Hz) – this is the SI unit of frequency.

The SI unit of period is the second. This is one of the seven **SI base units** from which all other SI units are derived. The hertz is an example of a **derived SI unit**.

> **MATHS REFERENCE**
> Derived units
> See Maths note 2.3

The frequency f and time period T are related:

$$T = \frac{1}{f} \tag{1}$$

which can also be written:

$$f = \frac{1}{T} \tag{1a}$$

As an oscillating object moves, the maximum **displacement** in either direction that it reaches from its **equilibrium position** is called the **amplitude**. The equilibrium (or mean) position is where the object comes to rest after its oscillations die down.

MATHS REFERENCE

Reciprocals

See Maths note 3.3

> ⚙ **ACTIVITY 2 PERIODIC OSCILLATIONS**
>
> By measuring the time period and frequency, investigate the motion of a variety of oscillating objects, such as those in Figure 2.2.

Displacement–time graphs

We often use displacement–time graphs to represent oscillations. Figure 2.3 shows such a graph for a metre rule that, when clamped to a bench with about 80 cm of its length projecting, oscillates with an amplitude of 30 mm and a frequency of 2.5 Hz.

A graph such as Figure 2.3 shows the 'shape' of an oscillation and is often referred to as a **waveform**. Waveforms like that in Figure 2.3, which have the same simple, smooth shape as graphs of $\sin\theta$ or $\cos\theta$ plotted against angle θ, are collectively described as **sinusoidal**.

PRACTICAL SKILLS REFERENCE

Scientific questions and information research

See Practical skills note 1.1

Planning and experimental design

See Practical skills notes 2.1–2.2

Carrying out practical work

See Practical skills notes 3.1–3.2

Analysis and interpretation of data

See Practical skills note 4.1

Conclusion and evaluation

See Practical skills note 5.1

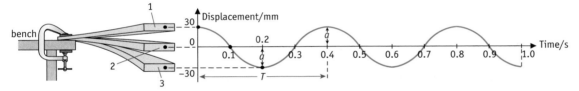

Figure 2.3 Displacement–time graph for a clamped metre rule

Sound waves produced by an oscillating object are detected when they set up oscillations with a similar waveform in a detector such as our ears or a microphone. The oscillations in a microphone can be displayed as a displacement–time graph using an oscilloscope or on a computer screen. Their waveform closely matches that of the sound source.

MATHS REFERENCE

Sine, cosine and tangent of an angle

See Maths note 6.2

Graphs of trigonometric functions

See Maths note 6.3

> ⚙ **ACTIVITY 3 EXPLORING WAVEFORMS WITH AN OSCILLOSCOPE**
>
> Use a cathode-ray oscilloscope (CRO) app on a smartphone or tablet or *PicoScope* to display a waveform produced by a sound source.
>
> Observe how the frequency and amplitude of the waveform are related to the pitch and loudness of the sound.

> ⚙ **ACTIVITY 4 EXPLORING WAVEFORMS WITH *AUDACITY***
>
> Use the sound analysis software *Audacity* to explore the waveforms of the sound from a variety of sources.

STUDY NOTE

For guidance on using *Audacity*, see *The Sound of Music* Additional Sheet 2.

Phase

We use the term **phase** ϕ (Greek letter phi) to describe the stage an oscillation has reached in its cycle. The two oscillations shown in Figure 2.4(a) are exactly in step. They are said to be **in phase**. Oscillations that reach their peaks and troughs at different times are said to have a **phase difference** $\Delta\phi$ between them. The phase of an oscillation is often expressed in terms of angles, drawing on the similarity between sinusoidal waveforms and graphs of sines and cosines.

When dealing with phase, angles can be expressed as degrees or, more commonly, in **radians**. One 'cycle' of a sine or cosine graph corresponds to one complete circle (360° or 2π radians).

MATHS REFERENCE

Degrees and radians

See Maths note 6.1

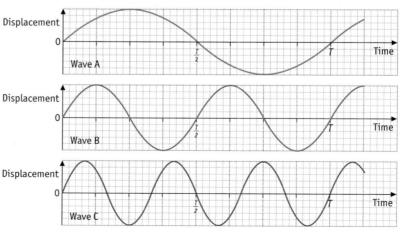

Figure 2.4 Graphs showing waveforms for oscillations that are (a) in phase $\Delta\varphi + 90°$, (b) in antiphase $\Delta\varphi + 180° = \pi$ radians, (c) in quadrature $\Delta\varphi + 90° = \dfrac{\pi}{2}$ radians, (d) the general case

STUDY NOTE

You may be wondering why phase differences are measured in units of angle. Later in the course, when you study simple harmonic motion in the chapter *Build or Bust?*, this connection will be made clearer.

STUDY NOTE

Radians may be abbreviated to rad or ^{c}. However, when π appears in a description of phase, the units of radians are taken for granted and are sometimes omitted.

In Figure 2.4(b) the oscillations are exactly half a cycle out of step; we say they have a phase difference of 180° or π radians. Such oscillations are said to be **in antiphase**.

In Figure 2.4(c) oscillation A is one-quarter a cycle ahead of B. A *leads* B by a phase difference of 90° or $\dfrac{\pi}{2}$ radians. Put another way, B *lags behind* A by $\dfrac{\pi}{2}$, or even, B *leads* A by $\dfrac{-\pi}{2}$.

Oscillations with a phase difference of $\dfrac{\pi}{2}$, or a quarter of a cycle, are said to be **in quadrature**.

Figure 2.4(d) shows the general case. A leads B by a fraction $\dfrac{t}{T}$ of a cycle. The phase difference is therefore $\left(\dfrac{t}{T}\right) \times 360°$ or $\left(\dfrac{t}{T}\right) \times 2\pi$ radians.

QUESTIONS

Q 1 Figure 2.5 shows three waveforms drawn to the same scale. Write down expressions relating the frequencies of **(a)** A and B, and **(b)** A and C.

Figure 2.5 Diagrams for Question 1

Q 2 Determine the phase difference between each of the pairs of oscillations shown in Figure 2.6.

(a)

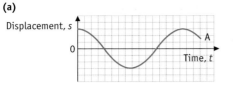 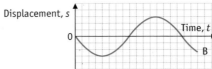

(b)

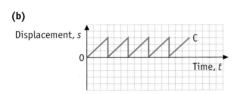 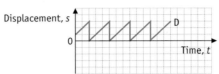

(c)

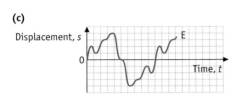 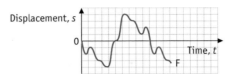

Figure 2.6 Graphs for Question 2

Q 3 On a sketch of a sinusoidal waveform (like Figure 2.6), use different colours to draw the following waveforms on the same axes:

(a) the same amplitude as the original and leading it by $\dfrac{\pi}{4}$ radians

(b) the same amplitude as the original and lagging behind it by 45°

(c) twice the amplitude of the original and leading it by $\dfrac{3\pi}{2}$ radians.

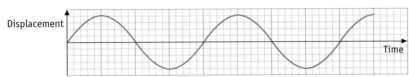

Figure 2.7 Waveform for Question 3

Q 4 **(a)** Write down a general expression, in degrees and in radians, for a phase change that would produce a wave identical to the original.

(b) What, if any, is the difference between waves that differ from wave A in Figure 2.5 by each of the following:

(i) $\dfrac{\pi}{8}$ radians?

(ii) 22.5°?

(iii) $\dfrac{17\pi}{8}$ radians?

(iv) −337.5°?

Q 5 Because the oscillations in Figure 2.5 have different frequencies, they will only be in phase at certain times. At what times are the following pairs in phase:

(i) A and B?

(ii) A and C?

(iii) B and C?

Figure 2.8 Circular wavefronts

1.3 Travelling waves

Oscillations can give rise to waves. For example, the oscillations of the clamped ruler in Figure 2.3 will give rise to a sound wave that propagates through the air.

More generally, a **wave** is an oscillation that travels through matter or space, transferring energy without transferring matter.

A tuning fork whose vibrating prongs are lowered into water will cause ripples to spread out in the water. These are **wavefronts**, lines joining points of equal phase (Figure 2.8).

You might have observed water waves in a ripple tank. The vibrating bar creates straight wavefronts.

There are two main classes of wave, both of which play a part in the production of sound from musical instruments, as you will see in Part 2. A **transverse** wave involves oscillations at right angles to the direction of wave propagation. In a **longitudinal** wave, the oscillations are along the direction of propagation.

Figure 2.9 Homemade wave machine

> ### ⚙ ACTIVITY 5 WAVES ON A SLINKY
>
> Using a slinky, generate and observe some transverse and longitudinal waves (Figure 2.10). Start with a single **pulse** (an oscillation that lasts for just one period) then try generating continuous waves.
>
> The PhEt interactive simulation 'wave on a string' is also a useful illustration.
>
> Mark one loop of the slinky and observe how it moves. Explore how to control the speed of the wave along the slinky. For example, try varying the tension in the slinky. Observe a single pulse as it reaches a fixed or a free end of the slinky.

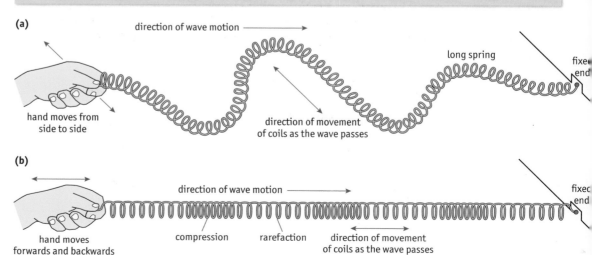

Figure 2.10 Using a slinky to generate (a) transverse and (b) longitudinal waves

In a water wave (Figure 2.11), the particles circulate rather than just moving up and down, thus exhibiting both longitudinal and transverse behaviour. The same is true of some earthquake waves.

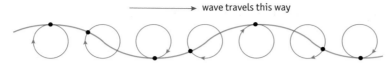

wave travels this way

Figure 2.11 The movement of particles in a water wave

QUESTION

Q 6 Use some of the terms introduced so far to describe the following motions:

(a) a tablecloth shaken to get rid of crumbs

(b) a train of railway trucks shunted by a locomotive

(c) a 'Mexican wave' in a stadium

(d) the stop–go motion of traffic in a jam.

Sound waves

Sound waves are longitudinal, as can be demonstrated with a loudspeaker cone. As the cone vibrates, it first compresses the air next to it and then immediately allows it to spread out again (rarefy) before repeating the cycle. A series of **compressions** and **rarefactions** travels outwards from the cone. The movements produced by loud sounds can make a candle flame flicker (Figure 2.12). Sound cannot travel in a vacuum, since the waves need a material that can be compressed or stretched.

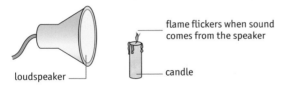

flame flickers when sound comes from the speaker

loudspeaker   candle

Figure 2.12 Demonstrating longitudinal oscillations associated with sound waves

In a human ear (Figure 2.13) the eardrum (a small membrane) is made to vibrate by the air compressions and rarefactions. These small vibrations are then amplified via a mechanical linkage of tiny bones. These larger pressure variations are detected by nerve endings within the inner ear.

A piezoelectric microphone (Figure 2.14) works in a very similar way to the ear. Variations of pressure caused by a sound wave exert tiny stresses on a piezoelectric crystal – a material that generates a voltage across it when stressed. This voltage can be detected as a small electrical signal.

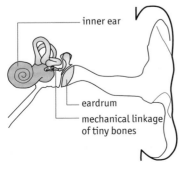

inner ear

eardrum
mechanical linkage of tiny bones

Figure 2.13 A human ear

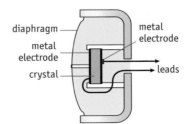

diaphragm
metal electrode
metal electrode
crystal
leads

Figure 2.14 A piezoelectric microphone

1.4 Graphs of travelling waves

There are several ways in which we can use graphs to represent travelling waves. Since transverse waves are perhaps easier to visualise, we will deal with them first and then apply the same ideas to longitudinal waves.

> ### ⚙ ACTIVITY 6 FREEZING A TRAVELLING WAVE
> Generate a travelling transverse wave on a rubber cord, rope or chain. If you do this in a darkened room, a strobe light can be used to 'freeze' the motion if the frequency of the strobe and the wave are suitably adjusted.

Transverse waves

Displacement–position graphs

The 'snapshot' that you should have seen in Activity 6 looks something like Figure 2.15, a displacement–position (or displacement–distance) graph. We can use such a diagram to define the **wavelength** λ as the distance between adjacent crests or, more generally, the distance between two adjacent places where the oscillations are in phase. The wavelength is also the distance between successive wavefronts.

The motion of each particle in Figure 2.15 is slightly out of phase with that of each of its neighbouring particles, and so the wave pattern travels as shown in Figure 2.16.

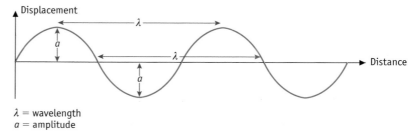

λ = wavelength
a = amplitude

Figure 2.15 A displacement–position graph of a travelling transverse wave

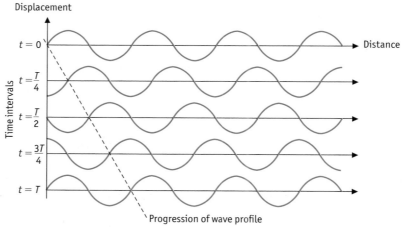

Figure 2.16 Successive 'snapshots' of a travelling wave

The wave equation

The wavelength λ and the frequency f of the wave are connected via the **wave equation**:

$$v = f\lambda \qquad (2)$$

where v is the speed of propagation of the wave. Note that Equation 2 applies to *all* types of wave.

STUDY NOTE

To review your knowledge and understanding of the wave equation, see *The Sound of Music* Additional Sheet 3.

QUESTION

Q 7 The human ear is sensitive to sounds between about 20 Hz and 20 kHz. (The ability to hear high frequencies diminishes with age. It can also be greatly reduced by prolonged exposure to loud sounds.) Taking the speed of sound in air as 340 m s⁻¹, calculate the corresponding range of wavelengths.

STUDY NOTE

You can test your own audible frequency range using the interactive book 'Sound Uncovered' from the Exploratorium.

Displacement–time graphs

We can represent the wave by drawing a displacement–time graph for just one particle in the material through which the wave is travelling, as we have already done for oscillating objects. You will have noticed that displacement–time and displacement–position graphs have very similar shapes. To be sure of distinguishing between these two sorts of graphs, make sure you *always* label the axes.

QUESTIONS

Q 8 Figure 2.17 shows a wave travelling in the positive x direction, away from the origin.

    (a) What are the wave's:

        (i) wavelength?

        (ii) time period?

    (b) Sketch a displacement–time graph for the particle marked A.

Q 9 A travelling wave with a speed of 300 m s⁻¹ has the displacement–time graph shown in Figure 2.18. Sketch a displacement–position graph for this same wave.

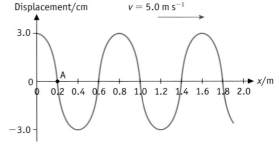

Figure 2.17 Diagram for Question 8

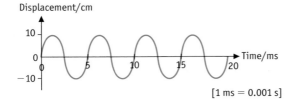

Figure 2.18 Diagram for Question 9

Longitudinal waves

Figure 2.19 shows a schematic diagram of the compressions and rarefactions in a sound wave. As you will see, there are various ways in which we can represent such a wave on a graph.

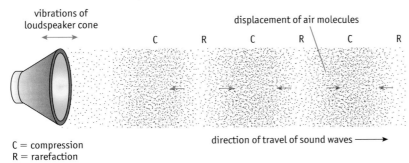

Figure 2.19 A 'snapshot' of a sound wave

Displacement–position and pressure–position graphs

One of the ways to turn Figure 2.19 into a graph, is to plot displacement against position and to define the amplitude as the maximum longitudinal displacement caused by the wave.

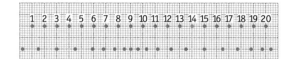

ACTIVITY 7 GRAPHS FOR A LONGITUDINAL WAVE

Figure 2.20 shows a row of twenty undisplaced particles, and below it the same particles displaced by the passage of a longitudinal wave. By tracing the motion of each particle, generate graphs of displacement versus position.

Figure 2.20 Diagram for Activity 7

Figure 2.21(a) shows the displacement–position graph for the wave of Figure 2.19. This graph looks 'transverse', even though it represents a longitudinal wave. The displacement is measured *along* the direction of wave motion (along the x-direction) but is plotted up the y-axis of the graph.

However, another way to turn Figure 2.18 into a graph is to plot pressure against position. This is shown in Figure 2.21(b). As you should have found in Activity 8, the two graphs are not in phase. Positions of maximum compression or rarefaction correspond to zero displacement, and positions of maximum displacement correspond to 'normal' pressure.

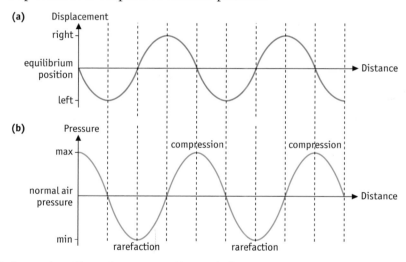

Figure 2.21 Displacement–position and pressure–position graphs for a longitudinal wave

Displacement–time and pressure–time graphs

We can also use displacement–time or pressure–time graphs to represent longitudinal wave motion in exactly the same way as transverse waves. If you look back at Questions 8 and 9, you will see that there is nothing in either question to indicate the type of wave – they apply equally to either type.

Oscilloscope traces

A microphone uses the small movements of its diaphragm to produce an electrical signal that mimics the variations of pressure or displacement in a sound wave. This signal can then be fed to a recording device, an amplifier or an oscilloscope (where the screen displays the variations). You make use of this in Activity 8.

ACTIVITY 8 SPEED OF SOUND

Determine the speed of sound in air using a two-beam oscilloscope, signal generator, speaker and microphone.

PRACTICAL SKILLS REFERENCE

Scientific questions and information research
See Practical skills note 1.1

Planning and experimental design
See Practical skills notes 2.1–2.2

Carrying out practical work
See Practical skills notes 3.1–3.2

Analysis and interpretation of data
See Practical skills note 4.1

Conclusion and evaluation
See Practical skills note 5.1

1.5 Superposition and standing waves

You have seen how an oscillating object can produce a sound wave. Yet what controls the frequency (the pitch) of the sound? How can a musical instrument be tuned to give a desired note? And why do notes of the same pitch sound different when played on different instruments? What determines the 'quality' of a sound?

Superposition

The answers to all the questions above involve **superposition** – the combination of two or more waves. When two or more waves arrive at the same place at the same time, the resultant displacement is equal to the sum of those due to the individual waves.

Since displacement is a vector quantity and can have negative values, superposition may lead to *smaller* resultant amplitude.

The effect is most noticeable if the waves combined are **coherent**, meaning that they are of the same frequency (or wavelength) and with a constant phase relationship. Figure 2.22 shows the result of combining two waves of the same frequency and phase but with different amplitude.

For sound waves, we could plot graphs using pressure rather than displacement: these too can simply be added together.

Note: the *ability* of waves to combine is known as *superposition*; what *happens* when they combine is called *interference*.

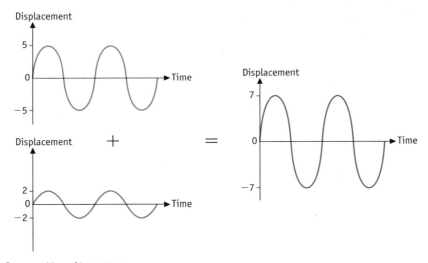

Figure 2.22 Superposition of two waves

Figure 2.23 Complex waves showing constructive and destructive superposition

---

⚙ **ACTIVITY 9 SUPERPOSITION**

Using the University of Salford's *Sounds Amazing* software, investigate what happens when two simple sinusoidal waves superpose.

In Activity 9 you should have seen examples of two special cases of superposition. If two waves combine so that they are always reinforcing one another, this is called **constructive superposition**; and if they are always cancelling one another, this is called **destructive superposition**.

QUESTIONS

Q 10 Sketch graphs similar to Figure 2.22 to show the resultant wave in each of the following cases:

(a) coherent waves of identical amplitude superposed in phase

(b) coherent waves of identical amplitude superposed with a phase difference of 90° or $\frac{\pi}{2}$ radians

(c) coherent waves of identical amplitude superposed with a phase difference of 180° or π radians.

Q 11 The driver of the jet-propelled car 'Thrust', which broke the world land speed record in 1997, sat directly between two high-powered jet engines. He would have been deafened but for a technique called 'active sound suppression', which involves generating sounds in the driver's headphones to cancel out the engine noise. What can you say about the sounds that would need to be generated?

Q 12 What conditions must two waves satisfy if they are to undergo:

(a) maximum constructive superposition?

(b) maximum destructive superposition?

Phase difference and path difference

Have you ever noticed a car radio getting louder and quieter as you drive along? This can be explained by superposition. Sometimes waves reach a single point by more than one route. For example, the car radio might pick up radio waves direct from the transmitter (path A in Figure 2.24) and also via a reflection from a building (a longer path B). These waves superpose, resulting in larger or smaller amplitude, depending on their **path difference**, which will change as you drive along.

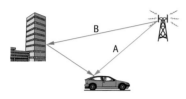

Figure 2.24 Radio waves taking two different paths, resulting in a path difference.

In Figure 2.24, if the path difference between routes A and B is a whole number multiple of the wavelength ($n\lambda$), constructive interference occurs and the resulting signal is strong (a **maximum**). This is another way of saying that the waves are arriving at the car in phase.

Conversely, if the path difference is half a wavelength, or 1½, 2½, etc. (more generally, $(n - \frac{1}{2})\lambda$), destructive interference gives a weaker signal (a **minimum**). The waves are arriving in antiphase.

To summarise:

Path difference, Δx = difference in distance from each source to a particular point (unit: metres)

Phase difference, $\Delta\phi$ = difference in phase of the waves at a point (unit: degrees or radians)

In general:

$$\Delta\phi = \frac{2\pi\Delta x}{\lambda} \tag{3}$$

In Activity 10 you will meet some examples of constructive and destructive superposition and practise explaining them in terms of path difference and phase difference.

Standing waves

Interesting things can happen when waves of a single frequency (or wavelength) travel back and forth 'on top of one another', as might happen if waves are reflected back and forth. Indeed, you might have observed in Activity 5 that a wave undergoes a phase change of 180° or π radians on reflection. Figure 2.25 shows the superposition of a 'red' wave travelling from left to right with a 'green' wave of the same frequency travelling in the opposite direction.

The waves could be:

● transverse, with the y-axis representing transverse particle displacement

● longitudinal, with the y-axis representing particle displacement along the direction of travel

● longitudinal, with the y-axis representing changes in pressure.

Superposition of the 'red' and 'green' waves gives the 'blue' resultant wave, which doesn't travel in either direction but merely remains where it is and changes profile as shown in Figure 2.26. The wave goes through the sequence 1, 2, 3, 4, 5, 4, 3, 2, 1 in one cycle. This type of wave is called a **standing wave** (or **stationary wave**). A point on the standing waves, such as P, Q or R where the value plotted on the y-axis is always zero, is called a **node** (there is *no* change). A point such as W, X, Y or Z, where the amplitude reaches a maximum, is called an **antinode**.

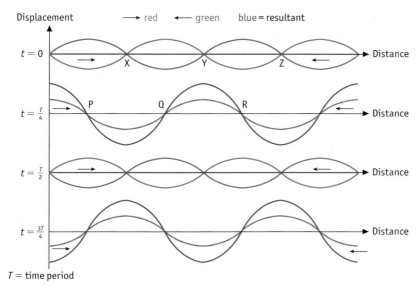

Figure 2.25 Superposition of travelling waves

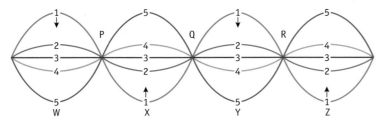

Figure 2.26 A standing wave

STUDY NOTE

Note that between two adjacent nodes, all points on a standing wave are in *phase* (unlike in a travelling wave). On opposite sides of a node, they are in *antiphase*.

⚙ ACTIVITY 10 STANDING WAVES

Generate and study some standing waves of various types. Examples might include: water waves in a bowl; waves on a cord or a slinky; sound waves in a tube; waves on a stretched wire.

QUESTIONS

Q 13 What is the distance on the standing waves between two adjacent nodes? (Express your answer in terms of the wavelength of the travelling waves.)

Q 14 The standing wave shown in Figure 2.27 was set up on a rubber cord attached at one end to a vibration generator oscillating at 150 Hz; the other end was fixed.

(a) On a copy of the diagram, label the nodes and antinodes.

(b) Determine the wavelength of the standing wave.

(c) Use the wave equation to find the speed of the wave along the rubber cord.

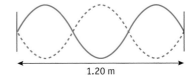

1.20 m

Figure 2.27 A standing wave on a rubber cord

1.6 Summing up Part 1

So far in this chapter you have learned how to describe oscillations and waves using words and mathematical expressions.

⚙ ACTIVITY 11 DESCRIBING WAVES

Look back through this chapter and your notes and make sure you understand the meaning of all the terms highlighted in bold. Then, for each of the following, write a sentence or two and sketch a labelled diagram to explain its meaning:

- wavelength
- wavefront
- antiphase
- longitudinal wave
- coherent
- superposition
- antinode
- standing wave.

2 Musical notes

In this part of the chapter, you will apply ideas about waves to two sorts of musical instrument and see how they produce notes. You will also see why the same note sounds different when played on different instruments.

2.1 Stringed instruments

Stringed instruments such as guitars or violins (Figure 2.28) produce a transverse standing wave on a string held between two fixed supports. The particles in the string are normally set into oscillation by plucking or bowing, but piano strings are struck by felted hammers.

Figure 2.28 Stringed instruments

The standing wave is generated by the superposition of the waves travelling along the string and being reflected at the support. A phase change of 180° (π radians) takes place at the reflection (Figure 2.29), so the incident and reflected waves always superpose destructively at that point and there will be a displacement node at both support.

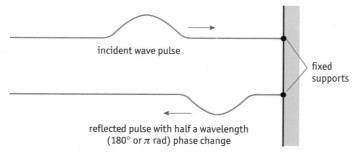

incident wave pulse

fixed supports

reflected pulse with half a wavelength (180° or π rad) phase change

STUDY NOTE

For more about the physics of stringed instruments, see *The Sound of Music* Additional Sheet 5.

Figure 2.29 Reflection at a fixed boundary produces a phase change that ensures there is a node at the boundary

For a string to have a node at each end (and possibly more between) means that, for a given string length, any certain precisely-fixed frequencies can sound. These are known as **resonant** frequencies. The lowest of these is called the **fundamental** frequency.

QUESTION

Q 15 **(a)** For Figure 2.30, write down:
    (i) a relationship between the wavelength λ of this wave and the length l of the string
    (ii) a relationship between the length l of the string and the frequency f and speed v of this wave.

(b) When we refer to 'the wavelength' and 'the speed' in part (b), do we mean the wavelength and speed of the transverse waves travelling along the string, or the wavelength and speed of the resulting sound waves in air?

(c) The string also produces other, higher frequency standing waves. Remembering to put a displacement node at each end, sketch two possible higher frequency standing waves on a string.

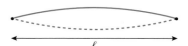
Figure 2.30 The fundamental frequency standing wave on a string

The sound box of a stringed instrument

As the string oscillates as a standing wave, it generates a succession of compressions and rarefactions in the air, which travel outwards as a sound wave (Figure 2.31).

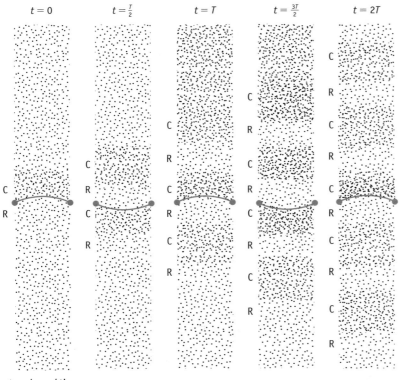

t = elapsed time
T = one time period

Figure 2.31 An oscillating string generates a sound wave

If the string were the only thing vibrating, then the sound would be barely audible because the string itself affects very little air. To make the sound louder, the string is attached to a sound box, which resonates with the string and sets a greater mass of air in motion, so the sound is louder.

QUESTIONS

Q 16 Classical guitars have a very obvious sound box to 'resonate' the sound. How do electric guitars achieve the same effect?

Q 17 Figure 2.32 shows part of a violin under construction, being tested by driving it at certain frequencies, with tea leaves on the surface of the wood. Explain what is happening to the tea leaves.

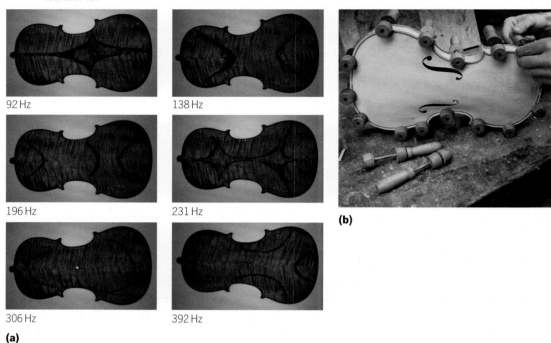

(a)

Figure 2.32 (a) Testing the sound box of a violin, and (b) making the sound box of a violin

Notes from a stringed instrument

Even if you are only vaguely familiar with a guitar (or any other stringed instrument), you will know that there are several ways in which the player can control the pitch (frequency) of the note.

PRACTICAL SKILLS REFERENCE

Planning and experimental design

See Practical skills notes 2.1–2.2

Carrying out practical work

See Practical skills notes 3.1–3.2

Analysis and interpretation of data

See Practical skills notes 4.1–4.2

Conclusion and evaluation

See Practical skills notes 5.1–5.2

⚙ ACTIVITY 12 WHAT AFFECTS THE NOTE PRODUCED BY A STRING?

Use a guitar or a sonometer (Figure 2.33) to explore one factor that affects the pitch of its note. Try to deduce a mathematical relationship between frequency and the factor you are investigating.

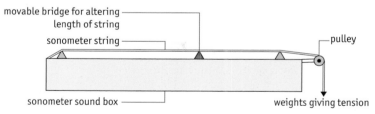

movable bridge for altering length of string
sonometer string
pulley
sonometer sound box
weights giving tension

Figure 2.33 A sonometer

In Question 15 you saw that the lowest-frequency standing wave that could fit on to a stretched string of length l has a wavelength λ where:

$$\lambda = 2l$$

This wavelength is related to the frequency f of oscillation, by the wave equation:

$$v = f\lambda \qquad \text{(Equation 2)}$$

where v is the speed of the transverse waves travelling along the string. We can therefore write:

$$f = \frac{v}{\lambda} = \frac{v}{2l} \qquad (4)$$

In Activity 12, you should have found that f is inversely proportional to the length l of the string: the shorter the string, the higher the note – as described by Equation 4.

You should also have found that the frequency does indeed depend on the tension and the mass per unit length of the string. Both of these factors affect the speed of transverse waves travelling along the string. In Activity 5 you will have seen that you can control the speed of waves along a slinky: the greater the tension, the greater the speed. The speed also depends on the mass per unit length of the string (or spring): the heavier the string, the lower the speed. The speed v is in fact related to the tension T and mass per unit length μ by the following equation:

$$v = \sqrt{\frac{T}{\mu}} \qquad (5)$$

Combining Equations 4 and 5 gives an expression for the frequency of the fundamental standing wave on a string:

$$f = \frac{1}{2l} \times \sqrt{\frac{T}{\mu}} \qquad (6)$$

Quantities and units

At first sight, Equation 5 looks rather unexpected. It is not at all obvious that a combination of tension and mass, involving a square root, should be equal to a speed. A good way of checking that any equation is likely to be correct is to consider its units. The units of the right-hand side must always be the same as the units of the left-hand side. If they are not, then the equation cannot be correct.

To carry out the check, write the units of each quantity in terms of their **SI base units**, which are listed in Table 2.1. All other SI units are **derived units** which are formed from some combination of the seven base units. For example, the SI unit of frequency, the hertz (Hz), is derived from the second: $1\,\text{Hz} = 1\,\text{s}^{-1}$. Derived units can often be worked out using familiar equations. For example, you can use the familiar equation $F = ma$ to express the units for force in terms of base units.

> **MATHS REFERENCE**
> SI units
> See Maths notes 2.2 and 2.3

> **MATHS REFERENCE**
> Derived units
> See Maths note 2.3

> **STUDY NOTE**
> In this chapter, only the base units m, kg and s are used.

Quantity	SI unit
Mass	kilogram, kg
Time	second, s
Length	metre, m
Electric current	ampere, A
Temperature	kelvin, K
Luminous intensity	candela, cd
Amount of substance	mole, mol

Table 2.1 The SI base units

> **WORKED EXAMPLE**
>
> **Q** Show that the wave equation (Equation 2) has the same SI units on each side
>
> **A** The left-hand side, speed (v) has units that are already a simple combination of SI base units: $\text{m}\,\text{s}^{-1}$.
> On the right-hand side:
> units of $f\lambda$ = units of frequency × units of length
> $\qquad = \text{Hz} \times \text{m} = \text{s}^{-1} \times \text{m} = \text{m}\,\text{s}^{-1}$
>
> **Q** Write the right-hand side of Equation 5 in terms of SI base units and hence show that the expression has units of $\text{m}\,\text{s}^{-1}$.
>
> **A** Tension T is a force so has SI units of newtons. Using $F = ma$:
> units of force = units of mass × units of acceleration = $\text{kg}\,\text{m}\,\text{s}^{-2}$
> Mass per unit length, μ:
> units of mass per unit length = $\dfrac{\text{units of mass}}{\text{units of length}}$ = kg/m = $\text{kg}\,\text{m}^{-1}$
> Units of $\dfrac{T}{\mu}$ = $\text{kg}\,\text{m}\,\text{s}^{-2} \div \text{kg}\,\text{m}^{-1}$ = $\text{m}^2\,\text{s}^{-2}$
> Units of $\sqrt{\left(\dfrac{T}{\mu}\right)}$ = $\sqrt{(\text{m}^2\,\text{s}^{-2})}$ = $\text{m}\,\text{s}^{-1}$

> **STUDY NOTE**
> Force, mass and acceleration
> See HFS Section 1.4

Figure 2.34 Pairs of similar instruments

QUESTIONS

Q 18 Explain which one of the following pairs of similar instruments (Figure 2.34) should produce notes with a higher range of frequencies:

(a) a bass guitar and a banjo

(b) a side drum and a timpani.

Q 19 (a) Show that Equation 4 has the same SI units on both sides.

(b) Use Equation 6 to explain the following:

(i) Before being played, stringed instruments are tuned by twisting a series of screws or pegs.

(ii) Violinists and guitar players press their fingers against the strings while playing.

(iii) In a piano, the strings that sound the high notes are much thinner than the strings that sound the low notes.

2.2 Wind instruments

Getting notes from a wind instrument (such as a saxophone or a flute) can be surprisingly difficult for a person trying it for the first time. The physics behind it is, however, straightforward to describe at a basic level.

> ### ⚙ ACTIVITY 13 PLAYING A WIND INSTRUMENT
>
> Read the passage below and answer Questions 20 to 25 that follow. Answers to many of the questions can be found in the passage and in earlier sections of this unit. Skim-read the passage first, to get an idea of what is in it, and then read the questions, so that on your second, more careful, reading of the article you will be able to pick out the important points.

Wind instruments (Figure 2.35 and 2.36) rely on the column of air molecules inside the tube of the instrument being made to oscillate as a standing wave. This can be done in several ways. Trumpets and other brass instruments are played with lip vibrations causing the air to oscillate; oboes and clarinets rely on a flexible reed vibrating as it is blown; recorders have a notched air vent at the top that protrudes into the air column slightly, setting up eddies in the air which generate molecular oscillations.

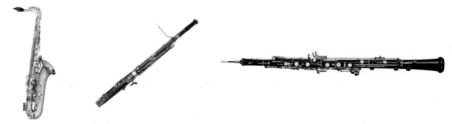

Figure 2.35 Wind instruments

STUDY NOTE

For more about the physics of wind instruments, see *The Sound of Music* Additional Sheet 6.

Figure 2.36 Blue Man Group 'Drumbone' performance

The standing wave of air vibrations makes the instrument and the air around it vibrate at the same frequency, generating a sound wave that travels outwards in all directions.

There are two basic categories of wind instrument:

● open tubes – a flute or a recorder behaves like this type of tube, with both ends open

● closed tubes – a clarinet behaves like this type of tube, with one end open and one closed; the closed end is the reed end.

The standing waves are set up because sound waves are reflected from either a closed or an open end. The wavelengths of the standing waves are governed by the following end conditions:

● At a closed end, air molecules are not free to move so their amplitude of vibration is zero (a displacement node) but the changes in pressure are maximum.

● At an open end, the amplitude of air molecule vibrations is a maximum (a displacement antinode) but the pressure does not change since it is equal to atmospheric pressure (a pressure node).

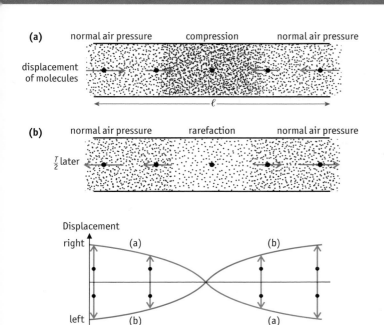

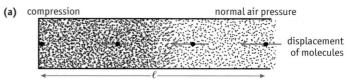

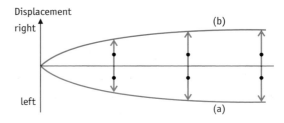

Figure 2.37 Fundamental standing wave in an open tube, e.g. recorder, oboe

Figure 2.38 Fundamental standing wave in a closed tube, e.g. clarinet, some organ pipes

Figure 2.37 shows the lowest frequency standing wave that can be set up in an open tube, and Figure 2.38 shows the lowest frequency standing wave that can be set up in a closed tube of the same length. As for a standing wave on a string, this **fundamental** frequency is the lowest of a series of possible resonant frequencies.

Note that a displacement node corresponds to a pressure antinode and vice versa.

When an instrument is played, opening or closing the holes along the tube controls the pitch. A an open hole, the air molecules can move freely and so the pressure does not change. So opening or closing the holes effectively alters the length of the tube in which a standing wave can be set up.

QUESTIONS

Q 20 Explain why the air molecule displacement graphs in the diagrams in Figures 2.37 and 2.38 have both positive and negative values.

Q 21 Sketch graphs showing how air pressure will vary with distance along each tube in Figures 2.37 and 2.38.

Q 22 What fraction of a wavelength λ corresponds to the tube length l for:

(a) an open tube fundamental?

(b) a closed tube fundamental?

Q 23 (a) From your answer to Question 22, work out an expression for the fundamental frequency of an open tube in terms of its length, l, and the speed of sound in air, v.

(b) Repeat (a) for a closed tube.

Q 24 What properties of a recorder do you think determine the fundamental frequency of the instrument?

Q 25 When playing a recorder, you need to cover up different numbers of holes to get different frequencies. In Figure 2.39 a black circle indicates a covered hole. On a sketch of Figure 2.39, mark the effective length of the tube in each case. Which of the two cases shown should give the lowest pitch (frequency) of note?

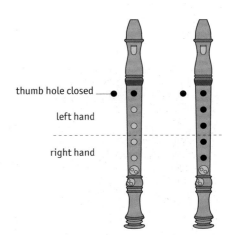

thumb hole closed

left hand

right hand

Figure 2.39 Fingering for two different notes on a recorder

STUDY NOTE

For guidance on using *Audacity* to analyse sounds, see Additional Sheet 4.

PRACTICAL SKILLS REFERENCE

Analysis and interpretation of data

See Practical skills notes 4.1–4.2

Conclusion and evaluation

See Practical skills notes 5.1–5.2

⚙ ACTIVITY 14 CAN YOUR RECORDER TELL YOU THE SPEED OF SOUND?

Your answers to Question 20 involved a relationship between the frequency of a note, the length of the tube and the speed of sound in air. Using this relationship, and with the help of *Audacity*, measure the speed of sound using a recorder.

FURTHER INVESTIGATION

If you have an opportunity in future, there are several aspects of this section that you could investigate further. Here are some suggestions:

- the frequencies of note produced by tapping a bottle partly filled with water or by blowing over its top
- two-dimensional standing wave patterns on a metal sheet attached to a vibration generator ('Chladni plates')
- the tensions, thicknesses and lengths needed to produce a given note from guitar or violin strings made from different materials
- the design and performance of sound boxes for stringed instruments
- the speed of sound by setting up a reflecting sound wave and detecting nodes and antinodes with smartphone decibel app or microphone
- the measurement of speed of sound in other materials.

2.3 Quality or timbre

Most people can recognise when notes from two different instruments have the same pitch (frequency). Yet even when played with the same volume (amplitude), they sound different.

The answer lies in harmonics, or overtones.

Harmonics and overtones

When a musical instrument is played, the air column or string does not vibrate with the simple 'tidy' vibration corresponding to the fundamental frequency. Rather, the vibration is a superposition of the fundamental frequency with many harmonics at smaller amplitudes. The resultant complex vibration has the same pitch as the fundamental, but the sound quality (timbre) is different. This characteristic sound depends, among other factors, on the shape of the instrument and the way it is played.

The sound produced when a violin plays middle C is made up of the fundamental (loudest) shown at the top of Figure 2.40 plus all the harmonics shown below, and more.

When these harmonics are superposed (as you saw in Activity 9 and Question 10), a complex waveform results such as that shown in Figure 2.41.

The frequencies and amplitudes of sinusoidal waves needed to make up a given sound can be found using a **spectrum analyser**, which splits up the sound into its component frequencies, rather as a prism splits light into its different frequencies or colours. The result is a sound **spectrum**, which is a plot showing the frequencies and amplitudes of these component sinusoidal waves (Figure 2.42a). Another violin might be played with a different bowing technique to produce a 'tinnier' sound with more treble (high frequency) overtones (Figure 2.42b).

STUDY NOTE

For guidance on using *Audacity* to analyse sounds, see *The Sound of Music* Additional Sheet 4.

⚙ ACTIVITY 15 A NOTE ABOUT NOTES

Use *Audacity* to explore the waveforms and frequency spectra of notes that sound similar in frequency and yet are different in quality. Look for waveforms that have similar periods (similar 'repeat distances' on the screen). Try comparing vowel sounds (recording yourself) such as 'oo' and 'ee'.

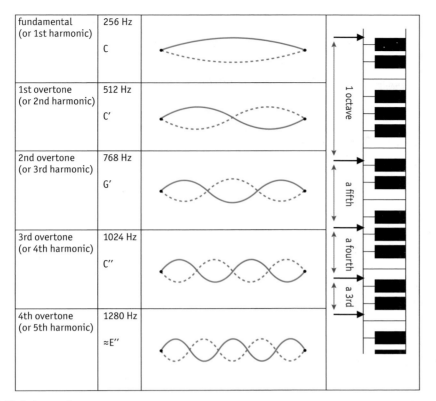

fundamental (or 1st harmonic)	256 Hz C		
1st overtone (or 2nd harmonic)	512 Hz C'		1 octave
2nd overtone (or 3rd harmonic)	768 Hz G'		a fifth
3rd overtone (or 4th harmonic)	1024 Hz C''		a fourth
4th overtone (or 5th harmonic)	1280 Hz ≈E''		a 3rd

Figure 2.40 Violin harmonics

STUDY NOTE

The mathematician Joseph Fourier (1768–1830) proved that any continuous wave could be produced as an infinite sum of sine and cosine waves.

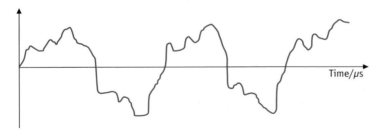

Figure 2.41 Complex waveform produced by the superposition of harmonics

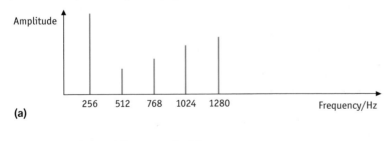

(a)

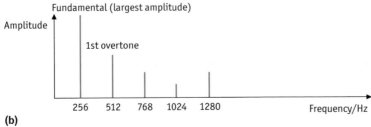

(b)

Figure 2.42 Sound spectra of the same note played on two different violins

Figure 2.43

Speech

A waveform of human speech (Figure 2.44 looks complex and untidy, but even this has a clear repetitive pattern or **periodicity**. You can pick out a basic period of about 10 m s, corresponding to a frequency of about 100 Hz. The spectrum of this waveform has a very large number of components.

Because the patterns in speech sounds are recognisable, spoken words can be converted into digital code as a particular word allowing the development of voice recognition software. Sometimes this coding causes higher frequency overtones to be lost, causing poor quality, such as mobile phone calls. For example, the treble sounds 'f' and 's' can be hard to distinguish.

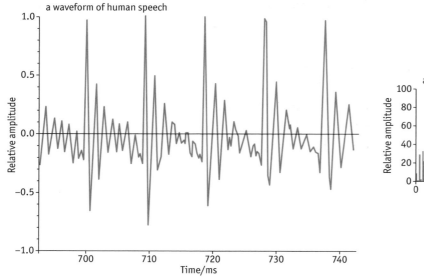

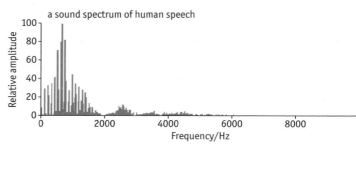

Figure 2.44 A waveform of human speech and its sound spectrum (a 'time plot' and a 'frequency plot')

2.4 Summing up Part 2

You should now be well versed in the science of sounds. You should be aware of what makes sounds different and how complex waveforms can be treated as combinations of simple sinusoidal waves. Activity 16 uses these ideas in the **synthesis** of familiar sounds. Synthesis means 'bringing together'. Activity 16 is about synthesis of complex sounds from simple components, and it also involves bringing together what you have learned in this part of the chapter.

Church organs (Figure 2.45) were the first **synthesisers**, combining sounds from different sets of pipes to create a huge range of timbers.

The idea is simple: if, by analysing a sound spectrum, you can pick out the main frequencies present in their correct proportions, then by reproducing those frequencies simultaneously you should get a reasonable copy of the sound. The more of the constituent frequencies you can reproduce, the better the copy will be. This method of reproducing synthetic sounds is often used by electronic devices and less sophisticated keyboards.

Sampling

The most realistic synthesised sounds are those that use the most detailed digital copy of the original sound. You can achieve this by sampling the original sound more often (**sampling rate**) and using more levels (**number of bits**). Real sounds also change even during a single note, with features called **attack**, **sustain** and **decay**. Many pop singers use an 'autotuner' that samples their voice and plays it back adjusted for frequency so that they always appear to sing in tune!

Figure 2.45 Organ pipes

⚙ ACTIVITY 16   ANALYSING AND SYNTHESISING SOUNDS

Use *Audacity* to explore the sound spectra of some synthesised sounds and compare them with the spectra of the same sounds produced naturally. Then explore the activity 'Fourier: Making Waves' from the University of Colorado interactive simulations website 'Phet'.

QUESTIONS

Q 26   In Question 15(c) you were asked to sketch some standing waves with frequencies higher than the fundamental. Do the same for closed and open tubes, labelling the displacement nodes and antinodes.

Q 27   A guitar string is 0.5 m long, has a mass per unit length of $3.75 \times 10^{-4}\,\mathrm{kg\,m^{-1}}$ and is held under a tension of 15 N.

    (a)   What is the frequency of its fundamental vibration?

    (b)   If the guitar player wishes to produce a note of frequency 400 Hz from this string (without re-tuning), how far along the string should the finger be placed?

Q 28   You may have witnessed a person breathing in helium gas and then speaking – the voice appears to sound much higher in pitch. Suggest a physical explanation for this effect.

Q 29   For the waveform shown in Figure 2.46, determine its period and (fundamental) frequency.

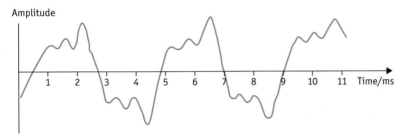

Figure 2.46 Waveform for Question 29

FURTHER INVESTIGATION

If you have the opportunity, here are some things that you might like to investigate:
- the frequency spectrum of a clarinet (or other instrument) as it plays through its complete range
- the frequency spectrum of notes from a plucked elastic band
- sounds produced from simple percussion instruments, e.g. a block of wood suspended and struck with a hammer
- the quality of sounds synthesised by a cheap keyboard (the cheaper the better!).

STUDY NOTE

The Sound of Music Additional Sheet 8 lists some websites that you might like to visit to extend your knowledge of waves, sound and light.

Figure 2.47 A CD player

3 Compact discs

Sometimes we want a permanent record of some favourite music, a famous voice or the strange sounds of whales. The permanent storage of that recording could be on a compact disc (CD; see Figure 2.47), as this is one of the popular formats for sound recordings. Digital Video Discs (DVDs) and Blu-ray Disc (BD) work in a similar way to CDs. In this part of the chapter you will explore many aspects of the physics required to manufacture a CD, DVD or Blu-ray disc player.

3.1 What's on the discs?

Compact discs store information in a way quite unlike the previous generations of discs, as we now discover.

Before the CD

Thomas Edison was the first person to record sound; he used wax cylinders. Another American, the German-born Emile Berliner, invented the flat disc-type record in Philadelphia in May 1888. In the early part of the 20th century the records were played back rotating at 78 revolutions per minute, so were called 78s. Later, a way was devised to store more music on vinyl discs that rotated more slowly – hence the name long-playing record, or LP. In all these types of storage, vibrations caused by sound waves are used to drive a tool that cuts a wavy groove into the surface of rotating record. The shape of the groove is similar to the waveform of the sound. This type of recording is known as **analogue** recording, as the stored information is an analogue, or copy, of the original sound. The sound is retrieved using a stylus, which is a flexible arm with a fine point that rests in the groove. As the record rotates the stylus moves with the wobbles in groove. These movements are converted to electrical signals, which are amplified and produce the sound in the speakers.

> ### ⚙ ACTIVITY 17 COMPARING DISCS
>
> Examine the surfaces of a CD and an LP (Figure 2.48) and their playback systems (just the visible exterior parts). Use any magnification available. Briefly describe the appearance of each surface and comment on how many grooves (if any!) you can see. Which surface is 'read' during play?
>
> Listen to two extracts of music, one from an LP and one from a CD played through the same amplifier. Comment on any difference in the quality of sound from the two systems you heard.

> ### ⚙ ACTIVITY 18 CDS – THE SOUND OF SCIENCE
>
> Read the article below and answer Questions 30 to 37 that follow. Answers to many of the questions can be found in the article. If you skim read the article first, you will get an idea of what is in it. Then read the questions so that on your second, more careful, reading of the article, you will be able to pick out the important points. Have a dictionary at hand to assist with any unfamiliar words.

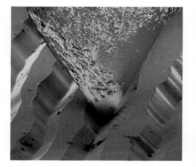

(a)

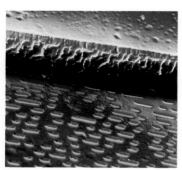

(b)

Figure 2.48 Magnified views of (a) an LP surface and (b) a CD

The sound of science

Compact discs offer better sound quality than vinyl discs, with up to an hour's uninterrupted playing time and, most important perhaps, greater durability. A compact disc will still play back perfectly even with a 2 mm hole drilled through the playing area, and handling a compact disc presents no problems as they are immune to a few scratches, dirt and grease. There are no grooves in the surface of the compact disc, and the CD player has no stylus. The audio information or signal recorded onto the disc is processed and stored there in a fundamentally different way, which is where computer electronics come in.

Storage and retrieval

Old music systems such as vinyl and tape were analogue storage and retrieval systems. In analogue systems the sound was recorded as a wobbly groove or varying magnetic field similar in form to the sound wave to be reproduced. CDs use **digital** recording – a completely different approach in which the sound is stored as **binary codes** of 0s and 1s. For the compact disc, Philips developed an elegant optical scanning system, using a low-powered laser to 'read' tiny bumps in a reflective metal surface (Figures 2.49 and 2.50).

STUDY NOTE

For more on binary code and digital signals, see *The Sound of Music* Additional Sheet 7.

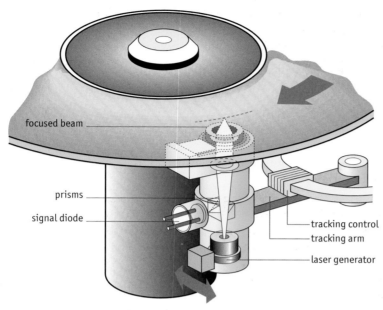

Figure 2.49 Playing a CD

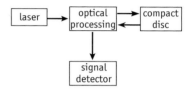

Figure 2.50 Block diagram of a CD player system

Metallic layer

Sandwiched by a protective plastic coating 1.6 mm thick, the silver metallic layer in the compact disc is etched with a spiral track of bumps of literally microscopic proportions. The pitch of the spiral is in fact 1.6 μm, which makes the 'micro grooves' of a conventional LP look quite big. When a beam of highly concentrated laser light is focused on this pattern, a reflected light signal is received from the flat surface, which is compared with the light reflected from the regions with bumps. In the player's optics, both reflected rays are passed to a photodiode, where superposition produces a series of electrical 'ones' and 'zeros'. Here the fundamental benefit of working with digits can be realised – it does not matter exactly how much light is received, because anything above a predetermined level is read as a 'one' and everything below that level as a 'zero'. Because the playback system only has to identify these two conditions, reproduction of the original information is theoretically perfect. The laser is accurately focused on the reflective metal layer so dust particles or marks on the plastic coating are ignored.

QUESTIONS

Q 30 **(a)** Does the CD system of sound recording use a digital or an analogue method?

(b) In a couple of sentences, explain the different between the two methods.

Q 31 What do you think the author means by 'optical scanning?' What is the equivalent for an LP?

Q 32 The distance between one turn of the spiral track and the next is called its 'pitch'.

(a) Write down the size of the pitch of a CD expressed in standard form.

(b) How broad can the light beam be if it is to distinguish between one set of bumps and another?

Q 33 The article mentions two materials. The compact disc has a 'reflective metallic layer' and a 'protective plastic coating'.

(a) What property, other than protective, must the plastic coating have?

(b) What is important about the metallic layer?

(c) Which reflection is more important: that from the metal or that from the plastic?

MATHS REFERENCE

Standard form
See Maths note 1.2

Q 34 Sketch diagrams to show:

(a) what is meant by a focused beam and a parallel beam

(b) how it is possible for an accurately focused beam to ignore dust particles and marks on the plastic surface.

Q 35 Reflection is mentioned many times. Write down what you understand by the term.

Q 36 The article includes a labelled diagram. What is:

(a) a signal diode?

(b) a tracking arm?

(c) a prism?

Q 37 Why must the spot of light focused on the metal surface of the CD be *wider* than the bumps on the surface?

3.2 Optical scanning

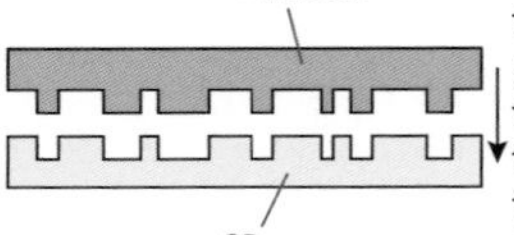

The digital information is coded on a CD as a series of small raised areas created as the playing disc is pressed from a master disc in which pits have been etched (Figure 2.51).

The pits are made, using a binary code, from audio measurements made 44 100 times a second. Each binary number represents the sound signal at one instant in time converted to a sequence of bumps or no bumps (rather like Braille) on a spiral track. Using this system we only have to read binary 1 or 0. For an optical reader this means detecting whether a light signal is 'on' or 'off'.

master

the pit pattern of the master is pressed into the first layer

CD

Figure 2.51 Pressing a CD from a master disc

Superposition

Somehow a series of bumps on a disc have to turn the light on and off as it scans over them. It is all done by waves – in particular, the property of waves known as **superposition**.

The following discussion, with Questions 38 to 40 and Activity 19, shows how superposition of coherent waves plays a key part in reading a CD.

STUDY NOTE

Superposition is discussed in Section 1.5 of this chapter (see pages 75–77).

QUESTIONS

Q 38 This question is about light waves A, B and C.

● Wave A has frequency f and amplitude a.

● Wave B has frequency f and amplitude $1.5a$, and is in phase with A.

● Wave C has frequency f and amplitude a, and is 180° out of phase with A.

State what an observer would see in each of the following situations. Give the frequency and amplitude of the resulting wave in each case and sketch graphs to illustrate your answers.

(a) (i) A is combined with B to give wave P.
(ii) A is combined with C to give wave Q.

(b) Wave B becomes 180° out of phase with A before combining with it to give wave R.

(c) Wave C becomes in phase with A before superposing with it to give wave S.

Q 39 For digital use the signal detector requires two states – the light is on or off.

(a) Look at your answers to Question 38 and decide which results are equivalent to 'on' and which 'off'.

(b) What are the requirements for two waves to produce total cancellation?

In practice, an electronic circuit can be calibrated to recognise 'on' signals for anything above a predetermined level of brightness, and if the light level falls below that the circuit records 'off'.

In our example the conditions for cancellation could then be set so that the two waves had to have the same period and be out of phase, and their amplitudes only need be similar not identical.

QUESTION

Q 40 If 'on' is taken to mean 'has an amplitude greater than a' and all other brightness levels are deemed 'off', reconsider your answer to Question 38(a).

Coherent waves

To get a steady signal from the superposition of two waves, they need to be **coherent**, otherwise the signal keeps changing (see Question 37). Light waves from two separate sources will be incoherent because the light is emitted in short random bursts, each lasting about a nanosecond. One way to be sure of getting coherent waves is to use a single beam of light. Yet how could a phase difference be caused across a single beam? It can be caused in several ways. Two parts of the wave could start together in phase, travel different distances and meet up again (Figure 2.52), or part of the wave could be **reflected** and meet up with the unreflected part (Figure 2.53).

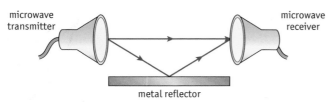

Figure 2.52 Superposition of waves that have travelled different paths

Figure 2.53 Superposition of reflected waves

Superposition in a CD player

In a CD player the laser light source produces a single beam with a diameter greater than the width of a raised bump (Figure 2.54). In the absence of a bump, all the light is reflected from the background surface with no phase difference across it – so it produces constructive superposition, i.e. the signal diode detects that the light is 'on' (Figure 2.55).

Figure 2.54 Bumps on a CD surface

However, when the light is reflected from an area with a bump, the middle of the beam is reflected from the top of the bump but the light either side of the bump has farther to travel. The light reflected from the top of the bump destructively interferes with the light reflected from either side of the bump.

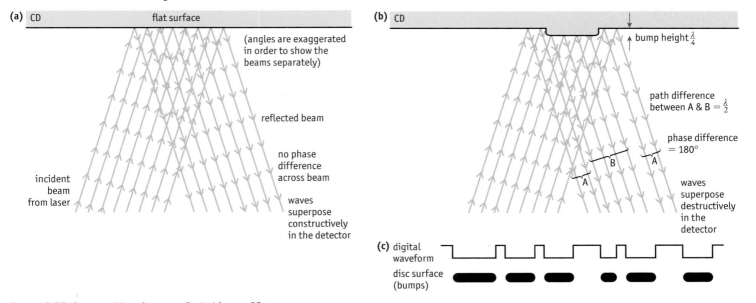

Figure 2.55 Superposition of waves reflected from a CD

Phase difference and path difference were introduced in Section 1.5 of this chapter.

In the presence of a bump, half the light will go to the background surface and back and get out of phase with the part reflected from the shorter route via the top of the bump. If the **path difference** Δx between the two reflected beams is carefully arranged, the **phase difference** $\Delta \varphi$ between them will give rise to destructive interference when they come together in the detector:

$$\Delta \varphi = \frac{2\pi \Delta x}{\lambda}$$

(Equation 3)

The light is recorded as 'off' by the signal diode even if the cancellation is not absolutely complete. The light beam moving over the spiral track gives a sequence of on–off signals, which is then processed to reconstruct the original sound.

In the case of the CD, one part of the light beam can destructively interfere with the other part because of a difference in the distance they both travel. This will only work if the laser light is **monochromatic** (i.e. of a single frequency) and the incident and reflected beams are coherent.

⚙ ACTIVITY 19 MODEL CD

Use the apparatus shown in Figure 2.56 to illustrate reading a CD. The 500 nm wavelength laser light used in a CD player is far too fine for laboratory use, so this apparatus uses electromagnetic waves with a wavelength of 3 cm to model the action. The size of the bumps is scaled up by the same factor as the wavelength.

Describe how this model works, using the terms *path difference* and *phase difference*.

Figure 2.56 A large-scale model of a CD and scanner

QUESTIONS

Q 41 (a) If two beams of light are to interfere destructively, what is the smallest possible difference in the paths travelled?

(b) If two beams of light interfere constructively, what are the possible differences in the paths travelled?

(c) If the wavelength of the light is 500 nm, how high must the bumps be on a CD to produce destructive interference?

3.3 Summing up Part 3

In this part of the chapter you have seen how information is encoded on CDs, and you have used ideas about superposition from earlier in the chapter to explain how the information can be read.

⚙ ACTIVITY 20 SUMMING UP PART 3

Check back through your work on this part of the chapter and make sure you understand the meaning of all the terms printed in bold.

QUESTION

Q 42 Blu-ray Discs use a light with a wavelength in air of 405 nm. Inside the plastic coating, the wavelength of this light is 270 mm. How high are the bumps on a Blu-ray Disc?

4 CD players

In this part of the chapter, attention turns to the production of the laser beam that is essential for reading a disc.

4.1 Laser

In Section 3.2 we said that the light beam in a CD player had to be monochromatic (single coloured) – that is, have a single frequency. The way to achieve this is to use a laser. In order to explain what is special about laser light, we will first look at light from sources that are not monochromatic.

Coloured light

You will probably have seen all the colours that make up white light separated out by a prism and displayed as a spectrum. This shows us what is there but doesn't explain how it got there. To understand about the lasers used in CD players, we need to develop a theory about light production.

In Activity 21 you will observe the spectra from various light sources. To display the spectra you need a **spectrum analyser** (a device that separates out the different frequencies present). This could be a prism, but a filter called a diffraction grating allows you to spread the colours over a wider range of angles so that they are more easily distinguished.

Modelling light

When we first thought about light it was enough to say that we need it in order to see. Then, perhaps through physics lessons, you learn that it involves energy transfer, and then you observe the phenomenon of superposition, which convinces you that light has wave properties.

STUDY NOTE

You will also use diffraction gratings in the chapter *Digging up the Past*.

> ⚙ **ACTIVITY 21 OBSERVING SPECTRA**
> Use a prism or a diffraction grating to observe the colours that make up the light from various sources. (See Figure 2.57.)

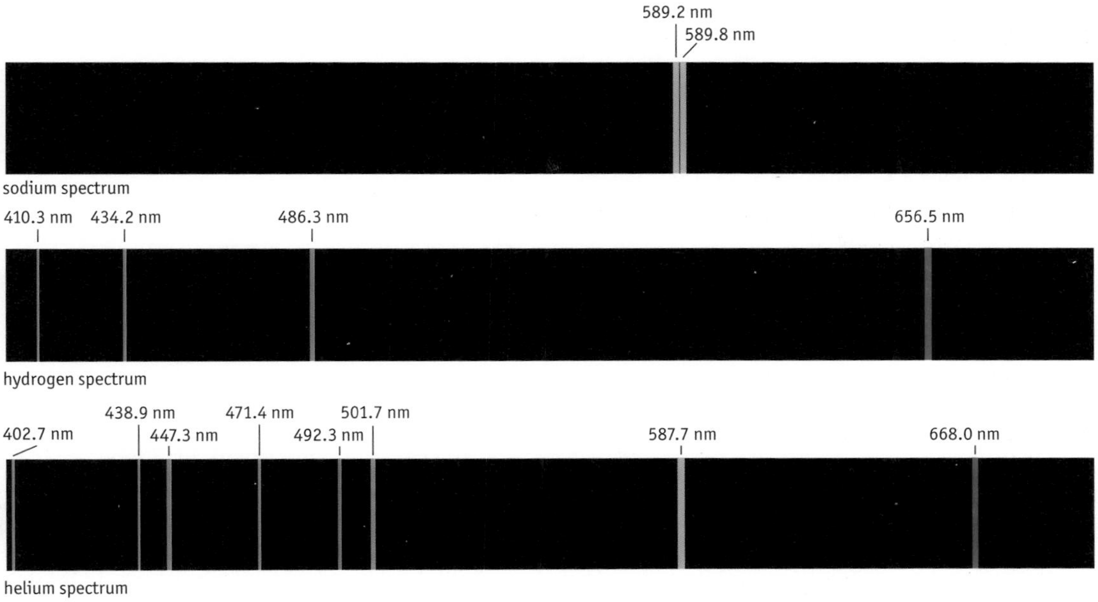

Figure 2.57 Light from various sources observed through a diffraction grating

This helps to explain colour and refraction – different wavelengths appear as different colours to humans, and refraction is linked to the wave speed. So, is it enough to say that light is a wave? Well, no. Once we get to the point of having to explain what is happening as light is created or absorbed, we need another way of looking at this thing called light; we need another **model**.

The energy emitted by a light source is the result of millions of individual events. Each event radiates a packet of energy, which means light also has to be modelled as a particle. A light particle is called a **photon**. These two models – wave and particle – describe different aspects of the phenomenon of light. Which one we use depends on the particular situation.

Both models can be used to describe colour. According to the wave model, colour depends on frequency: violet light has a higher frequency than red light (about twice as high). However, according to the particle model, colour depends on energy: a violet photon transfers more energy than a red photon (about twice as much). The two models are related via the Planck equation:

$$E = hf \qquad\qquad (7)$$

where E is the energy of the photon and f is the frequency of the wave. The constant h is known as the **Planck constant**: $h = 6.63 \times 10^{-34}\,\text{J s}$.

QUESTIONS

$c = 3.00 \times 10^8\,\text{m s}^{-1}$

$h = 6.63 \times 10^{-34}\,\text{J s}$

Q 43 (a) Copy and complete Table 2.2 so that it contains data relating to the wave and photon models of light.

(b) How do the values of photon energy help explain warnings about sunburn?

Colour	Wavelength λ/nm	Frequency f/Hz	Photon energy E/J
Infrared	775		
Red	656		
Green	486		
Blue	434		
Purple	410		
Ultraviolet	389		

Table 2.2 Some of the lines in the hydrogen spectrum

Q 44 Power is the rate at which energy is transferred. A power of 1 W corresponds to $1\,\text{J s}^{-1}$. A laser for a CD player has a power of 0.2 mW and a wavelength of 775 nm.

(a) What is the frequency of the light?

(b) At what rate does the laser emit photons?

(c) What difference would it makes to your answers if the laser had a shorter wavelength but the same power?

MATHS REFERENCE

Manipulating powers on a calculator

See Maths note 1.4

Atomic line spectra

In Activity 21 you will have seen some **line spectra** – light that contains only a few distinct colours separated by gaps, rather than a continuous range. This light was emitted by atoms in an electrical discharge tube. Each element has its own distinctive set of colours.

The photon model of light can help explain the origin of atomic line spectra. In a discharge tube, energy is transferred from the electrical supply to the atoms in the gas, giving their electrons additional energy. The electrons lose this extra energy by emitting light – each photon given out corresponds to a single electron losing energy. When the negative electrons are bound to the positive nucleus in an atom, they can only have certain energies, which are known as electronic **energy levels**. The photons they emit correspond to electrons jumping between these levels. By analysing the energies of photons given out by excited atoms, it is possible to work out their energy levels.

As hydrogen is the simplest element (just one electron), its line spectrum is the one most readily worked out. Some of the calculated energy levels for hydrogen are shown in Figure 2.58, with arrows indicating some of the possible energy transitions.

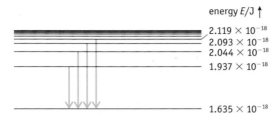

energy E/J ↑

2.119 × 10⁻¹⁸
2.093 × 10⁻¹⁸
2.044 × 10⁻¹⁸

1.937 × 10⁻¹⁸

1.635 × 10⁻¹⁸

0

Figure 2.58 An energy level diagram for a hydrogen atom

QUESTIONS

Q 45 Calculate the energy transitions corresponding to the four arrows in Figure 2.58, and match them up with four of the lines listed in your answer to Question 43.

Q 46 Without doing any calculations, what can you say about the photon emitted when an electron makes a transition to the lowest energy level in Figure 2.58 (called the **ground state**)?

Wave-particle duality

If light can be represented as a wave *and* as a stream of particles, what exactly is light and what do you have to do about it? Both models are 'right' in that they each explain some aspects of the behaviour of light, and we have to treat light as behaving *like* waves part of the time and *like* particles at others – notice that we have not said that light *is* either of these.

QUESTIONS

Q 47 Given a choice between the wave and photon models, say which you think best explains each of the following:

(a) a light source produces a line spectrum

(b) a ray of light is reflected.

Q 48 'A photon is the means by which the energy carried by the waves is ultimately delivered and takes effect.'

(a) What does the speaker of this quotation mean about energy being delivered?

(b) How does this short statement indicate when to use the wave and particle models?

Laser light

A **laser** emits light of just one frequency. In other words, it has a special sort of line spectrum corresponding to just one energy transition. Laser light has two other unusual properties, both of which are useful in the CD player:

● the light is emitted in a narrow beam rather than coming out in all directions

● the emission is coherent – different atoms emit light in phase with one another, rather than randomly.

The name laser stands for **l**ight **a**mplification by **s**timulated **e**mission of **r**adiation. This phrase relates to the way that a laser produces light, which is in turn related to the light's special properties.

A directed beam of coherent monochromatic light is produced if excited atoms are stimulated to emit a photon in a chosen direction. An identical photon will do this. One photon enters the excited atom and two leave (the light is 'amplified'). The photons travel in the same direction, have the same wavelength and are in phase with one another (see Figure 2.59).

First, we need to get the atoms excited, which means an electron in the atom moves to higher energy orbit. The energy from an electric current or discharge through the material works well at exciting the atoms. After a short time the electrons will fall back to a lower energy and a photon will be emitted; this is called spontaneous emission (Figure 2.59a). Mirrors are used to ensure that some of these photons are kept travelling up and down the space, stimulating others to 'get in step'. A small hole in one mirror allows a small proportion to escape as a laser beam.

If an excited atom is disturbed by a photon of the same energy as its excitation, it will be stimulated to emit its photon in time with the disturbing photon. This is called stimulated emission of radiation. The stimulated photon will have the same phase, frequency and direction as the disturbing photon (Figure 2.59b).

Many types of material can be made to 'lase'. Sometimes a gas is used; but to get a compact, robust portable laser, solid materials are used. The laser for a CD player must be extremely small. To get an intense monochromatic light from a small component, the answer is to use a semiconductor material – most commonly gallium arsenide. The disadvantage of a semiconductor laser is that the beam spread is about 10°, so lenses are used to make a parallel beam as shown in Figure 2.49.

STUDY NOTE

You will learn about the properties of lenses in the chapter *Spare Part Surgery*.

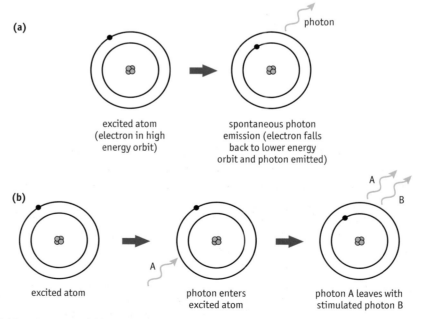

Figure 2.59 (a) Spontaneous and (b) stimulated emission of radiation

ACTIVITY 22 JELLY LASER

A simple demonstration (Figure 2.60) shows the principal elements in a laser.

SAFETY NOTE

Do not allow light from the flash gun or the laser to shine directly into anyone's eye.

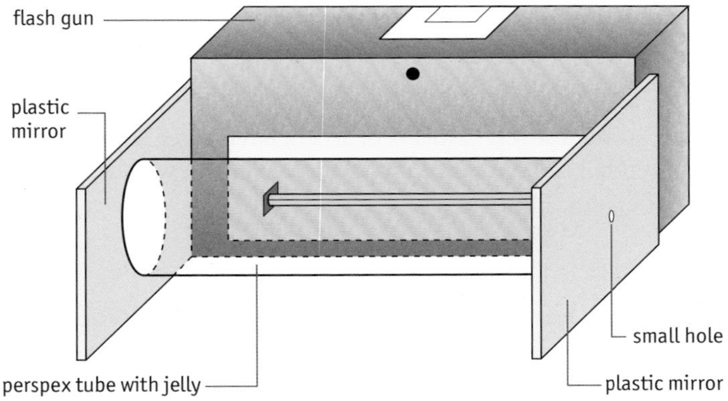

Figure 2.60 A jelly laser

Detecting the signal

Our journey around the working of a CD player is almost complete. There is just space for a word or two about the light detector. The digital signal is going to need electronic decoding and processing before the final sound is heard. All this requires a transfer of energy from a light to an electrical signal. A suitable component is a photodiode (Figure 2.61). When a photon hits it surface, the energy is absorbed by an electron, which then moves, i.e. it contributes to an electric current.

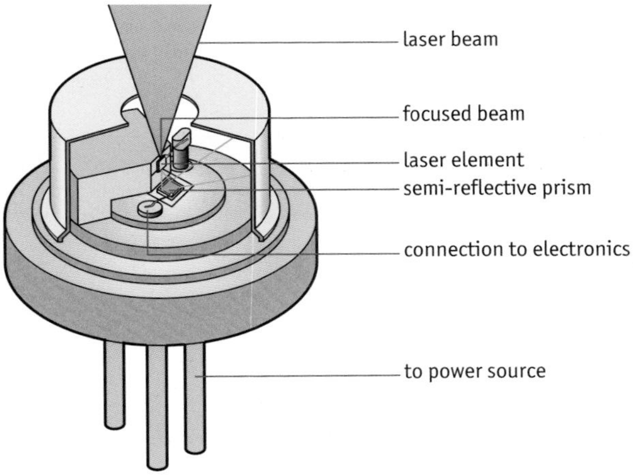

Figure 2.61 Detecting the signal

4.2 Summing up Part 4

This part of the chapter and Part 4 have covered many of the bits and pieces contained within a compact disc player. To summarise what you have learnt, it is a good idea to bring all the parts together. Activities 33 to 35 and the questions that follow are designed to help you do this.

ACTIVITY 23 SUMMING UP PART 4

Skim through Part 4 of this chapter and make sure that your notes include a clear definition or explanation of each of the terms printed in **bold** type. Look back at the article about CDs in *The Sound of Science* Section 3.1, and see how it relates to what you have been learning.

ACTIVITY 24 HOW IT WORKS

Set up a large-scale model of the optical system of a CD player (see Activity 19) that could be displayed at an open day or parents' evening. Prepare a brief explanation of your model (either written or spoken) that would be suitable for GCSE students or other visitors.

LINK THE LEARNING

5 Encore

In this chapter you have studied several aspects of the behaviour of sound and light. This concluding section is intended to help you to look back over the whole chapter and consolidate your knowledge and understanding.

5.1 Waves

In studying this unit you have learned some fundamental pieces of physics that all relate to waves. You have been studying sound waves in air, waves on stretched strings and light waves. Much of what you have learned about waves in this chapter can be applied to other natural and man-made phenomena that can be described and explained in terms of waves – earthquakes, microwave ovens and starlight are just three examples in addition to those you have met in this chapter. However, there are also some important differences between the various types of waves.

⚙ ACTIVITY 25 WAVES

Table 2.3 lists properties of waves that you have studied in this chapter. Copy the table. Use ticks and crosses to show which properties apply to which type of wave and which are common to waves of all types. If you made a large copy of this table you could add brief notes in each box – as has been done in the second row.

STUDY NOTE

You could extend your research into waves by listing some of the websites listed on *The Sound of Music* Additional Sheet 8.

Property	Type of wave			
	sound waves	waves on string	light waves	all
Obeys wave equation $v = f\lambda$				
Speed depends on material	✓	✓ $v = \sqrt{\dfrac{T}{\mu}}$	(See the later chapter *Good Enough to Eat*)	✓
Can travel in a vacuum				
Transverse				
Longitudinal				
Undergoes reflection				
Phase change of π when reflected at 'hard' boundary				
Undergoes superposition				

Table 2.3 Summary of wave properties for Activity 25

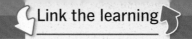

5.2 Questions on the whole chapter

Q 49 In the manufacture of microchips, sizes and positions have to be measured very precisely. This may be done using a laser, as shown schematically in Figure 2.62.

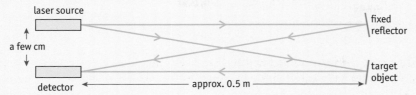

Figure 2.62 Measuring small changes in position

The detector measures the intensity of light produced by the superposition of the two light beams. Small changes in the intensity indicate small changes in position of the 'target' object. By using light of wavelength 600 nm, we can measure changes in position as small as 0.15 nm.

(a) Figure 2.63 shows two waves arriving at the detector in phase. Suppose the 'target' is moved away from the source through 150 nm. How much further, approximately, does the light beam now have to travel via the target to reach the detector?

Figure 2.63 Waves arriving at a detector

(b) Draw a diagram to show the two waves that now arrive at the detector and the resultant signal.

Q 50 Ruari and Rachel are talking about different kinds of waves. Ruari is certain that both sound and light from a spaceship travel through outer space so that you can hear and see the engine. Rachel says that you only get sound effects in *Star Wars* films. What do you think?

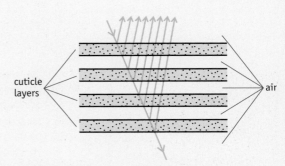

Figure 2.64 Reflection and refraction by thin layers

Q 51 This question is about the vivid colours seen in the wings of many moths, butterflies and birds. These so-called iridescent colours are produced by superposition when light is partially reflected and partially refracted by one or more thin layers of cuticle (scaly material) and then recombines as shown in Figure 2.64.

Figure 2.65 shows the light paths through a single cuticle layer. If light of a particular wavelength undergoes constructive superposition, when beams 2 and 3 recombine, then the cuticle layer appears to 'shine' with light of that colour.

(a) (i) What happens to the amplitude when two waves constructively superpose?

(ii) How must the *phases* of beams 2 and 3 be related if constructive superposition is to take place when they recombine?

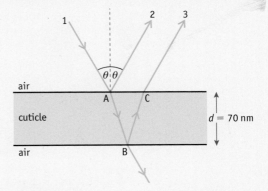

Figure 2.65 Light paths through a single cuticle layer

(b) Light reflected at A, the upper surface of the cuticle, *undergoes a phase change of 180° or π radians*. Explain what is meant by this phrase in italics.

(c) In order for beams 2 and 3 to superpose constructively when $\theta = 0°$, what must be the relationship between the wavelength, λ, and the thickness, d?

(d) Explain why different colours are seen when the cuticle is looked at from different angles.

> **STUDY NOTE**
>
> You will learn more about refraction in the chapter *Good Enough to Eat*; you don't need to know about refraction to answer this question.

Q 52   Some of the energy levels in a helium
atom are shown in Figure 2.66.

————————————————— 3.50×10^{-18}

————————————————— 2.95×10^{-18}

(a) Calculate the frequency of the three
different photons that can be emitted
when an electron moves between
these energy levels.

energy E/J ↑

(b) One of the lines in the helium
spectrum has a wavelength 447 nm.
What is the energy of a photon of
this radiation?

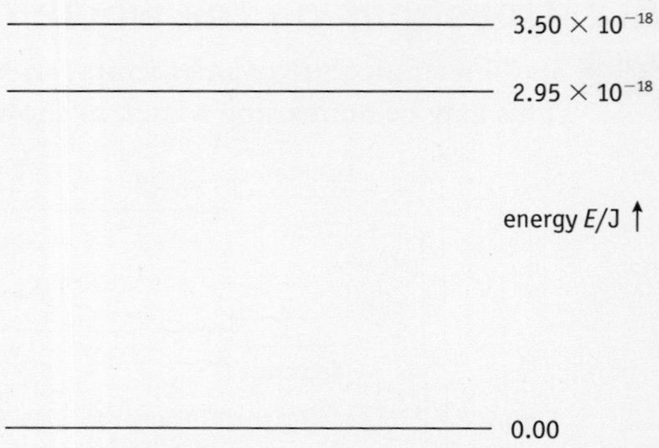

————————————————— 0.00

Figure 2.66 Electron energy levels in a helium atom

5.3 Achievements

Now you have studied this chapter you should be able to achieve the outcomes listed in Table 2.4.

TABLE 2.4 ACHIEVEMENTS FOR THE CHAPTER *THE SOUND OF MUSIC*

	Statement from Examination Specification	Section(s) in this chapter
1	know and understand the distinction between base and devised quantities and their SI units	1.2, 2.1
2	demonstrate their knowledge of practical skills and techniques for both familiar and unfamiliar experiments	1.2, 1.4, 2.1, 2.2
5	be able to communicate information and ideas in appropriate ways using appropriate terminology	2.2, 3.1, 3.2, 4.2
59	understand the terms *amplitude*, *frequency*, *period*, *speed* and *wavelength*	1.2, 1.4, 3.2
60	be able to use the wave equation $v = f\lambda$	1.4, 3.2
61	be able to describe longitudinal waves in terms of pressure variation and the displacement of molecules	1.3, 1.4
62	be able to describe transverse waves	1.4
63	be able to draw and interpret graphs representing transverse and longitudinal waves including standing/stationary waves	1.4, 1.5
64	CORE PRACTICAL 6: Determine the speed of sound in air using a two-beam oscilloscope, signal generator, speaker and microphone	1.4
65	know and understand what is meant by *wavefront*, *coherence*, *path difference*, *superposition*, *interference* and *phase*	1.5, 2.1, 2.2, 3.2
66	be able to use the relationship between phase difference and path difference	1.3, 3.2
67	know what is meant by a *standing/stationary wave*, and understand how such a wave is formed, know how to identify nodes and antinodes	1.5, 2.1, 2.2
68	be able to use the equation for the speed of a transverse wave on a string: $$v = \sqrt{\frac{T}{\mu}}$$	2.1
69	CORE PRACTICAL 7: Investigate the effects of length, tension and mass per unit length on the frequency of a vibrating string or wire	2.1
90	understand how the behaviour of electromagnetic radiation can be described in terms of a wave model and a photon model	3.2, 4.1
91	be able to use the equation $E = hf$ that relates the photon energy to the wave frequency	4.1
95	understand atomic line spectra in terms of transitions between discrete energy levels and understand how to calculate the frequency of radiation that could be emitted or absorbed in a transition between energy levels	4.1

Answers

Q 1 (a) $f_A = \dfrac{f_B}{2}$ because the period of A is twice that of B.

(b) $f_A = \dfrac{f_C}{3}$ because A has three times the period of C.

Q 2 (a) $\Delta\phi = 90°$ or $270° \left(\dfrac{\pi}{2} \text{ or } \dfrac{3\pi}{2} \text{ radians}\right)$

(b) $\Delta\phi = 120°$ or $240° \left(\dfrac{2\pi}{6} \text{ or } \dfrac{4\pi}{3} \text{ radians}\right)$

(c) $\Delta\phi = 180°$ (π radians)

Q 3 See Figure 2.67.

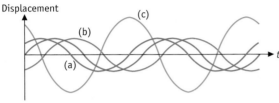

Figure 2.67 The answers to Question 3

Q 4 (a) The phase difference must correspond to a whole number of cycles, i.e. by $360n°$ or by $2\pi n$ radians, where n is a whole number.

(b) They are all the same.

$\dfrac{\pi}{8}$ radians = 22.5° so (i) and (ii) are the same.

$\dfrac{17\pi}{8} = 2\pi + \dfrac{\pi}{8}$ so (iii) is the same as (i) and (ii).

$-337.5° = 22.5° - 360°$ so (iv) is also the same as (i), (ii) and (iii).

Q 5 (i) A and B are in phase at times 0 and T.

(ii) A and C are in phase at times 0, $\dfrac{T}{2}$ and T.

(iii) B and C are in phase at times 0 and T.

Q 6 (a) The motion of the cloth approximates to a travelling transverse wave pulse with an amplitude and frequency that depends on how it is shaken.

(b) The motion of the trucks approximates to a travelling longitudinal wave pulse.

(c) The Mexican wave is a travelling transverse wave of roughly constant amplitude and speed.

(d) If the traffic is confined to one lane its motion approximates to a series of longitudinal pulses. If lane changing is possible then there is also some transverse motion.

Q 7 Using Equation 2, wavelength $\lambda = \dfrac{v}{f}$

$$= \dfrac{340\,\text{m s}^{-2}}{20\,\text{Hz}}$$

$$= \dfrac{340\,\text{m s}^{-2}}{20\,\text{s}^{-1}}$$

$$= 17\,\text{m}$$

Similarly, when $f = 20\,\text{kHz}$, $\lambda = 17 \times 10^{-3}\,\text{m}$

$$= 17\,\text{mm}$$

Q 8 (a) (i) $\lambda = 0.8\,\text{m}$

(ii) $f = \dfrac{v}{\lambda}$

$$= \dfrac{5.0\,\text{m s}^{-1}}{0.8\,\text{m}}$$

$$= 6.25\,\text{s}^{-1}\ (= 6.25\,\text{Hz})$$

$$T = \dfrac{1}{f} = \dfrac{1}{6.25\,\text{s}^{-1}} = 0.16\,\text{s}$$

(b) See Figure 2.68.

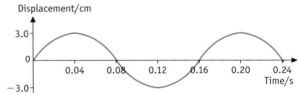

Figure 2.68 The answer to Question 8(b)

Q 9 See Figure 2.69. The period T is 5 ms (5×10^{-3} s) so the wavelength can be found using Equations 1 and 2:

$$\lambda = \dfrac{v}{f} = v \times T$$

$$= 300\,\text{m s}^{-1} \times 0.005\,\text{s}$$

$$= 1.5\,\text{m}$$

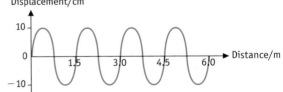

Figure 2.69 The answer to Question 9

Q 10 See Figure 2.70.

(a)

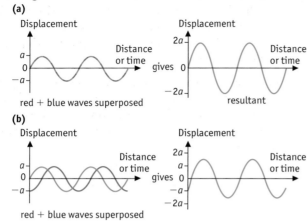

red + blue waves superposed   gives   resultant

(b)

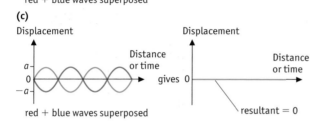

red + blue waves superposed   gives

(c)

Displacement   Displacement

red + blue waves superposed   gives   resultant = 0

Figure 2.70 The answers to Question 10

Q 11 The sound must have the same amplitude as the engine noise, but be in antiphase with it.

Q 12 In both case the waves must have the same amplitude and frequency. For **(a)** they must be in phase and for **(b)** they must be in antiphase.

Q 13 Distance between nodes $= \dfrac{\lambda}{2}$

Q 14 **(a)** See Figure 2.71.

(b) $\lambda = 0.80\,\text{m} = \dfrac{2}{3}$ of 1.20 m.

(c) $v = f\lambda = 0.80\,\text{m} \times 150\,\text{Hz}$
$\qquad = 120\,\text{m s}^{-1}$

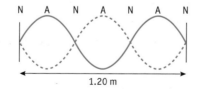

N A N A N A N

1.20 m

Figure 2.71 A standing wave on a rubber cord with nodes and antinodes labelled

Q 15 **(a)** $l = \dfrac{\lambda}{2}$ so $f = \dfrac{v}{2l}$

(b) We are referring to the transverse waves on the string because it is these waves that superpose to form the standing waves that define the fundamental frequency of the string's vibration. (The sound waves that are generated in the air have the same frequency as these vibrations, but travel at a different speed and so have a different wavelength.)

(c) Any two higher frequency standing waves (harmonics), e.g. as shown in Figure 2.72.

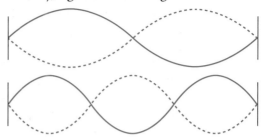

Figure 2.72 Possible answers to Question 15(c)

Q 16 In an electric guitar, the vibrations are amplified electronically.

Q 17 As the wood vibrates, the tea leaves are set in motion and settle at places where the wood is not moving, i.e. at the nodes. The pattern of tea leaves therefore reveals a two-dimensional standing wave. (Such standing waves are sometimes called Chladni vibrations after the 19th-century scientist who first investigated them.)

Q 18 **(a)** Banjo, **(b)** Picolo, **(c)** Side drum. In each case, the smaller instrument produces the higher-pitched notes because the standing waves that correspond to its fundamental vibration will be shorter and hence of higher frequency. (We can only compare similar instruments in this way because there are other factors that affect the speed of the waves set up within the instrument and therefore the frequency of the fundamental vibration.)

Q 19 **(a)** The SI units of the quantities on the right-hand side of Equation 6 are:

length l m

tension T N $1\,\text{N} = 1\,\text{kg m s}^{-2}$

mass per unit length μ kg m^{-1}

So the SI units of the right-hand side are:

$$\frac{1}{\text{m}} \sqrt{\frac{\text{kg m s}^{-2}}{\text{kg m}^{-1}}} = \frac{1}{\text{m}} \sqrt{\text{m}^2 \text{s}^{-2}}$$

$$= \frac{1}{\text{m}}\,\text{m s}^{-1}$$

$$= \text{s}^{-1}$$

As $1\,\text{s}^{-1} = 1\,\text{Hz}$, the right-hand side has the correct units for frequency.

(b) (i) Twisting the screws adjusts the tension in the strings so that they produce the desired notes. The greater the tension T the higher the frequency of vibration of a given string and so the higher the pitch of its note.

(ii) Placing a finger on the string shortens the length *l* that is free to vibrate. The shorter the string the higher the frequency of its vibration and so the higher the note it produces.

(iii) Reducing the mass per unit length μ of a string increases the frequency of its vibration and so raises the pitch of its notes. (If all the strings of a piano were the same thickness, they would have to have a very large range of lengths and the high-note strings would have to be held under much greater tension than the low-note strings. Using strings of different thickness reduces the extremes of length and tension that are needed, making the instrument easier to construct and use.)

Q 20 Sign indicates the direction of displacement and the molecules oscillate first to one side of their equilibrium position and then to the other.

Q 21 See Figure 2.73.

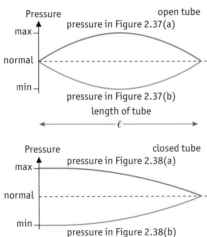

Figure 2.73 The answers to Question 21

Q 22 **(a)** Open tube: there is a displacement antinode at each end, so $l = \dfrac{\lambda}{2}$

(b) Closed tube: the length of the tube is the distance from node to antinode, i.e. $l = \dfrac{\lambda}{4}$

(Compare with answers to Question 15.)

Q 23 **(a)** From Equation 2, $f = \dfrac{v}{\lambda}$.

For an open tube:

$\lambda = 2l$ (see Question 22) so $f = \dfrac{v}{2l}$

(b) For a closed tube, $\lambda = 4l$ so $f = \dfrac{v}{4l}$

Q 24 The fundamental frequency depends primarily on the length of the air column from the tip of the mouthpiece to the nearest open hole. (The width of the tube might also affect the frequency, as would the overall pattern of uncovered holes.)

Q 25 The vibrating air column extends approximately from the mouthpiece to the first uncovered hole as shown in Figure 2.74. Case (b) gives the lower note because it has a longer air column than (a) – it has a larger uninterrupted row of covered holes.

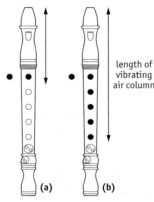

Figure 2.74 The answers to Question 25

Q 26 Your answers should resemble Figure 2.75. Standing waves in tubes have displacement nodes at closed ends and displacement antinodes at open ends. Possible answers to Question 26. Standing waves in a tube (a) with two open ends (b) with one open and one closed end.

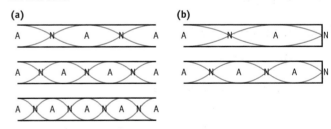

Figure 2.75 The answers to Question 26

Q 27 **(a)** Substituting values into Equation 6:

$$f = \frac{1}{0.5\,\text{m}} \times \sqrt{\frac{15\,\text{N}}{3.75 \times 10^{-4}\,\text{kg m}^{-1}}}$$

$$= \frac{1}{0.5\,\text{m}} \sqrt{(4 \times 10^{4})\,\text{m}^2\,\text{s}^{-2}}$$

$$= 400\,\text{Hz}$$

(b) The frequency is to be doubled, therefore the length of vibrating string must be halved, so the finger must be placed 0.25 m from the end.

Q 28 Helium changes the resonant frequency of the mouth cavity because sound waves travel faster in helium, amplifying the higher frequency overtones. (The common myths are that helium makes vocal cords vibrate faster, see, for example, YouTube video 'Why does helium make your voice sound funny?' by Naked Science Scrapbook.)

Q 29 Time period $T \approx 4.3$ ms, so $f \approx \dfrac{1}{0.0043\,\text{s}} = 233\,\text{Hz}$

Q 30 **(a)** Digital

(b) An analogue method replicates the waveform as a continuous signal, either electrical or mechanical (a stylus oscillating along a record groove). A digital system measures a series of sound samples and converts each value into a binary number.

Q 31 An optical system is one that uses light. If you look up scanning in a large dictionary you get many choices. Our context is an electronic one, so 'to move a beam of light in a predetermined pattern over a surface to obtain information' is probably what the author means. In other words, a laser beam will be moved along a spiral path from the centre to the edge of a CD. A stylus or pick-up is used with LPs.

Q 32 **(a)** 1.6×10^{-6} m (This could also be written $1.6\,\mu\text{m}$, as $1\,\mu\text{m} = 10^{-6}$ m)

(b) In a perfect world the beam could have a diameter of 1.6×10^{-6} m, but in practice it must be smaller to allow for wobbles and imperfections in the focusing of the light.

Q 33 **(a)** The plastic coating must be transparent so that the light can reach the metallic layer.

(b) The information is stored in the metallic layer as a spiral track of bumps.

(c) The important reflection takes place at the metal surface to collect the information codes in its bumps.

Q 34 The beam does not focus at the surface of the plastic, but lower down, on the metal layer. At the surface, it is wide enough so that the amount of light blocked by a speck of dust is not critical (see Figure 2.76).

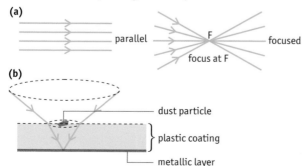

Figure 2.76 Diagram for the answer to Question 34

Q 35 You should have drawn a diagram similar to Figure 2.77, illustrating which angles are equal when light rays change direction at a reflecting boundary. Reflection is not a property of light alone: sounds, light and balls reflect from surfaces, often with some loss of energy.

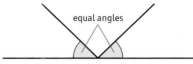

Figure 2.77 Diagram for the answer to Question 35

Q 36 **(a)** The diode is a photodiode that absorbs light to produce an electrical signal.

(b) The tracking components control the movement of the laser light so that it keeps on the spiral track as the disc turns.

(c) A prism is a block of transparent material – glass or similar – with a triangular cross-section.

Q 37 The beam must be wider than the bump to ensure that *some* of the beam is reflected from the surrounding surface and *some* from the bump. If *all* the beam was reflected from the bump there would be no path difference across the beam and no destructive interference.

Q 38 All resultant waves have period T, frequency f.

(a) (i) P amplitude $2.5a$, brighter than A or B individually.

(ii) Q amplitude zero, totally dark.

(b) R amplitude $0.5a$, fainter than either A or B.

(c) S amplitude $2a$, brighter than either individually.

Q 39 **(a)** Combination Q is 'off'. All the others are 'on'.

(b) They must have exactly the same frequency and amplitude and be 180° out of phase.

Q 40 Now both Q and R count as 'off'.

Q 41 **(a)** The smallest path difference between the two beams is half a wavelength. This gives a 180° phase difference.

(b) It must be zero or a whole number of wavelengths, i.e. $n\lambda$ where n is a whole number.

(c) 125 nm high since a half wavelength difference is achieved by an outward and return journey to make the 250 nm (half wavelength) difference.

Q 42 Bump height $= \dfrac{\lambda_{\text{plastic}}}{4} = \dfrac{270\,\text{nm}}{4} = 67.5\,\text{nm}$

Q 43 (a) See Table 2.5.

Colour	Wavelength λ/nm	Frequency f/Hz	Photon energy E/J
Infrared	775	3.87×10^{14}	2.57×10^{-19}
Red	656	4.57×10^{14}	3.03×10^{-19}
Green	486	6.17×10^{14}	4.09×10^{-19}
Blue	434	6.91×10^{14}	4.58×10^{-19}
Violet	410	7.32×10^{14}	4.84×10^{-19}
Ultraviolet	389	7.71×10^{14}	5.11×10^{-19}

Table 2.5 The answers to Question 43(a)

(b) Photons of ultraviolet radiation have more energy than those of visible or infrared radiation, so they can cause ionization and do more damage. Labels on barrier creams refer to their ability to absorb ultraviolet radiation.

Q 44 (a) $f = \dfrac{c}{\lambda}$

$$= \frac{3.00 \times 10^8 \, \text{m s}^{-1}}{775 \times 10^{-9} \, \text{m}}$$

$$= 3.87 \times 10^{14} \, \text{Hz}$$

(b) Energy of single photon

$E = hf$

$$= 6.63 \times 10^{-34} \, \text{J s} \times 3.87 \times 10^{14} \, \text{Hz}$$

$$= 2.56 \times 10^{-19} \, \text{J}$$

$$\left\{ \begin{array}{c} \text{number of photons} \\ \text{emitted per second} \end{array} \right\} = \left\{ \begin{array}{c} \text{total energy emitted} \\ \text{per second} \\ \hline \text{energy of each photon} \end{array} \right\}$$

$$= \frac{0.2 \times 10^{-3} \, \text{J s}^{-1}}{2.56 \times 10^{-19} \, \text{J}}$$

$$= 7.80 \times 10^{14} \, \text{s}^{-1}$$

Note that we have included the units at each step, and this gives sensible units for the final answer, i.e. a number per second.

(c) The photon energy would be greater, so there would need to be fewer photons per second in order to deliver the same power.

Q 45 Going from energy level 3 to level 2, the energy lost by the electron is:

$$(1.94 - 1.63) \times 10^{-18} \, \text{J} = 3.02 \times 10^{-19} \, \text{J}$$

From Table 2.4, this corresponds to the energy of a photon of red light (give or take a slight difference in the third figure due to rounding). Similarly, the transitions from level 4 to 2, 5 to 2 and 6 to 2 correspond, respectively, to the photon energies for the green, blue and violet light that you calculated for Table 2.4.

Q 46 Even the smallest possible transition to the ground state (from level 2 to level 1) involves an electron losing 1.635×10^{-18} J, which is larger than any of the photon energies corresponding to visible light, so this radiation lies in the ultraviolet (or even shorter wavelength) part of the spectrum.

Q 47 (a) Line spectra can only be explained using the particle model.

(b) Many aspects of reflection can be explained using either model, but not the phase change – so the wave model is better.

Q 48 (a) The speaker seems to mean that when a beam of light meets a surface it is absorbed in packets as photons.

(b) When light is emitted or absorbed it seems to behave as a particle, but on its travels it behaves as a wave.

GOOD ENOUGH TO EAT

Why a chapter called *Good Enough to Eat?*

Everyone has to eat, and for the most part we enjoy the taste and textures of food as well as the social aspects of eating. Foods have to be manufactured and packaged so that they can be transported and stored safely and affordably. They also need to be labelled so that we know what we are eating.

The food production industry is enormous. In 2014, Nestlé, the world's largest food, drink and confectionery producer, was making over 8500 different products (Figures 3.1 and 3.2) to be sold in more than a hundred countries, and employing over 300 000 people. In 2014, Nestlé's sales amounted to £60 billion.

Physicists have a part to play in most stages of the design and development of food production processes. Physics principles are used to assess the raw materials' quality and condition. Ingredients must be weighed and mixed and brought together to form a homogeneous mass at a specified temperature. Food manufacture often involves the product flowing along pipes, being pushed through orifices or shaped in moulds, each of which is affected by the physical properties of the materials. The product must be tested to check that it has the desired properties. Finally, the product needs to be packaged for safe storage and distribution, which means that the physical nature of the packaging is important. Labelling, date stamping and detecting contaminants during processing all involve important elements of physics.

Figure 3.1 Confectionery products

OVERVIEW OF PHYSICS PRINCIPLES AND TECHNIQUES

In this chapter you will see how the flow properties of liquids are affected by concentration and temperature, and how they can be measured or compared. Products need to be tested (for example, to ensure that a biscuit provides a suitable 'crunch'), and in this part of the chapter you will learn about materials testing and such factors as hardness, brittleness and toughness. You will learn how to use light to measure the sugar concentration of raw materials and so learn about refraction and polarisation of light. Material properties feature again in the final part of the chapter, on packaging, where you will also see how physics relates to aspects of health and safety.

During the course of this chapter you will learn about instrumentation and calibration, and you will be introduced to some important techniques and measuring instruments. You will learn how to read a vernier scale, how to use a micrometer screw gauge and how to treat experimental errors and uncertainties.

In this chapter you will extend your knowledge of:

- forces and motion and using graphs from *Higher, Faster, Stronger*
- the behaviour of light from *The Sound of Music*.

In other chapters you will do more work on:

- forces and motion in *Transport on Track*
- bulk properties of materials in *Spare Part Surgery* and *Build or Bust?*

In *Good Enough to Eat* you will see how physics principles are used in the confectionery industry – in particular, the manufacture of biscuits and chocolates.

Figure 3.2 Confectionery products

1 Physics in the food industry

Stephen Beckett has many years' experience of working as a professional physicist at the Nestlé Research and Development Centre in York. Here, he provides an introduction to the place of physics in the food and confectionery industry.

1.1 Physics in the food and confectionery industry

Chocolate making, and indeed the food industry as a whole, is not at first sight an obvious place to need physics. Yet closer inspection shows that the industry needs and uses physics to an ever-increasing degree. Not only is food processing the UK's biggest industry, it is also one that is currently in the middle of big changes from an essentially craft-based industry to a highly automated one requiring critical control. This makes the challenge and the opportunity for physicists even greater.

Food has the advantage over many industrial products in that if it is processed well, and to the customer's liking, then a repeat purchase is likely in the very short term, unlike other industries whose products may last for many years. It does, however, have an extra challenge in that the products must be absolutely safe to eat and obey the food laws. You cannot, for instance, help chocolate to melt in the mouth by something that tastes nasty or, even worse, makes the consumer ill. It is always worth remembering that food is bought because of how it looks and tastes, not because of the clever science that has been used to make it. Science can, however, help to manipulate the taste and texture of a product, ensure that it is relatively consistent from day to day (not an easy task when your raw ingredients are always varying) and indeed help to ensure a product's safety.

In addition, science can help to make the industry more efficient by optimising processing and other factors such as extending shelf-life so that a product can be made all the year round, rather than having operators and expensive machinery employed for only a few weeks.

Further research

When a box of chocolate assortments becomes old, the centres containing nuts are usually the first ones to turn a white colour. This is known as 'bloom' and is when the fat from the sweet comes to the surface and sets there.

The reason why it is worse in the nut sweets is because the nuts contain a fat that is mainly liquid at room temperature, whereas most of the fat within chocolate (cocoa butter) is solid. The soft nut fat reacts with the cocoa butter and softens it and also migrates through the sweet to the surface. In order to obtain more information about this process, magnetic resonance imaging (as used in body scanners) has been used at the University of Cambridge to monitor the changes in the position of the nut fat taking place within the sweets.

So, every time you buy a KitKat, Mars Bar or Crunchie, it has been produced with the aid of physics. The chocolate industry, however, still has a lot of physics that remains to be done. Not only is a simple method required to detect plastic in chocolate but other problems remain, such as the measurement of the three-dimensional contraction of chocolate as it sets in the mould, or of its stickiness as it melts in the hand. Perhaps you have the solution!

Stephen Beckett has written further comments to accompany some other sections as you progress through the chapter.

PRACTICAL SKILLS REFERENCE

Information research

See Practical skills notes 1.2–1.4

⚙ ACTIVITY 1 FOOD WEB

Use the Internet to find some more background information about the food industry. If you want to find out more about the variety of food products, or if you are wondering whether your future might be in this field of employment, go to www.pearsonhotlinks.co.uk, search for this title and activity. You can investigate further using the websites listed.

The Answers website provides a good introduction to the food industry. If you would like to find out more about Nestlé then go to their website, which provides insight into the company, its research, products, sales, staffing and history.

Figure 3.3 Chocolate manufacture has a long history

For more about chocolate, its history and its production (Figure 3.3) visit the Encyclopaedia Britannica and Exploratorium websites and search for 'chocolate'.

The website 'Wayne's this and that' also contains information about chocolate.

⚙ ACTIVITY 2 HOW BIG? HOW DENSE?

Manufacturers need to monitor their production, and they need to know how precise their measurement is. Make measurements to determine the volume and density of different sweets, and estimate the uncertainty in your measurements.

STUDY NOTE

For guidance on using measuring instruments, see EAT Additional Sheet 1

MATHS REFERENCE

Experimental measurements

See Maths note 7.1

Combining uncertainties

See Maths note 7.5

STUDY NOTE

For further guidance on using uncertainties see EAT Additional Sheet 2.

Figure 3.4 The enrobing process

Figure 3.5 Mis-shapen chocolates

Figure 3.6 A consistometer used to perform a line spread test

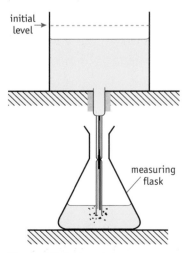

Figure 3.7 Redwood viscometer

2 Going with the flow

In many industrial processes it is essential to get liquids flowing at an appropriate speed to match the needs of the process. In the manufacture of chocolates or chocolate biscuits, the chocolate needs to flow at a rate that allows the correct thickness to be placed on a biscuit or soft centre or to fill a mould, and to keep up the required rate of production. Physics is essential to the description, understanding, measurement and control of the flow.

2.1 Flowing chocolate

> ⚙ **ACTIVITY 3 FLOWING CHOCOLATE**
>
> Read the following short article in which Stephen Beckett describes aspects of chocolate manufacture. Then make notes of how physics is, or might be, used in the circumstances that he mentions. Expand on any points you can, suggesting techniques and equipment that might be used for sensing, testing or control.

Chocolate differs from most other foods in that it is solid at room temperature and yet easily melts in the mouth. This is because the fat it contains has a melting point below that of blood temperature. In confectionery manufacture, chocolate is produced as a liquid to pour into moulds or to pour over (enrobe) a sweet centre, before being cooled to enable the fat to set (Figure 3.4). Incorrect flow properties will result in a poor-quality product. This may take the form of mis-shapes (Figure 3.5) where the chocolate runs down the sweet but instead of flowing through the open grid on which the sweet is enrobed it sticks to it, forming a sort of foot.

In aerated products, such as Aero bars, the flow properties of the chocolate will affect the size of the air bubbles. Weight control also becomes difficult, with thick chocolate sticking on top of the centre and sides and making it overweight. Too thin a chocolate may run off the centre altogether, allowing it to pick up or lose moisture and so be more likely to deteriorate.

The flow property of chocolate is in fact very complex. Only about one-third is made up of fat that is capable of melting at moderate temperatures and helping chocolate to flow. The remainder consists of solid particles (sugar, cocoa and milk solids) that must be coated with fat for them to flow smoothly past one another when the chocolate is being processed or melted in the mouth. This high solids content makes the chocolate flow in what is known as a non-Newtonian manner. In other words, its viscosity depends on how quickly it is moving. It is in fact a bit like tomato ketchup or non-drip paint, in that it becomes runnier when stirred or mixed quickly.

In addition, the more fine particles there are, the bigger the surface area to be coated by fat to enable the chocolate to flow and so the thicker the chocolate becomes. Once again physics becomes important in that it is used to measure the size distribution of these solid particles. This is done by dispersing the chocolate in a liquid and then shining a laser through the dispersion; the distribution can be calculated from the relative intensity of the light scattered at different angles.

2.2 Viscosity

How fast liquids flow is partly dependent on their **viscosity**, a factor describing their resistance to flow. Loosely speaking, the lower the viscosity of a fluid (a liquid or gas), the 'runnier' it is. Tar and treacle are very **viscous**, while water has low viscosity. Devices for comparing and measuring viscosity are called **viscometers**.

Comparing viscosities

One of the simplest tests for comparing viscosities is known as the line spread test and uses a device known as a consistometer (Figure 3.6). A fixed quantity of liquid is allowed to flow out of a container and spread over a flat surface. How far or fast it spreads provides a measure of the liquid's viscosity. Another instrument, the Redwood viscometer (Figure 3.7), involves allowing the liquid to flow through a narrow tube driven by its own head of pressure. (This instrument was first developed by French physiologist and physicist Jean Léonard Poiseuille (1797–1869), who used it to study blood flow.) Both these tests are used in the food industry.

Text near Figure 3.7 diagram: initial level, measuring flask

Defining viscosity

The line spread and Redwood tests are useful for comparing the behaviour of fluids, but they do not give an absolute measurement of viscosity. For this we can use a falling ball viscometer, an instrument developed by Irish physicist George Gabriel Stokes (1819–1903), which involves timing a ball falling at constant speed through a fluid. The instrument has been adapted for use in the chocolate industry: as chocolate is opaque, a rod is attached to the ball so that its movement can be monitored (Figure 3.8).

Stokes was able to quantify viscosity by studying the force exerted on a spherical object as it moves through a fluid, or when a fluid flows past it. (There is equivalence between a ball-bearing moving through a still fluid and a fluid moving past a stationary ball-bearing.) This **viscous drag** force is described by the relationship known as **Stokes's law**:

$$F = 6\pi r \eta v \tag{1}$$

where r is the radius of the sphere, v the velocity of the fluid relative to the sphere and η the coefficient of viscosity of the fluid (or commonly, just 'the viscosity') (η is the Greek letter eta). The direction of the force is opposite to that of the velocity. Equation 1 can be rearranged to get an expression for η:

$$\eta = \frac{F}{6\pi r v} \tag{1a}$$

From this we can see that the SI units of η are $\mathrm{N\,s\,m^{-2}}$. To give you an idea of typical values, the viscosity of water at 20 °C is $1.000 \times 10^{-3}\,\mathrm{N\,s\,m^{-2}}$, and that of air at 27 °C and a pressure of 1 atmosphere is $18.325 \times 10^{-6}\,\mathrm{N\,s\,m^{-2}}$. (Note that the temperatures are quoted – the viscosities of most fluids are highly dependent on temperature.)

Figure 3.8 Chocolate falling ball viscometer

MATHS REFERENCE
Manipulating units
See Maths note 2.2

Drag force

For a small sphere moving slowly through a fluid, the viscosity described by Stokes's law is the main contribution to drag. However, there is also a drag force that depends on the density of the fluid (the moving object has to push fluid out of its path). For large objects moving at high speed this drag force is much larger than the viscous drag, but in the falling ball viscometer it is much smaller and can be ignored in comparison to the viscous drag.

Archimedes in the balance

Figure 3.9 shows the forces acting on a sphere falling through a fluid. The sphere's weight acts downwards, and in addition to the drag force there is another upwards force: the **upthrust** or **buoyancy force**. This force always acts on an object immersed in a fluid, and it arises because the object displaces some of the fluid around it. When getting into or out of a bath or swimming pool, we feel lighter or heavier, and in this way become aware of the upthrust provided by the water. A similar force acts in air, too, and the weight we measure on bathroom scales is very slightly less than it would be in a vacuum. Indeed, anything that is completely or partially immersed in a fluid will experience an upthrust or buoyancy force, be it a skydiver, a ship or a falling ball-bearing.

The size of the upthrust is described by **Archimedes' principle**: 'When a body is partially or totally immersed in a fluid, the upthrust is equal to the weight of the fluid it displaces.' Legend has it that Archimedes (*c.*287–212 BCE) discovered this while in his bathtub and then ran through the streets of Syracuse in Sicily, where he lived, shouting 'Eureka' (meaning 'I found it'). He was at the time trying to develop a method of checking that the king's crown really was made of pure gold as the maker had claimed.

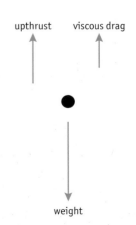

Figure 3.9 Forces on a falling ball

STUDY NOTE

For more on density see EAT Additional Sheet 3

The size of the upthrust, U, depends on the volume, V, of displaced fluid and its **density**, ρ:

$$U = \rho V g \qquad\qquad (3)$$

If an object is *fully* immersed in a fluid then it displaces its own volume of fluid and V equals the object's volume. However, if the object is only partially immersed then V is less than the volume of the object.

A simple way of thinking about upthrust is to consider a floating object. Its weight must still be acting downwards, but with the upthrust force acting against the weight, the forces are in equilibrium and the object remains at rest. Now think of an object fully immersed in fluid. If the upthrust exceeds the weight there will be a net upward force that will push the object upwards towards the surface until it is only partially immersed and displaces exactly its own weight of fluid. If, on the other hand, the upthrust on the fully immersed object is less than the object's weight, there is a resultant downward force and so the object sinks.

When an object falls through a fluid, it first accelerates due to the net downward force (weight minus upthrust). However, it also experiences a drag force that increases with speed, so the resultant downward force is reduced as speed increases. When the net force reaches zero, the object can no longer accelerate and it falls with a constant downward velocity called its **terminal velocity**.

> ⚙ **ACTIVITY 5 ARCHIMEDES' PRINCIPLE**
> Demonstrate Archimedes' principle by weighing an object in air and immersed in water.

Questions 1 to 4 take you through some calculations relating to the forces involved in a falling ball viscometer.

QUESTIONS

These questions refer to a ball-bearing of radius $r = 1.0 \times 10^{-3}$ m, made of steel with a density ρ_{steel} falling through oil with density ρ_{oil} and viscosity η.

$$\rho_{steel} = 7.8 \times 10^3 \,\text{kg m}^{-3}$$

$$\rho_{oil} = 920 \,\text{kg m}^{-3}$$

$$\eta = 8.4 \times 10^{-2} \,\text{N s m}^{-2}$$

The gravitational field strength, g, is $9.81 \,\text{N kg}^{-1}$.

A sphere with radius r has volume $V = \dfrac{4\pi r^3}{3}$.

STUDY NOTE

For more about units and dimensions see EAT Additional Sheet 3

Q 1   **(a)** Show that η has SI units N s m^{-2}. Then express these units in terms of the SI base units m, kg, s.

       (b) Assuming that Stokes's law applies, calculate the viscous drag on the ball-bearing when it is travelling through the oil at a speed of $2.0 \times 10^{-2} \,\text{m s}^{-1}$.

Q 2   Calculate **(a)** the volume of the ball-bearing, **(b)** its mass and **(c)** its weight.

Q 3   When the ball-bearing is immersed in the oil, what are **(a)** the volume, **(b)** the mass and **(c)** the weight of the oil that it displaces?

Q 4   Using your answers to Questions 1 to 3, **(a)** state the size of the upthrust acting on the ball-bearing and then **(b)** calculate the size and direction of the net force acting on the ball-bearing.

Measuring viscosity

In a falling ball viscometer, the ball-bearing is selected so that it reaches it terminal velocity after travelling only a short distance through the fluid.

Referring back to Questions 1 to 4, we can then write down an expression for the forces acting on the ball-bearing, which must combine to give a resultant force of zero – in other words, the magnitudes of the forces must be related as follows:

upthrust + drag forces = weight

Ignoring the drag force that depends on density, we can write:

$$\frac{4\pi r^3 \rho_{\text{fluid}} g}{3} + 6\pi r \eta v = \frac{4\pi r^3 \rho_{\text{steel}} g}{3} \qquad (2)$$

To learn more about viscous drag visit the Brookfield Engineering website (go to www.pearsonhotlinks.co.uk, search for this title and click on this activity).

> ⚙ **ACTIVITY 6 MEASURING VISCOSITY: HOW 'RUNNY' IS IT?**
> Use a falling ball viscometer to determine the viscosity of honey or syrup at a particular temperature. Plan your experiment carefully and decide how best to analyse your measurements, taking account of any experimental uncertainties.

Calibration

A falling ball viscometer allows us to measure viscosities of fluids fairly directly. Once this has been done, then fluids of known viscosity can be used to **calibrate** other viscometers – that is, to establish a relationship between the performance of a particular viscometer and the actual viscosity of any fluids used. For example, your results from Activity 6 could be used to calibrate the consistometer or the Redwood viscometer that you used earlier; you could relate the flow of a fluid in a given time to its viscosity.

Figure 3.10 shows another type of viscometer popular in the food industry – the viscous drag viscometer. Here the liquid under test is contained within the outer cylinder, which is rotated at constant speed. As a result of the viscous properties of the liquid, this drags the inner cylinder round against the force of the spring S, moving a pointer over a scale. The position of the pointer indicates the liquid's viscosity, but there is not a simple relationship between the movement of the pointer and the viscosity of the liquid with the viscous drag viscometer.

> ⚙ **ACTIVITY 7 CALIBRATION**
> Discuss how you would go about calibrating a viscous drag viscometer. Suggest a value for the viscosity of the liquid that moved the pointer to the position shown in Figure 3.11.

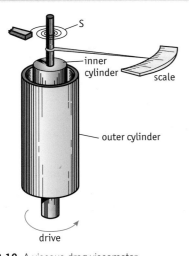

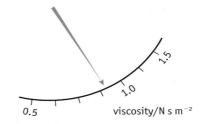

Figure 3.11 Pointer on scale

Figure 3.10 A viscous drag viscometer

PRACTICAL SKILLS REFERENCE

Planning and experimental design
See Practical skills notes 2.1–2.2

Carrying out practical work
See Practical skills notes 3.1–3.2

Analysis and interpretation of data
See Practical skills notes 4.1–4.2

Conclusion and evaluation
See Practical skills notes 5.1–5.2

STUDY NOTE

See EAT Additional Sheets 1 and 2 for guidance on measurement and uncertainty

PRACTICAL SKILLS REFERENCE

Planning and experimental design
See Practical skills notes 2.1–2.2

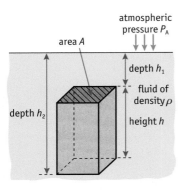

Figure 3.12 Rectangular block immersed in fluid

QUESTIONS

Q 5 If you were provided with a forcemeter, a measuring cylinder, some water, a piece of cotton and an object that could be immersed in the measuring cylinder, outline how you could check Archimedes' principle. (You will need to know that $g \approx 10\,\text{N}\,\text{kg}^{-1}$ and that the density of water is $1000\,\text{kg}\,\text{m}^{-3}$.)

Q 6 The pressure P at a depth h within a fluid is given by $P = \rho g h$, where ρ is the fluid's density and g is the gravitational field strength. By considering the pressures at the top and bottom surfaces of the rectangular object of area A shown in Figure 3.12, demonstrate that the upthrust must be equal to the weight of the fluid displaced.

Q 7 Under what conditions can you ignore the upthrust acting on an object in a fluid?

Q 8 Suppose that when Archimedes compared the weight of the king's crown immersed in water with the same crown weighed in air, the ratio came to 0.948. If the density of gold is 19.3 times that of water, was the crown solid gold?

Q 9 The website 'urban myths' claims that a man in California tied a number of balloons filled with helium to his chair in the garden, with a view to gently hovering above the neighbourhood. The moment he cut the anchoring cord he shot upwards to a height of about 4000 m. Several hours later a helicopter rescued him after he was spotted by an airline pilot.

(a) If the combined mass of the man and the chair was 70 kg, calculate their weight.

(b) Show that the upthrust in newtons from the balloons is about 13 V where V is the total volume of the balloons in cubic metres. The density of air is $1.29\,\text{kg}\,\text{m}^{-3}$.

(c) Write down an expression, in terms of V, for the weight of the helium in the balloons. The density of helium is $0.18\,\text{kg}\,\text{m}^{-3}$.

(d) Calculate the total volume of the balloons required just to lift the man and his chair from the ground. Assume the weight of the balloon fabric is negligible.

(e) Estimate the number of party balloons required for this feat. (You can assume a party balloon to be spherical and you will need to estimate a typical size.)

(f) Explain why you can ignore any viscous drag force in the previous calculation.

Q 10 Some motor oils are labelled 'viscostatic'. From the name, what behaviour might you expect these oils to have over a wide range of temperatures?

2.3 More about flow

Laminar/streamlined flow or turbulence?

Stokes's law relies on the flow of the liquid past the ball-bearing being **streamlined** or **laminar** and not **turbulent**. In streamlined or laminar flow the liquid does not make an abrupt change in direction or speed, and adjacent layers within the fluid only mix on a molecular scale – the word 'laminar' means 'layered'. With turbulent flow there is a lot of mixing and a series of eddies (little whirlpools) are produced along the object's path (see Figure 3.13).

Turbulence is the unsteadiness that we observe in smoke billowing away from bonfires, the flapping of sails on yachts or of a flag on a flagpole, or the buffeting that one occasionally feels on an aeroplane. Turbulence gives rise to heating as energy is transferred to the fluids; this is usually unwanted and reduces the efficiency of a process.

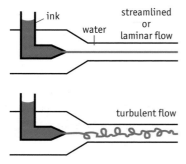

Figure 3.13 Streamlined and turbulent flow patterns

Designers consider the aerodynamics of cars in order to promote streamlined or laminar low, as turbulence would increase fuel consumption. Similarly, a professional speed skier will purchase clothing and adopt a posture that aims to achieve a streamlined flow of air past the body and so allow him to go faster. Likewise, less energy will be needed to move fluids in a factory if turbulence is avoided. The flow of chocolate onto centres needs to be as laminar as possible in order to produce a fairly even coating without air bubbles.

In this short activity you will be able to see the difference between laminar and turbulent flow. Connect a piece of transparent plastic tubing to a laboratory water tap and arrange for a length of it to be horizontal before going into a sink. Fill a syringe with ink and pass the syringe needle into the tube just where it becomes horizontal. Turn the tap on slowly and squeeze some ink into the tube.

Compare, and comment on, the pattern of movement of the ink as the flow of the water is increased from slow to fast.

Thixotropy

A number of foods display the interesting property of **thixotropy**. Margarine in its container at normal temperatures will not flow. However, on exerting a force with a knife in order to spread it, the margarine's viscosity lessens and it flows. When that force is removed, the margarine's viscosity again rises and it acts like a solid on the bread. This behaviour identifies it as a thixotropic material. You can see similar effects with chocolate spread, tomato ketchup and mayonnaise (Figure 3.14).

Figure 3.14 Some thixotropic foods

ACTIVITY 9 STIRRING CUSTARD

In this activity you will be able to observe behaviour known as negative thixotropy (rheopexy).

Put two heaped teaspoons of custard powder into a cup. Mix in up to two spoonfuls of water until, when the custard is stirred slowly, it is just runny. Now stir quickly and note what happens.

FURTHER INVESTIGATION

If you let honey or syrup pour from a spoon or jar, it forms a small hill with a few spirals at the summit as shown in Figure 3.15. Might this perhaps provide a means of determining viscosity? What variables might be worth investigating?

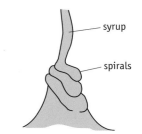
syrup

spirals

Figure 3.15 Syrup hill

2.4 Measuring and controlling flow rates

The measuring of flow rates is vital in the confectionery industry if one is to maintain consistency of the product; for example, the same thickness of chocolate on the sweet's centre or in the mould for shaped chocolate (Figure 3.16). One way to do this would be to measure the mass or volume collected in a given time interval and then determine the **mass flow rate** (the mass per unit time) or **volume flow rate** (the volume per unit time). However, this would interrupt the process, and it is preferable to use a flowmeter that can be left in position all the time. There is a tutorial that explains this very clearly at the Omega website, details of which can be found at www.pearsonhotlinks.co.uk.

Figure 3.16 Chocolate moulds

Being able to measure rates of flow is not enough; their control is essential too. Mostly this is achieved using valves and pumps, but a rather more novel method is being considered at Michigan State University in the USA. In 1996 researchers in their Agricultural Engineering Department found molten chocolate to be an electro-rheological fluid; that is, one in which electric fields affects its viscous properties. The stronger the electric field the more viscous the fluid. An extremely strong field can make the fluid solid.

An electric field is a region in which a charged object experiences a force. Electric fields are produced when objects become charged. You may have generated an electric field yourself by rubbing a comb on your clothes and seeing how it can then pick up small pieces of paper or make your hair stand up a little. More controllably, you can produce an electric field by connecting a potential difference between a pair of conducting plates.

STUDY NOTE

You will learn more about electric fields in the later chapter *The Medium is the Message*.

The electro-rheological effect was first discovered in 1948. Since then a number of applications have been considered and developed. These include a clutch for a motor vehicle in which the coupling between the engine, clutch and finally the wheels is controlled by the viscosity of the material in the clutch. The more viscous the fluid, the greater the coupling and the faster the vehicle will go. The viscosity is controlled by an electric field placed across the material.

QUESTION

Q 11 Suggest how electro-rheology might be used in the making of a chocolate-coated product.

2.5 Summing up Part 2

This part of the chapter should have given you some insight into the flow properties of materials and how they can be measured. Use Activities 10 and 11, and Questions 12 to 15, to check your progress and understanding.

> **⚙ ACTIVITY 10 SUMMING UP PART 2**
> Look back through your work and ensure that your notes include a clear definition, explanation or description of each of the terms printed in bold type.

> **⚙ ACTIVITY 11 GOING WITH THE FLOW**
> Draw a series of annotated sketches to illustrate the following:
> (i) very viscous flow   (iv) streamlined flow
> (ii) flow with little viscosity   (v) turbulent flow.
> (iii) a thixotropic material
> In the cases of the first three, list some materials that would behave as described.

QUESTIONS

Q 12 For each of the following, say whether it applies to A upthrust, B viscous drag, C both or D neither.

(a) has SI units of newtons (N)

(b) always acts upwards

(c) can act in the absence of a fluid

(d) depends on the relative speed of the body and fluid

(e) depends on the size of the body

(f) depends on the shape of the body

Q 13 In a test of some motor oil, a ball-bearing of radius 0.5×10^{-3} m was dropped down the centre of a wide container of oil and quickly reached a terminal velocity of 0.03 m s^{-1}.

(a) What is meant by *terminal velocity* and what can be said of the forces acting on the ball-bearing when it reaches its terminal velocity?

(b) Why is it important that the width of the container is much greater than the diameter of the ball-bearing?

(c) Calculate the upthrust or buoyancy force on the ball-bearing. (The density of this motor oil is 900 kg m^{-3} at this temperature.)

(d) Given that the density of the steel from which the ball-bearing was made is 7860 kg m^{-3} and g, the gravitational field strength, can be taken as 9.81 N kg^{-1}, calculate the weight of the ball-bearing.

(e) The fall through the oil was such that Stokes's law could be applied. Calculate the viscosity η of the oil.

Q 14 One simple type of flowmeter is the light-gate flowmeter. When conducting experiments with dynamics trolleys you will probably have used light-gates to time the movement of a known length of card past a fixed point. The light-gate consists of a source of light (a bulb or a light-emitting diode (LED)) that shines on to a photodiode. When the beam is interrupted, the change of illumination triggers an electronic timer, which is stopped when the illumination is restored.

The same principle can be used in a flowmeter (Figure 3.17). Here, a rotating propeller blade, driven by the flowing liquid, repeatedly interrupts the illumination. The meter registers the frequency of interruptions, i.e. the number of 'darkenings' per second.

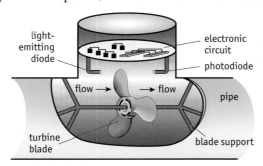

Figure 3.17 Cutaway of light-gate flow meter

The data in Table 3.1 were collected from a light-gate flowmeter. Explain whether they indicate that output frequency is proportional to flow rate for this type of meter.

Mean output frequency/Hz	Mean volume flow rate/L s^{-1}
12.5	0.15
13.9	0.17
16.0	0.20
18.9	0.23

Table 3.1 Flowmeter data for Question 14

Q 15 It is often more relevant to measure mass flow rate than volume flow rate (for example, when charging customers for gas).

(a) Suggest why measuring the mass of gas is more appropriate than measuring its volume when charging a customer.

(b) Explain how mass flow rate can be calculated from volume flow rate.

Q 16 Figure 3.18 shows a vortex-shedding flowmeter. When a non-streamlined obstruction is placed in a section of pipe, a series of vortices or eddies are produced non-symmetrically by the fluid flowing past. Mounted within the obstruction are two heated NTC thermistors. The eddies cool the thermistors, which increases their resistance.

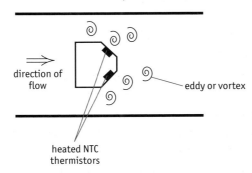

Figure 3.18 Vortex-shedding flowmeter

STUDY NOTE

You will learn more about thermistors in the later chapter *Technology in Space*.

(a) Tables 3.2 and 3.3 show data collected for this type of meter for obstructions of diameters 10 mm and 5 mm.

Speed of flow/m s^{-1}	Time for 20 vortices to pass/s	Frequency of vortices/Hz
0.5	2.00	
1.0	0.98	
1.5	0.66	
2.0	0.50	
2.5	0.40	

Table 3.2 Data for a vortex flowmeter: 10 mm obstruction

Speed of flow/m s^{-1}	Time for 20 vortices to pass/s	Frequency of vortices/Hz
1.0	0.50	
1.5	0.33	
2.0	0.25	
2.5	0.20	

Table 3.3 Data for a vortex flowmeter: 5 mm obstruction

(i) Copy and complete the 'Frequency of vortices' column in each table.

(ii) What appears to be the relationship between the speed of flow and frequency of vortices for an obstruction of given size?

(iii) For any one speed of flow, what appears to be the relationship between the diameter of the obstruction and the frequency of the vortices?

(b) Suggest a problem that might occur with this type of meter if the vortex frequency became very high.

3 Testing, testing ...

3.1 Good enough to eat?

It is no use developing a product that no-one will buy. You are likely to try a new food or sweet just to see what it tastes like, and you may decide to purchase it again if it tastes nice. Yet what makes a popular product, and how do manufacturers know this?

What qualities do we look for in a chocolate, biscuit or sweet? The flavour is very important, and this will be determined by the chemical composition of the food. Another important factor is the texture, which for some people, and especially young children, can make all the difference between liking and disliking the food.

Consider what happens when you put a food in your mouth: it triggers a number of sensations. When you discuss this with others and explain what it is that you like or dislike about these sensations, you need to be able to describe what happens so that others can understand. We use a large number of words for these sensations. A sweet manufacturer may employ tasting panels (Figure 3.19) to find out what the people like and dislike. Below, a member of a tasting panel comments on the need to agree on exactly what each word means.

Figure 3.19 A tasting panel

The company has tasting panels to comment on texture, flavour and smell. When testing for flavour we have a number of references to compare with the test flavours, but we don't do that for texture. We were recruited through an advertisement in the local press and we spend one day a week testing. We did a lot of training and have regular training sessions. We have to discuss the product and come up with a description that we all agree with, although of course, no opinion is wrong and people do taste things very differently sometimes.

When the panel formed we spent a long time defining different words. For example, chewy means partly how much it sticks to your teeth – how flexible it is. Some sweets are compact: they go into a ball and move around your mouth more than others do. Brittle means it breaks into shards – sharp-edged pieces – easily and quickly when you bite it. Crunchy means it makes a noise when you chew it. A sticky sweet sticks to your teeth and leaves a residue. It might be creamy or grainy or something else – we have defined all these descriptions.

When we do a profile for a product we start by saying what it looks like and what it feels like. Then we bite into it. Some products have a very different surface to the inside, so we comment on that, and on the initial bite. We time things like how long we suck before we bite, and how long the sweet lasts in the mouth. Finally, we comment on the aftertaste.

Once tasters are experienced enough to give consistent descriptions, they can be employed in rating the attributes of various products. Frequently, some 30 to 60 attributes will be judged on scales of 1–5, 1–7 or 1–9. These data are fed into a computer, which then constructs a star or spider diagram (Figure 3.20) to display the so-called sensory profile of the product.

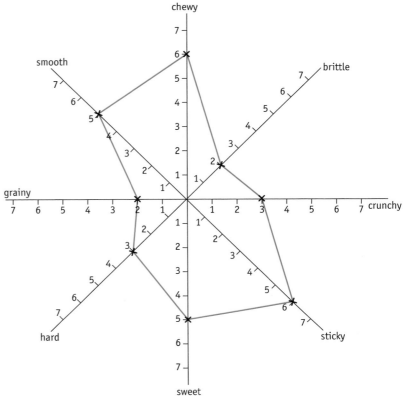

Figure 3.20 A star or spider diagram

> ⚙ **ACTIVITY 12 DESCRIBING FOOD**
>
> Make a list of the words you might use to describe the texture of some foods or confectionery. Combination products such as KitKat, Lion bar, Mars bar, Picnic and Snickers will give you opportunities to deal with a number of textures and tastes. Construct star/spider diagrams for your chosen products.

Human tasters give a subjective definition of what happens inside their mouth, described in words, with no measurement of how hard one has to chew to break food. The taster commenting earlier does measure the time to suck a sweet, to melt it and the time before it is soft enough to bite, but on the whole tasting panels are not concerned with measurement. However, research has been done to match sensory factors, such as chewiness, stickiness and hardness, to the tester, and the minute electrical signals are recorded as the product is eaten. These are then commented on.

The need for objective measurement arises when foods are to be produced on a large scale. The manufacturer must ensure that the product is always the same. You would be very surprised if you bought a food product one week and then the next week you bought the same product and found that the taste or texture was different. Is it possible to measure qualities such as brittleness or chewiness? To describe behaviour quantitatively we need to be more definite about the meaning of the words, replacing verbal description with measurements. We must investigate and measure how the food deforms when a force or combination of forces is applied to it.

3.2 Crunching and chewing

There are many material properties of interest to food and confectionery makers. The way foods deform, stretch or break under an applied force is related to the sensations we experience when eating them. It is essential that sweets that are designed to be bitten can indeed be bitten without breaking your teeth – they must not be too **hard**.

A hard material is one that is not readily scratched or indented. There is no absolute measure of hardness, but it is easy to rank samples in order of hardness according to whether they scratch or can be scratched by one another.

Much of the testing in the food industry concerns the behaviour of foods under compression (Figure 3.21) because the manufacturers are interested in what happens to food when we chew or bite it. However, tensile ('pulling') tests are also used (Figure 3.22). Some sweets, such as strawberry or cola laces (see Activity 15), are often gripped with the teeth and pulled to break them, so their tensile behaviour is of interest.

The results of tensile and compressive tests are often displayed as graphs. From a load–extension graph such as that in Figure 3.23, we can measure the stiffness of a material.

Figure 3.21 Compression testing of a cake

Figure 3.22 Tensile testing of pasta

STUDY NOTE

In the tests used to produce Figure 3.23, compressions were defined to be positive and extensions negative.

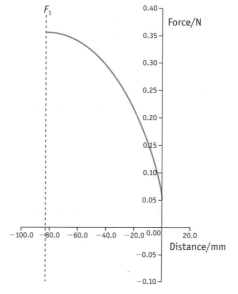

Figure 3.23 Load–extension graph for noodles

As you saw in the earlier chapter *Higher, Faster, Stronger*, the **stiffness** k is defined as:

$$k = \frac{F}{x} \qquad\qquad (4)$$

where F is the applied force and x the resulting extension. The stiffness depends on the size and shape of the sample, as well as on the material from which it is made. A thick sample will be stiffer than a thin one of the same material, and a long sample will be less stiff than a short one. However, provided the samples are all of a standard size and shape, graphs like that in Figure 3.23 provide a quick visual way to compare stiffness. A **stiff** material is one such as seaside rock (Figure 3.24) that does not easily change shape when a force is applied, so its force–extension (or force–compression) graph will be steep – a large load produces only a small deformation.

When the load is removed, some materials (such as jelly cubes or sweets, Figure 3.25) will spring back to their original shape; such materials are said to be **elastic**. Others, described as **plastic** materials (such as well-chewed chewing-gum, Figure 3.26), will remain deformed. Many materials are elastic under small loads, up to their **elastic limit**, but deform plastically when subjected to larger loads.

STUDY NOTE

In the chapter *Spare Part Surgery* you will see how the stiffness of a material (rather than a particular sample) can be defined and measured.

Figure 3.24 Seaside rock, a stiff foodstuff

Figure 3.25 Jelly, an elastic foodstuff

Figure 3.26 Chewing gum, which is plastic when well chewed

There are various ways in which a material can be deformed plastically. A **ductile** ('drawable') material is one that can readily be pulled out by a tensile force into a longer, thinner shape (for example, well-chewed gum), and a **malleable** ('hammerable') material can be deformed under compression. All ductile materials are malleable but not all malleable materials are ductile; some, like fudge (Figure 3.27), may tear apart under tension.

Tensile or compression testing can also measure the force needed to break a sample. Again, the actual force needed depends on the size and shape, but compression of standard samples gives information about strength; a **strong** material is one that requires a large force to make it break.

The way in which foodstuffs break is of great interest to manufacturers and consumers. A **brittle** material is one that easily cracks, for example a boiled sweet, hard toffee or a biscuit; such foods might loosely be described as 'crunchy'. An applied force is unable to deform the brittle material; they are usually stiff and show essentially no plastic deformation. Instead, the load causes small cracks to spread rapidly. Sometimes, as with wafers, this behaviour arises because there are many small air gaps within the structure that are unable to stop cracks spreading.

In contrast to brittle materials, a **tough** material deforms plastically and can withstand dynamic loads such as shock or impact. A tough material requires a large force to produce a small deformation – in other words, a large amount of **work** must be done on the material in order to produce a small plastic deformation. Few foodstuffs can be described as tough according to this definition (apart, perhaps, from some meats); it is a term more usually applied to materials such as Kevlar®, which is used to make bullet-proof vests (Figure 3.28).

Figure 3.27 Fudge, a malleable foodstuff that breaks apart under tension

Figure 3.28 Bullet-proof vest made of Kevlar

STUDY NOTE

In the chapter *Higher, Faster, Stronger*, you saw that work is defined as the product of the resultant force and the distance moved in the direction of the force.

STUDY NOTE

For guidance on measurement and uncertainty, see EAT Additional Sheets 1 and 2.

PRACTICAL SKILLS REFERENCE

Planning and experimental design

See Practical skills notes 2.1–2.2

Carrying out practical work

See Practical skills notes 3.1–3.2

Analysis and interpretation of data

See Practical skills notes 4.1–4.2

Conclusion and evaluation

See Practical skills notes 5.1–5.2

ACTIVITY 13 BRITTLE AND DUCTILE TOFFEE

Investigate how modifying the structure of toffee changes its physical properties.

ACTIVITY 14 TOUGH COOKIES

Compare the toughness of different sweets, chocolate bars (such as Curly Wurly bars) and biscuits.

ACTIVITY 15 STRETCHY SWEETS

Investigate the behaviour of strawberry or cola laces under tension. Display your results using graphs and use appropriate technical terms to describe the behaviour of your samples.

QUESTION

 Table 3.4 lists some measurements obtained from hanging masses on a sweet called a Glow-worm. When the load is removed, the Glow-worm slowly goes back to its original length. It was 8.0 cm long at the start of the test, and its cross-section was an equilateral triangle with sides of 1 cm.

(a) Plot a graph to display the data from Table 3.4.

(b) Use appropriate words to describe and explain what was happening to the Glow-worm during this test.

(c) Using your answers to parts (a) and (b), describe what the texture of a Glow-worm would be like as you ate it.

Mass of load/g	Length/cm
20	8.6
30	8.8
40	9.1
50	9.5
60	9.9
70	10.0
90	10.6
150	11.6
200	12.6
250	13.4
300	14.2
400	15.0

Table 3.4 Tensile tests on a Glow-worm

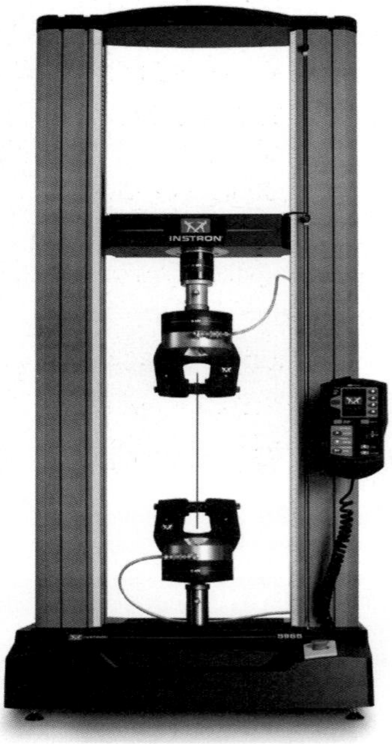

More testing

Standard tests in industry are normally carried out by machines that automatically measure the forces needed to cause different deformations. Figure 3.29 shows one widely used machine, the Instron Universal Testing Machine. The moving part of the machine is driven vertically to compress or stretch the sample, and the drive is connected to a chart recorder so the force and distance can be recorded. It can perform tests in tension, compression or bending, and can be used for many materials including wood, plastic and adhesives. There are different models, some developed specifically for the food industry, and accessories for performing different tests can be attached to the machine as required. The model shown here can apply a force in the range from 2 N to 5 kN, and the speed of deformation can vary from 0.02 to 50 cm min^{-1}.

Figure 3.29 Instron Universal Testing Machine

Food manufacturers use a variety of tests in addition to straightforward compressive and tensile testing. One common test is the three-point bend test, shown in Figure 3.30, which determines the 'bendiness' of a wafer. This test is used in many industries; for example, steel rails and PVC window frames are tested in this way.

Another test used to monitor the crispness of wafers is shown in Figure 3.31. A wafer is snapped in front of a microphone, and its waveform and frequency spectrum displayed. The sound produced, and so the shape of the waveform and frequency spectrum, depends on the crispness or bendiness of the wafer.

STUDY NOTE

For more about sound and frequency spectra see the chapter *The Sound of Music*.

Figure 3.30 Three-point bend test

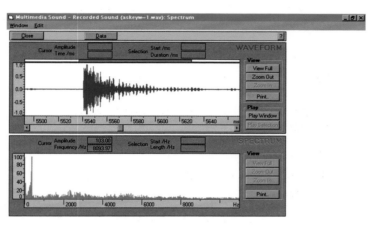

Figure 3.31 Waveform and frequency spectrum of a breaking wafer

⚙ ACTIVITY 16 BENDY WAFER

Devise and carry out a three-point bend test on a wafer.

In 1988 Michael McIntyre and James Woodhouse of Cambridge University suggested that Chladni figures, the patterns on resonant surfaces, might by used to analyse material properties. This suggestion was followed up for wafers by Simon Livings, who went on to work at the Centre Recherche Nestlé in Switzerland, as part of his doctoral project. He placed glitter on the top surface of wafers, positioned them near a loudspeaker and observed the patterns as the wafer resonated.

FURTHER INVESTIGATION

Materials testing provides scope for a variety of investigations using foodstuffs or other materials. You could explore the sounds produced by snapping brittle foods, and try to relate the results to other properties of the materials such as stiffness or strength, or perhaps you could investigate Chladni figures on resonating wafers. Alternatively, you might like to devise a completely different 'crispness' test for wafers. You could investigate how the 'crispness' varied with water content of wafers left exposed to damp air, or how the stretchiness and strength of spaghetti or noodles varied with the quantity of water absorbed.

You could also try to devise tests to measure other physical aspects of food materials, such as 'stickiness'. A good test must by easy to use and should give reproducible results, i.e. the same test applied on different occasions to the same sample should give results within a relatively small range of uncertainty.

PRACTICAL SKILLS REFERENCE

Planning and experimental design

See Practical skills notes 2.1–2.2

Carrying out practical work

See Practical skills notes 3.1–3.2

Analysis and interpretation of data

See Practical skills notes 4.1–4.2

Conclusion and evaluation

See Practical skills notes 5.1–5.2

3.3 Summing up Part 3

In this part of the chapter you have learned about the so-called **mechanical properties** of materials. You have focused on the food industry, however these tests, and the terms used to describe the materials, are applicable wherever materials are tested and used.

Activity 17 and Questions 18 to 21 are intended to help you look back through this part of the chapter and check what you have learned.

> ### ⚙ ACTIVITY 17 PICK AND MIX
> Select a variety of sweets or other foodstuffs and use the words malleable, ductile, elastic, plastic and brittle, as appropriate, to describe their properties.

QUESTIONS

Q 18 Control of high volume manufacturing production, such as the steel industry, is achieved through regular sampling and testing of the product. In one test, a rod of steel approximately the size of a pencil was subject to an increasing tension (T), and the resulting extension (x) measured. Table 3.5 lists the results.

$T/10^3$ N	0	5	10	15	20	25	30	35
$x/10^{-6}$ m	0	12	24	36	48	60	74	100

Table 3.5 Data for Question 18

(a) Plot a graph to show these results.

(b) Use the straight-line region to calculate the stiffness of the sample.

(c) Indicate on the graph with a letter P the limit of proportionality and mark with an E a possible position of the elastic limit.

(d) A second sample of the steel is stiffer, weaker and brittle. Add a line on your graph showing a possible line for this sample.

Q 19 Suggest some everyday foods that illustrate the difference between hard and tough.

Q 20 Figure 3.32 shows the results of compression tests on Gouda cheeses.

(a) Describe what happens to the stiffness of Gouda cheese as it ages.

(b) What happens to the strength of the cheese as it ages? (Strength as in physical property, not as in taste!)

(c) What effect do the cumin seeds have on the physical properties of the cheese? Suggest a reason for this effect.

Q 21 Imagine that you are working in the quality control area of a textile factory. You are asked to select four threads from a large number to demonstrate to some visitors which threads are:

(a) strong but not stiff

(b) stiff but not strong

(c) both strong and stiff

(d) neither strong not stiff.

If you tested the threads by hand, what would you look for to identify each of (a) to (d)?

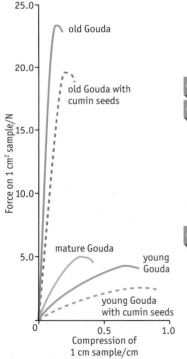

Figure 3.32 Compression tests on Gouda cheeses

4 Sweetness and light

The confectionery industry, and indeed the food industry in general, is a very large user of sugar. Sugar produced in the UK comes from sugar beet (Figure 3.33) and most imported sugar comes from sugar cane. Sugar beet is recognised as one of the most financially secure, major arable crops in the UK, and around 3600 growers are involved in the industry.

A typical harvested beet contains 16.0% sugar, 75.9% water, 2.6% soluble non-sugar and 5.5% pulp, but both beet and cane can vary in quality. Beet samples are analysed for their sugar content, and farmers are paid according to the percentage of sugar in their beet.

In this part of the chapter you will explore two techniques for analysing the sugar content of solutions, both of which use light. You will learn about how light refracts as it passes through boundaries and about the polarisation of light.

Figure 3.33 Collecting sugar beet

4.1 Refractometry

The speed at which light travels through a medium depends on the atomic structure of the material. Electrons in the atoms absorb energy from the waves and re-radiate it. The facility with which they do this determines the speed at which the waves can travel.

The value normally quoted as the speed of light is actually its speed in a vacuum, which is where it travels most easily and therefore fastest. Light travels more slowly in all other materials. Generally the speed of light in air is taken to be the same as that in a vacuum, as the two values are extremely close. The speed of light in a sugar solution depends on its concentration. So, if you can devise a method for measuring that speed, you can determine the concentration.

Physicists characterise transparent substances in terms of their **refractive index**, which is defined as the ratio of the speed, c, of light in a vacuum to the speed of light, v, in the material:

$$\text{refractive index, } n = \frac{\text{speed of light in a vacuum}}{\text{speed of light in a material}} = \frac{c}{v} \qquad (5)$$

As light travels most rapidly in a vacuum, $n \geq 1$ for all materials. The refractive index of air is usually taken to be 1.

QUESTION

Q 22 Given that light travels at $3.00 \times 10^8 \, \text{ms}^{-1}$ in air, what is the speed of light in each material in Table 3.6?

Material	Refractive index between air and the material
Glass	1.47
Water	1.33
Polystyrene	1.60

Table 3.6 Data for Question 22

STUDY NOTE

There are many different types of glass, and the refractive index of each type depends on its composition. Table 3.6 refers to just one type of glass.

Figure 3.34 shows a ray of light crossing from one medium into another where the speed of light is different. The ray meets the boundary at a slanting angle and, as a result, the path of the ray changes as it crosses the boundary. This effect is known as **refraction**. Note that it is conventional to measure the angles with respect to the **normal** line (at right angles to the boundary), not with respect to the boundary itself. If the ray strikes the boundary along the normal line, then the speed will change but the direction will not.

When a ray of light crosses a boundary into a medium where the speed is less (for example, from air into glass), the path of the ray will be refracted towards the normal. If the speed increases as it crosses the boundary then the ray will be refracted away from the normal. A wave model of light (Figure 3.35) helps explain this. When a wave front meets a boundary at an angle, part of it

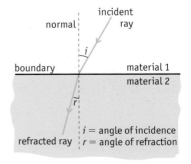

Figure 3.34 A light ray crossing a boundary

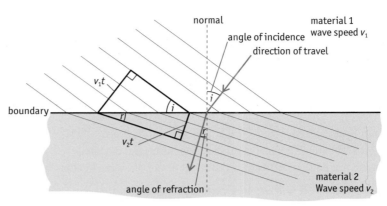

Figure 3.35 Waves crossing a boundary

slows down before the rest, causing the wavefront to swing round and change direction. We get a similar experience when a car swerves into the kerb because the inside wheels meet a large puddle of water. The slowing effect turns the vehicle.

Snell's law of refraction

The amount by which a ray of light is refracted while crossing the boundary between two materials depends on the difference in speeds. So, if we can arrange for light to travel from a material with a known speed of light (refractive index) into another, measuring the amount of refraction should enable us to determine the refractive index of the second material. To do this, we need a mathematical way of relating the amount of refraction to the refractive indices of the two materials. We can develop an equation that will do this job by considering Figure 3.35.

In a time t, the wavefront passing though material 1 will travel a distance $v_1 t$, while the part of the wavefront in material 2 covers a distance $v_2 t$. By drawing right-angled triangles as shown in Figure 3.35, we can write down some useful relationships. The triangles share a hypotenuse, so:

$$\frac{v_2 t}{\sin r} = \frac{v_1 t}{\sin i} \tag{6}$$

Cancelling t, multiplying by $\sin i$ and dividing by v_2, we can write the relationship known as **Snell's law**:

$$\frac{\sin i}{\sin r} = \frac{v_1}{v_2} \tag{6a}$$

It is more useful to have an equation involving refractive index, which we can obtain using Equation 5:

$$n_1 = \frac{c}{v_1}$$

$$n_2 = \frac{c}{v_2}$$

(where c is the speed of light in vacuum), so that:

$$\frac{\sin i}{\sin r} = \frac{n_2}{n_1} \tag{7}$$

or:

$$n_1 \sin i = n_2 \sin r \tag{7a}$$

Equation 7 can also be written as:

$$n_1 \sin \theta_1 = n_2 \sin \theta_2 \tag{8}$$

where θ_1 is the angle between the ray direction and the normal in material 1, and θ_2 is the angle in material 2. Equation 8 reminds us that the relationship between speeds and angles does not depend on the direction of travel (it does not matter which angle we call the angle of incidence).

QUESTION

(a) There are two materials in Figure 3.34. If they are air and glass, which is which? What helped you to decide?

(b) If you interchanged the materials, what would be different?

(c) If a ray is incident along the normal, what happens to it in the second material?

(d) Now imagine the materials are altered so that the ray of light is refracted less. How would the angle, *r*, alter?

⚙ ACTIVITY 18 MEASURING REFRACTIVE INDEX
Trace rays of light through a rectangular block of transparent material or a rectangular tank of sugar solution, and measure the angles at the interfaces (Figure 3.36). Then use Snell's law to calculate the refractive index of that material.

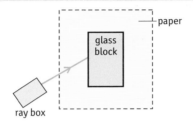

Figure 3.36 Diagram for Activity 18

Reflection and refraction at a boundary
While carrying out Activity 18, you will have noticed that the rays of light crossing a boundary reflect as well as refract. In Activity 19, you will explore this effect in more detail.

⚙ ACTIVITY 19 RAY TRACING ON THE WAY OUT
Using blocks of various shapes (as in Figure 3.37), look at light as it comes out of a block and see how a single beam can be split into two parts.

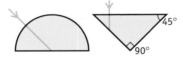

Figure 3.37 Block shapes for Activity 19

In Figure 3.38 light emerges from a dense material into a less dense one, for example from a Perspex block into air. It is incident on a boundary where both reflection and refraction are possible. Your sketches from Activity 19 will show that while reflection is always possible refraction does not always occur. The largest possible internal angle of incidence that will allow light to emerge is called the **critical angle**, *C*. If the light cannot refract out of the block we say that there is **total internal reflection** (sometimes abbreviated to TIR).

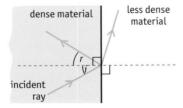

Figure 3.38 Light emerging from a block

As the angle of incidence on the boundary increases towards the critical angle, so the angle of refraction gets closer to 90°. A ray of light cannot be refracted by more than 90°, which is why TIR happens once the angle of incidence is equal to or greater than *C*.

PRACTICAL SKILLS REFERENCE

Planning and experimental design
See Practical skills notes 2.1–2.2

Carrying out practical work
See Practical skills notes 3.1–3.2

Analysis and interpretation of data
See Practical skills notes 4.1–4.2

Conclusion and evaluation
See Practical skills notes 5.1–5.2

Using Snell's law:

$$n_1 \sin\theta_1 = n_2 \sin\theta_2 \qquad \text{(Equation 8)}$$

we can figure out how the critical angle depends on the refractive indices. As θ_1 gets closer to C, so θ_2 gets closer to 90°, and with that $\sin\theta_2$ approaches 1. At the critical angle, we have:

$$n_1 \sin C = n_2 \qquad (9)$$

or:

$$\sin C = \frac{n_2}{n_1} \qquad (9a)$$

> **MATHS REFERENCE**
>
> Reciprocals
> See Maths note 3.3

Usually we are dealing with a situation involving a ray of light emerging from a solid or liquid material into air, so that n_2 is the refractive index of air (taken to be 1). This gives:

$$\sin C = \frac{1}{n_1} \qquad (10)$$

Percentage concentration of sugar by mass	Refractive index
0	1.333
5	1.340
15	1.348
20	1.364
25	1.372
30	1.381
35	1.390
40	1.400
45	1.410
50	1.420
55	1.431
60	1.442
65	1.453
70	1.465
75	1.478
80	1.491
85	1.504

Table 3.7 Refractive index of sugar solutions at 20 °C

⚙ ACTIVITY 20 CONNECTIONS

Look back at your results for Activity 19 and find the size of the critical angle for one of the blocks. Use this value to determine the refractive index for the material of the block.

Refractometry of sugar solutions

Refractometry is used in determining the payouts to farmers dependent on the concentration of sugar in sugar beet and in other situations such as judging the ripeness of pineapples in the field. Table 3.7 shows how the refractive index of sugar solution changes with concentration.

In principle, the concentration of a sugar solution can be determined from its refractive index. Figure 3.39 shows an Abbé refractometer, which can measure refractive index with a precision of ±0.001 or better. In Activity 21 you will use a model Pulfrich refractometer. Both of these instruments are used to measure the critical angle, and in this way determine the refractive index. Questions 24 and 25 will help you prepare for Activity 21.

QUESTIONS

Q 24 **(a)** Referring to Figure 3.34 (page 125), write down the relationship(s) between the angles i and r, the speed of light v_1 and v_2 in the materials 1 and 2, and the refractive index n.

(b) Say what is meant by critical angle, and write down the relationship(s) between critical angle, C, and refractive index.

Q 25 **(a)** Plot a graph of the data in Table 3.7. (A spreadsheet would be an ideal way of dealing with this.)

(b) Describe in words and, if appropriate, in mathematical terms the relationship between concentration and refractive index.

(c) What would be the percentage concentration of a sugar solution that had a refractive index of 1.470 at 20 °C?

The principle of the Pulfrich refractometer is shown in Figure 3.40. The idea is that you look through the glass block at a mark on its far edge and trace the path of the light for which the mark just disappears. In Figure 3.40(a), light passing through the liquid and glass block is partially blocked by the mark on the edge of the block. This makes the mark visible. In Figure 3.40(b), the light reflects off the inner surface of the glass block before it reaches the mark, so the mark cannot be seen at this angle. Figure 3.40(c) shows the critical situation where the mark *just* appears or disappears as the viewing angle is changed very slightly.

We can use Snell's law (Equation 8) to describe the situation at the glass-liquid boundary:

$$n_\ell \sin \theta_\ell = n_g \sin\theta_g$$

Figure 3.39 Abbé refractometer

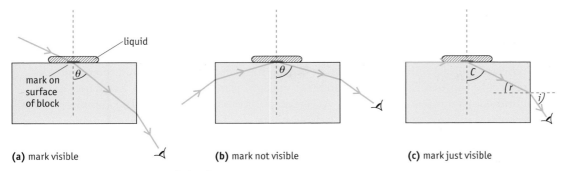

(a) mark visible   **(b)** mark not visible   **(c)** mark just visible

Figure 3.40 The principle of the Pulfrich refractometer

where the subscripts ℓ and g refer to the liquid and the glass. In Figure 3.40(c), the angle in the glass is C, and on the liquid side of the boundary the angle is 90°. Since sin 90° = 1, we have:

$$n_\ell = n_g \sin C \tag{11}$$

At the air/glass boundary:

$$n_a \sin i = n_g \sin r \tag{Equation 8}$$

The block of glass is rectangular, so we can see that:

$$C = 90° - r \tag{12}$$

Taking the sin of both sides of Equation 12:

$$\sin C = \sin(90° - r) = \cos r \tag{13}$$

Substituting from Equation 13 into Equation 11:

$$n_l = n_g \cos r \tag{14}$$

which we can rearrange to get:

$$n_g = \frac{n_i}{\cos r} \tag{14a}$$

We can then combine Equation 14 with Equation 8 to get a relationship between the angles that we can measure, and the refractive index of the liquid, without involving the refractive index of glass:

$$n_a \sin i = \frac{n_i}{\cos r} \times \sin r = n_l \tan r \tag{15}$$

Finally, we can use the fact that $n_a = 1$, and divide by tan r, to get a simpler equation:

$$n_l = \frac{\sin i}{\tan r} \tag{16}$$

MATHS REFERENCE

Sine, cosine and tangent of an angle

See Maths note 6.2

PRACTICAL SKILLS REFERENCE

Carrying out practical work

See Practical skills notes 3.1–3.2

Analysis and interpretation of data

See Practical skills notes 4.1–4.2

Conclusion and evaluation

See Practical skills notes 5.1–5.2

⚙ **ACTIVITY 21 REFRACTOMETRY**

Use a model Pulfrich refractometer to determine the refractive index of some sugar solutions. Use your results to plot a calibration graph and in this way determine the concentration of an unknown sugar solution.

4.2 Polarimetry

You may already be familiar with polarised light through the use of polarising sunglasses, which reduce the intensity of light passing through them and are particularly effective at reducing glare from reflecting surfaces. If you place two polarising sunglasses lens to lens, and rotate one pair with respect to another, then you will find that the light passing through the two lenses varies in brightness as you rotate one of them. At certain positions the light is blocked completely; this arrangement is referred to as 'crossed polarising filters' (see Figure 3.41).

Figure 3.41 View through crossed and uncrossed polarising filters

STUDY NOTE

An electric field is a region in which a charged particle experiences a force. The direction of the electric field is defined as the direction of the force on a positive charge. A magnetic field is a region in which a magnet (e.g. a compass needle) experiences a force; its direction is defined as that in which the north-seeking pole of a compass needle would point.

You will learn more about electric fields in *The Medium is the Message*.

George Wheelwright III first produced Polaroid material in the USA in 1938. It is made by stretching a piece of plastic to align its long chain molecules and then dipping in into iodine solution, so that iodine atoms become attached to the chains and line up along them. Polaroid is a trade name; more correctly and generally, such a piece of plastic should be called a **polarising filter**.

To explain how polarising filters work – and to see what they have to do with the concentration of sugar solutions – we need to think about the nature of light waves.

Light waves, and all other electromagnetic waves, are *transverse* – that is, they involve oscillations at right angles to their direction of travel. What is actually oscillating is an electric and a magnetic field at right angles to each other and to the direction of travel, as shown in Figure 3.42.

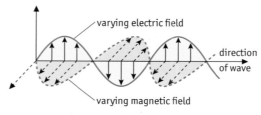

Figure 3.42 An electromagnetic wave

Polarised waves

We can model the behaviour of light using transverse waves on a rope. If you shake the end of a rope up and down, you produce a travelling wave where the oscillations take place only in a vertical plane; we describe the waves as **polarised** or, more correctly, **plane polarised**. If you shake the rope in all transverse directions, you still produce a transverse rolling wave, but now the oscillations are no longer confined to a plane and the wave is **unpolarised**. If the rope passes through a narrow slit, as in Figure 3.43, only those oscillations parallel to the slit can get through, so the slit turns unpolarised into polarised waves – it acts as a polarising filter.

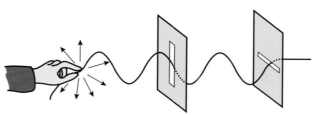

Figure 3.43 Demonstrating polarised waves on a rope

If polarised waves encounter a second polarising filter parallel to the first, they can travel through unimpeded, but if the slit is at 90° to the first then it completely blocks their passage and the slits behave like crossed Polaroids. With the second filter at an intermediate angle, waves still emerge through it; their amplitude is reduced and the plane of polarisation is parallel to the second slit.

If you repeat this exercise with *longitudinal* waves (e.g. on a Slinky) then the slits have no effect on the passage of the waves – they always get through the slits. Longitudinal waves cannot be plane polarised. The fact that polarising filters affect electromagnetic waves shows that the waves *must* be transverse in nature.

Rotating the plane of polarisation

Light is blocked by crossed polarising filters because the two filters are aligned at 90° to one another. However, there are some materials that rotate the plane of polarisation of light. Sugar solution is one such **optically active** material; others include turpentine and many plastics, particularly when stretched. If you place an optically active material between two crossed polarising filters, then some light can emerge, and you need to rotate one of the polarising filters to produce extinction again.

Some materials, including most naturally occurring sugars, cause a clockwise rotation when you look at the light coming towards you; these materials are said to be **dextrorotatory**. Materials that cause an anticlockwise rotation are described as **laevorotatory**.

⚙ ACTIVITY 22   EXPLORING POLARISATION

Use a rope and a Slinky to demonstrate the polarisation of transverse waves, and to show that longitudinal waves cannot be plane polarised.

Use two polarising filters to observe the behaviour of some optically active materials. Look through a single polarising filter at light reflected at a shallow angle from a polished surface (e.g. a bench top) and explain why sunglasses with polarising filters are particularly good at reducing glare.

We can measure the rotation of the plane of polarisation with a polarimeter (Figure 3.44). In its simplest form, a polarimeter capable of studying liquids consists of two polarising filters, one fixed and one that can be rotated against a protractor scale, with a tube of liquid placed between them.

⚙ ACTIVITY 23   POLARIMETRY

Use a polarimeter to measure the rotation of the plane of polarisation for some sugar solutions, and to therefore explain how polarimetry can be used to measure sugar concentrations.

FURTHER INVESTIGATION

In Activity 22 you probably observed colours produced by optically active materials between crossed polarising filters. You might like to devise a method to explore how the rotation of the plane of polarisation depends on wavelength. Alternatively, you could look into variations with temperature.

Engineers sometimes make plastic models of structures (such as bridges) and observe them through crossed polarising filters; the colour and intensity of light that emerges changes according to the load on the structure, indicating where the structure is under greatest stress. You might think of devising a way to explore this phenomenon.

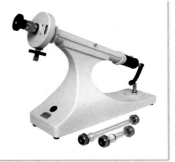

Figure 3.44 A polarimeter

PRACTICAL SKILLS REFERENCE

Planning and experimental design

See Practical skills notes 2.1–2.2

Carrying out practical work

See Practical skills notes 3.1–3.2

Analysis and interpretation of data

See Practical skills notes 4.1–4.2

Conclusion and evaluation

See Practical skills notes 5.1–5.2

QUESTION

Q 26 The data in Table 3.8 were obtained using sugar solutions of the same concentration throughout and by varying the length of the light path through the solution. Table 3.9, on the other hand, shows how the rotation of the plane of polarisation varied with concentration for a single light path length.

Length of light path L/dm	Rotation angle θ/deg
0.2	7
0.4	14
0.6	20
0.8	27
1.0	34

Table 3.8 Data for Question 26: single concentration (1 dm = 10^{-1} m)

Concentration of solution c/g ml^{-1}	Rotation angle θ/deg
0.25	17
0.50	33
0.75	50

Table 3.9 Data for Question 26: single length of light path

Plot graphs of the data in Tables 3.8 and 3.9 and then describe, in mathematical terms, how the rotation angle θ depends on the concentration c and length L of the light path through the solution.

4.3 Summing up Part 4

In this part of the chapter you have used two aspects of the behaviour of light to measure sugar concentration. In doing so, you have reviewed and extended your knowledge of waves from the earlier chapter *The Sound of Music*.

ACTIVITY 24 SUMMING UP PART 4

Spend a few minutes checking through your work on this part of the chapter. Make sure that you understand *all* the key terms printed in bold.

Look back at your work from *The Sound of Music*, and extend your table from Activity 25 in that chapter by adding and completing a row at the bottom with 'can be plane polarised' in the left-hand column.

ACTIVITY 25 MEASURING CONCENTRATION

Compare and evaluate the two methods you have used to measure sugar concentration. Which method do you think is better? Take account of the following:

- cost of equipment
- amount of sugar solution needed
- ease of use
- reliability of results.

PRACTICAL SKILLS REFERENCE

Conclusion and evaluation

See Practical skills notes 5.1–5.2

QUESTION

Q 27 The specific rotation of an optically active solution is defined as

$$specific\ rotation = \frac{\theta}{cL}$$

(Equation 17)

where θ is the rotation in degrees, c is the concentration in g ml^{-1} for a substance in solution (or, for a pure substance, its density in g ml^{-1}), and L is the length of the light path (or depth of substance) in decimetres (1 dm = 10^{-1} m).

(a) What is the specific rotation of a sugar solution that produced a rotation of the plane of polarisation of 33° with a concentration of 0/5 g ml^{-1} and a light path of 1 dm?

(b) Some materials will, for a 1 dm light path, rotate the plane of polarisation by many hundreds of degrees. Since it is not feasible to measure more than 360° directly, suggest how you might calculate their specific rotation.

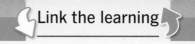

LINK THE LEARNING

5 Wrapping up

In this final part of the chapter, you will look at some other aspects of physics in the food industry and then review the work that you have done in earlier parts of the chapter.

5.1 Food quality and safety

It is important to ensure that foods, including confectionery, are fit to eat. Government regulations have a role to play in this. The Food Safety Act (1990) and The Food Safety (Temperature Control) Regulations (1995) are two important pieces of legislation covering the food chain from the farm to the shop.

At each stage, the manufacture and processing of food must conform to high standards of quality. The relevant techniques, procedures and management systems are specified in 'British Standards'. The procedures for certification are independently inspected, and a company would lose its certificate if it failed to reach the required standards. Stephen Beckett of Nestlé Research and Development comments below on how physics is involved.

> The development and use of instrumentation is perhaps one of the most important areas for physicists in the food industry. Some of this is for safety and must be carried out on-line, e.g. foreign material detectors; other instruments are for quality control, e.g. temperature and humidity. Even these are not as simple as they may at first appear. An item containing a metal object must be detected and rejected when the product is passing at the rate of several hundred per minute, and a simple, robust device for detecting pieces of plastic within chocolate has still to be invented. In addition, the chocolate's temperature must be monitored and controlled to within a fraction of a degree to ensure that it is glossy and has a good 'snap' when broken.

As you would expect, hygiene and safety are paramount. To ensure that any potential hazards are identified in a food production system, a Hazard and Critical Control Points (HACCP) system was developed. The first such system was designed in the USA in the 1960s to ensure the safety of the food for astronauts (Figure 3.45) as getting food poisoning in space would be quite a problem! The key principles of HACCP involve:

- identifying steps in food production where significant hazards occur

- identifying critical control points (CCPs) where it is essential to remove the hazards

- establishing critical limits that describe the difference between safe and unsafe

- establishing the means of monitoring and controlling the hazards

- keeping records

- verifying that the system is working correctly.

The hazards could be biological ones, such as salmonella in chicken. They could also be chemical hazards, related to the cleaning materials or lubricants used on the production line, or physical hazards, such as pieces of glass, metal, stones or wood getting into the food.

Figure 3.45 NASA Shuttle astronaut Rhea Seddon having a meal on the Space Shuttle

ACTIVITY 26 PHYSICAL HAZARDS IN FOOD

In a small group, discuss your suggestions and ideas concerning the following:

- the types of physical hazards that could potentially contaminate food in the course of production
- the possible source(s) of these contaminants
- the techniques you might be able to use to detect such contaminants
- the techniques you might use to keep out such contaminants.

Make notes on your discussions as you will need them for Activities 25 and 26.

If you have the opportunity to visit a food production company, you may be able to identify some of their critical control points, together with what is done to ensure monitoring and control at these points.

Figure 3.46 A confectionery product going through a wrapping machine

5.2 Packaging

Most confectionery products are wrapped to preserve them in good condition. There is a vast number of wrapping materials in use, mainly plastic-based, including cellulose acetate, polyester, polyethylene, polypropylene, polyvinyl chloride, nylon-6 and polyvinylidene chloride, among others; the aluminium foil wrap of many chocolate bars is a good example of a non-plastic material. Stephen Beckett puts the final production stage (Figure 3.46) into perspective:

> Packaging plays an important part in the chocolate confectionery industry, as it is often the only thing that a would-be purchaser sees. It is important to ensure therefore that the wrapper has been put on correctly. Major chocolate brands are produced at a rate of several million per day, and it is impossible to see moving parts of the wrapping machines to determine what happens when something goes wrong. In such cases high-speed video cameras can be of great benefit in being able to slow down the motion and help determine the cause of the fault.

ACTIVITY 27 WHICH PACKAGING?

Your task here is to make a recommendation on the ideal wrapping material(s) for a white chocolate covered Crunchie bar that is wrapped at a rate of 1000–1500 bars per minute. Write a report giving reasons for your recommendations.

5.3 The final product

The following activities are designed to help you look back over your work in this chapter. In doing so, make sure you have a full record of your work and that you are familiar with the key terms printed in bold earlier in the chapter.

ACTIVITY 28 COPING WITH HAZARDS

Design a double-page spread (perhaps using computer graphics) for a magazine that shows how some physical hazards could be detected and coped with in the food industry. Support your diagrams with a short paragraph outlining the physics involved in the techniques employed. Use your discussion notes from Activity 26 to help you.

ACTIVITY 29 SWEET PHYSICS

Write a short educational pamphlet titled 'Sweet physics' about physics in the confectionery industry, which might be useful for visitors to a confectionery company. Use your notes on the whole chapter to help you with this.

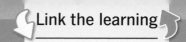

5.4 Questions on the whole chapter

 Q 28 A student wants to measure the density of the sugar mix used to make aniseed balls. He measures the diameters of 5 different balls with a micrometer screw gauge and obtains the following results: 10.2, 10.7, 10.1, 10.3, 10.5 mm. He weighs 10 balls, and obtains a mass of 11.16 g.

(a) **(i)** What is the mean diameter and its uncertainty?

(ii) What is the percentage uncertainty in the diameter, and in the radius?

(iii) What is the volume of one ball? Give your answer in mm^3 and in cm^3.

(b) If the balance reads to ± 0.01 g, what is the percentage uncertainty in the total mass, and in the mass of 1 ball?

(c) What is the density of the sweet? Give your answer in g cm^{-3} and in kg m^{-3}.

(d) **(i)** What is the uncertainty in the density?

(ii) How many significant figures should you give in the value for the density?

(iii) Write the density with the appropriate number of significant figures and its uncertainty.

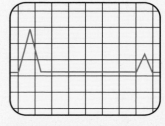

Figure 3.47 Schematic oscilloscope trace for Question 23 1 division = 1 cm

Q 29 A student wanted to build a model of a surveyor's ultrasound 'tape measure'. She connected a signal generator to a speaker, next to a microphone. The output from the microphone was connected to a storage oscilloscope. The timebase of the oscilloscope was set at 2 m s cm^{-1}. The speed of sound was taken as 335 m s^{-1} ± 10 m s^{-1}. The student switched the generator on and off very quickly, and obtained a trace similar to that in Figure 3.47.

(a) **(i)** Estimate the time between the signal received from the speaker and the echo.

(ii) Calculate the distance travelled by the sound in that time, and so the distance away of the wall that reflected the sound.

(b) **(i)** If the position of each pulse can be judged ± 0.1 cm, calculate the uncertainty in the time for the signal to return.

(ii) Calculate the percentage uncertainty in the time for the signal to return.

(c) Calculate the percentage uncertainty in the speed of sound.

(d) **(i)** Calculate the actual uncertainty in the distance to the wall.

(ii) State the distance to the wall with the correct number of significant figures, and its uncertainty.

 Q 30 When water vapour in the atmosphere cools, it condenses to form droplets of liquid water. This forms clouds. If the droplets cool further, they freeze to form ice pellets, which fall from the cloud. By the time they reach the ground they have usually melted again to form rain, but sometimes they reach the ground as hail. When the ice pellets melt, they break up into small water droplets, which reach their terminal velocity before they hit the ground. Hailstones can cause a lot of damage because they are larger and more massive and travel faster than raindrops.

(a) Explain, with the aid of a diagram, how the forces on an object falling through a viscous fluid bring it to a terminal velocity.

(b) Write down an expression for the forces on a raindrop of radius r and density ρ_{water}, when it has reached a terminal velocity v while falling through air of density ρ_{air} and viscosity η.

(c) Given that $\rho_{air} \ll \rho_{water}$, rearrange your answer to (b) to obtain an expression for v.

(d) Given that $\rho_{ice} \approx \rho_{water}$, explain why hailstones reach the ground travelling faster than raindrops.

Q 31 In 1809 Étienne-Louis Malus (1775–1812) discovered that light can be partially or completely polarised by reflection from a shiny surface.

(a) Explain how you could use a polarising filter to demonstrate that light has become polarised on reflection.

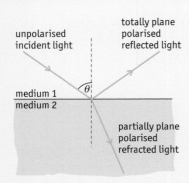

unpolarised incident light

totally plane polarised reflected light

medium 1
medium 2

θ

partially plane polarised refracted light

Figure 3.48 Obtaining polarised light by reflection

(b) David Brewster (1781–1868) discovered that totally polarised light can be obtained on reflection when the refractive index μ of the reflecting material equals the tangent of the angle of incidence of the light, as shown in Figure 3.48. (The angle at which this happens is known as the Brewster angle.)

(i) If the refractive index from air to glass is 1.5, what must the angle of incidence be in order to produce totally plane-polarised light on reflection?

(ii) What would be the angle of reflection of this polarised light from the glass surface?

(c) When light is polarised by reflection from glass, only about 8% of the light is reflected; the rest enters the glass. Suggest and explain how you might boost this percentage using glass reflective surfaces *only*.

5.5 Achievements

Now you have studied this chapter you should be able to achieve the outcomes listed in Table 3.10.

	TABLE 3.10 ACHIEVEMENTS FOR THE CHAPTER *GOOD ENOUGH TO EAT*	
	Statement from Examination Specification	Section(s) in this chapter
1	know and understand the distinction between base and derived quantities and their SI units	2.2
2	demonstrate their knowledge of practical skills and techniques for both familiar and unfamiliar experiments	2.2, 3.2, 4.1, 4.2
3	be able to estimate values for physical quantities and use their estimate to solve problems	2.2, 5.4
4	understand the limitations of physical measurement and apply these limitations to practical situations	1.1, 2.2, 3.2, 4.1, 4.2, 5.4
5	be able to communicate information and ideas in appropriate ways using appropriate terminology	2.5, 5.2, 5.3
49	be able to use the equation density $\rho = \dfrac{m}{V}$	1.1
50	understand how to use the relationship upthrust = weight of fluid displaced	2.2
51	be able to use the equation for viscous drag (Stokes's Law), $F = 6\pi\eta rv$. Understand that this equation only applies to small spherical objects moving at low speeds with laminar flow (or in the absence of turbulent flow) and that viscosity is temperature dependent	2.2
52	CORE PRACTICAL 4: Use a falling ball method to determine the viscosity of a liquid	2.2
53	be able to use the Hooke's law equation, $\Delta F = k\Delta x$, where k is the stiffness of the object	3.2
55	(part) be able to draw and interpret force–extension and force–compression graphs. Understand the terms limit of proportionality, elastic limit, yield point, elastic deformation and plastic deformation and be able to apply them to graphs	3.2
71	know and understand that at the interface between medium 1 and medium 2: $n_1\sin\theta_1 = n_2\sin\theta_2$ where refractive index is $n = \dfrac{c}{v}$	4.1
72	be able to calculate *critical angle* using $\sin C = \dfrac{1}{n}$	
73	understand the term critical angle and be able to predict whether total internal reflection will occur at an interface	4.1
74	understand how to measure the refractive index of a solid material	4.1
81	understand what is meant by plane polarization	4.2

Answers

Q 1 **(a)** The numbers 6 and π have no units, so the units of η are

$$\frac{N}{m \times m\,s^{-1}} = N\,s\,m^{-2}$$

$$1\,N = 1\,kg\,m\,s^{-2}$$

so, in SI base units,

$$N\,s\,m^{-2} = kg\,m\,s^{-2} \times s \times m^{-2} = kg\,m^{-1}\,s^{-1}$$

(b) Using Equation 1:

$$F = 6\pi\eta r v$$

so:

$$F = 6\pi \times 8.4 \times 10^{-2}\,N\,s\,m^{-2} \times 1.0 \times 10^{-3}\,m \times 2.0 \times 10^{-2}\,m\,s^{-1}$$

$$= 3.2 \times 10^{-5}\,N$$

Q 2 **(a)** $V = \dfrac{4\pi \times (1.0 \times 10^{-3}\,m)^3}{3}$

$$= 4.2 \times 10^{-9}\,m^3$$

(b) Mass $m_{steel} = \rho_{steel}\,V$

$$= 7.8 \times 10^3\,kg\,m^{-3} \times 4.2 \times 10^{-9}\,m^3$$

$$= 3.3 \times 10^{-5}\,kg$$

(c) Weight of ball-bearing $= m_{steel}\,g$

$$= 3.3 \times 10^{-5}\,kg \times 9.8\,N\,kg^{-1}$$

$$= 3.2 \times 10^{-4}\,N$$

Q 3 **(a)** Volume $= 4.2 \times 10^{-9}\,m^3$ as the ball-bearing will displace its own volume.

(b) Mass of oil $m_{oil} = \rho_{oil}\,V$

$$= 920\,kg\,m^{-3} \times 4.2 \times 10^{-9}\,m^3$$

$$= 3.9 \times 10^{-6}\,kg$$

(c) Weight of displaced oil $= m_{oil}\,g$

$$= 3.9 \times 10^{-6}\,kg \times 9.8\,N\,kg^{-1}$$

$$= 3.8 \times 10^{-5}\,N$$

Q 4 **(a)** Upthrust = weight of displaced oil

$$= 3.8 \times 10^{-5}\,N$$

(b) Upward force = upthrust + viscous drag force

$$= 3.8 \times 10^{-5}\,N + 3.2 \times 10^{-5}\,N$$

$$= 7.0 \times 10^{-5}\,N$$

Weight of ball-bearing $= 3.2 \times 10^{-4}\,N$ acting downwards

There is therefore a net downwards force of magnitude F, where:

$$F = 3.2 \times 10^{-4}\,N - 0.7 \times 10^{-4}\,N$$

$$= 2.5 \times 10^{-4}\,N$$

Q 5 Weigh the object in air by suspending it from the forcemeter by the cotton.

Pour some water into the measuring cylinder to about halfway and note the volume.

Lower the object, still attached to the forcemeter, completely into the water, but don't let it touch the bottom.

Note the new forcemeter reading and the new level of water in the measuring cylinder.

The difference between the two forcemeter readings gives the upthrust.

The difference between the two levels in the measuring cylinder gives the volume of water displaced (which is also the volume of the object).

Calculate the mass of water displaced and therefore its weight, which should be equal to the upthrust.

Q 6 See Figure 3.12 (page 113).

Pressure exerted by water on top of block $= P_A + h_1\rho g$

Downward force on top of block $= (P_A + h_1\rho g)A$

Pressure exerted by water at bottom of block $= P_A + h_2\rho g$

Upward force on bottom of block $= (P_A + h_2\rho g)A$

So net upward force on block $= (h_2 - h_1)\rho g A$

$$= h\rho g A$$

Volume of fluid displaced = volume of block $= Ah$

Mass of fluid displaced $= \rho Ah$

Weight of fluid displaced $= \rho Ahg$, which is the same as the net upward force

Q 7 The upthrust on an object may be ignored when its density is very much greater than the density of the surrounding fluid.

Q 8 Using symbols:

C_a = weight of crown in air

C_w = weight of crown in water

W_d = weight of water displaced

ρ_w = density of water

ρ_c = density of crown

V = volume of crown = volume of water displaced

By Archimedes' principle, we know that:

$$C_w = C_a - W_d$$

and we are told that:

$$\frac{C_w}{C_a} = 0.948$$

so we can write:

$$\frac{(C_a - W_d)}{C_a} = 0.948$$

and so:

$$1 - \frac{W_d}{C_a} = 0.948$$

$$\frac{W_d}{C_a} = 1 - 0.948 = 0.052$$

However, we can also say that:

$$C_a = V\rho_c g$$

and:

$$W_d = V\rho_w g$$

so:

$$\frac{\rho_w}{\rho_c} = \frac{W_d}{C_a}$$

or:

$$\frac{\rho_c}{\rho_w} = \frac{C_a}{W_d} = \frac{1}{0.052} = 19.3$$

This is the density ratio of pure gold to water, so the crown must be made of pure gold.

Q 9 **(a)** If the combined mass of man and chair is M, then their weight is
$$W = Mg = 70\,\text{kg} \times 9.81\,\text{N}\,\text{kg}^{-1} = 690\,\text{N}$$

(b) Upthrust = weight of air displaced

$$= \text{volume of balloons} \times \text{density of air} \times g$$

$$= \frac{V}{\text{m}^3} \times 1.28\,\text{kg}\,\text{m}^{-3} \times 9.81\,\text{N}\,\text{kg}^{-1}$$

$$= \frac{V}{\text{m}^3} \times 12.65\,\text{N} \approx 13\,V/\text{m}^3\,\text{N}$$

(V/m^3 means the volume in units of m^3)

(c) Weight of helium = $V \times$ density of helium $\times g$

$$= \frac{V}{\text{m}^3} \times 0.18\,\text{kg}\,\text{m}^{-3} \times 9.81\,\text{N}\,\text{kg}^{-1}$$

$$= \frac{V}{\text{m}^3} \times 1.77\,\text{N} \approx 1.8\,V/\text{m}^3\,\text{N}$$

(d) When the man just leaves the ground without accelerating significantly, the forces acting on him are just about balanced.

Upthrust = weight of man + weight of helium

$$12.65\frac{V}{\text{m}^3}\text{N} = 690\,\text{N} + 0.18\frac{V}{\text{m}^3}\text{N}$$

$$10.88\frac{V}{\text{m}^3} = 690$$

$$V = \frac{690\,\text{m}^3}{10.88} \approx 6.3\,\text{m}^3$$

(e) Suppose a typical party balloon has radius $r = 0.15\,\text{m}$.

$$\text{Volume} = \frac{4\,\pi r^3}{3} = 0.0141\,\text{m}^3$$

$$\text{Number of balloons} = \frac{63\,\text{m}^3}{0.0141\,\text{m}^3} \approx 4.5 \times 10^4.$$ Your value will depend on your estimate of the balloon's size.

(f) The viscous drag force calculated using Stokes's equation (Equation 1) is much smaller than the other forces acting. The main contribution to the drag force on large objects (balloons, man and chair) is the density-dependent force, as an object pushes air out of the way and creates turbulent motion. Viscous drag is only significant for very small objects moving slowly (no turbulence).

Q 10 You might expect them to have the same coefficient of viscosity over a range of temperatures – visco (viscosity) and static (the same). (In reality this is not actually so, but the changes of viscosity are such as to enable the vehicle to function satisfactorily regardless of the temperature changes. For extremes of temperature, oils are specially formulated to provide suitable viscosity.)

Q 11 By changing the electric field at certain points in the flow, the rate of flow of the chocolate could be changed in order to alter the thickness of a coating or take account of the change of speed of a production line.

Q 12 **(a)** A   **(b)** A   **(c)** D

(d) B   **(e)** C   **(f)** B

Q 13 **(a)** The terminal velocity is the greatest steady velocity reached by the falling ball-bearing. It is reached when the forces acting on the ball-bearing are balanced.

(b) If the bearing is similar in diameter to the container then the oil will need to pass through a narrow space to get past. This means there is a steeper velocity gradient across the fluid and therefore a greater force on the ball. There is also more likely to be turbulence, as the liquid will flow at a faster speed to get the same volume of fluid past the ball, which is necessary for the ball to move at a particular velocity.

Stokes's law only applies to laminar flow. (Also, if you use large ball-bearings, the viscous drag might not be the main drag force; the density-dependent drag force will become significant – regardless of the size of the container.)

(c) Upthrust $= \dfrac{4\pi r^3 \rho_{oil} g}{3}$

$= \dfrac{4}{3}\pi \times (0.5 \times 0^{-3}\,\text{m})^3 \times 900\,\text{kg m}^{-3} \times$
$\hspace{6cm} 9.81\,\text{N kg}^{-1}$

$= 4.62 \times 10^{-6}\,\text{N}$

(d) Weight $= \dfrac{4\pi r^3 \rho_{steel} g}{3}$

$= \dfrac{4\pi}{3} \times (0.5 \times 10^{-3}\,\text{m})^3 \times 7860\,\text{kg m}^{-3} \times$
$\hspace{6cm} 9.81\,\text{N kg}^{-1}$

$= 4.03 \times 10^{-5}\,\text{N}$

(e) From Equation 2:

viscous drag force = weight − upthrust

$6\pi r \eta v = 4.03 \times 10^{-5}\,\text{N} - 4.62 \times 10^{-6}\,\text{N}$

$\eta = \dfrac{(4.03 \times 10^{-5}\,\text{N}) - (4.62 \times 10^{-6}\,\text{N})}{6\pi \times 0.5 \times 10^{-3}\,\text{m} \times 0.03\,\text{m s}^{-1}}$

$= 1.26 \times 10^{-1}\,\text{N s m}^{-2}$

Q 14 If you plot the data on a graph, the points lie almost on a straight line, suggesting that the output frequency is proportional to the flow rate.

Q 15 **(a)** The fluid will expand and contract as temperature changes, so customers would be charged incorrectly.

(b) Mass = density × volume, so mass flow rate = density × volume flow rate. (Some flowmeters incorporate densitometers that automatically measure the density and compensate for any changes.)

Q 16 **(a)** **(i)** See Tables 3.11 and 3.12
(ii) The speed of flow is directly proportional to the frequency of vortices. As one doubles the other also doubles.
(iii) The diameter of the obstruction is inversely proportional to the frequency of vortices. As one doubles, the other halves; as one is reduced to a third, the other triples.

Speed of flow/m s⁻¹	Time for 20 vortices to pass/s	Frequency of vortices/Hz
0.5	2.00	10
1.0	0.98	20
1.5	0.66	30
2.0	0.50	40
2.5	0.40	50

Table 3.11 Table 3.2 completed (10 mm obstruction)

Speed of flow/m s⁻¹	Time for 20 vortices to pass/s	Frequency of vortices/Hz
1.0	0.50	40
1.5	0.33	61
2.0	0.25	80
2.5	0.20	100

Table 3.12 Table 3.3 completed (5 mm obstruction)

(b) If the frequency of vortices was very high there might not be enough time for the thermistors to heat up again before the next vortex cooled it. Then the vortices would not be detected.

Q 17 **(a)** See Figure 3.49. Notice that this graph is plotted using g and cm: if you worked out the load in newtons and the extension in m, your graph would have the same shape, but the numbers on the axes would be different. A mass of 10 g has a weight of approximately 0.1 N, so when the mass is 20 g the load is 0.2 N. You could also have plotted extension rather than total length, in which case your graph would start at the origin.

(b) The behaviour was elastic throughout (the Glow-worm returned to its original length when the load was removed). It was not very stiff (despite being quite thick, it doubled its length under a moderate load). As it extended it became slightly stiffer (the graph curves upwards, so load ÷ extension is greater when the extension is large).

(c) The Glow-worm would feel quite 'rubbery' and stretchy when chewed; it would deform and spring back.

Q 18 **(a)** The graph should look like the line through the marked points in Figure 3.50.

(b) Since the line is straight and passes through the origin, you can read one pair of values from the line to find the gradient; using a point a long way from the origin gives a smaller uncertainty.

stiffness $= \dfrac{\text{force}}{\text{extension}}$

$= \dfrac{25 \times 10^3\,\text{N}}{60 \times 10^{-6}\,\text{m}}$

$= 4.2 \times 10^8\,\text{N m}^{-1}$

(c) P is at the end of the straight region (Figure 3.50); E is between P and the end of the line. The elastic limit is the point beyond which the sample no longer returns to its original shape when the load is removed. Unlike P, E does not have an exactly predictable position, except that it must be after P and before the sample has broken.

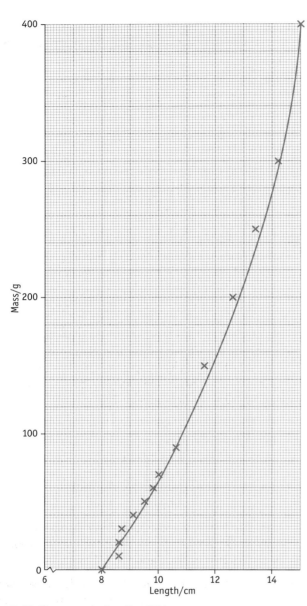

Figure 3.49 The answer to Question 17(a)

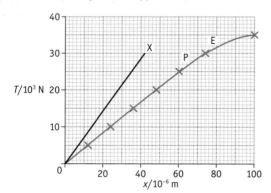

Figure 3.50 The answer to Question 18

(d) See Figure 3.50. The line is steeper (since it is stiffer), ends (at **X**) without curving (which indicates brittle behaviour with no plastic deformation before fracture) and ends at a lower value of force (since the sample is weaker).

Q 19 There are many possible examples that you might enjoy discussing. 'Mints with a hole' are hard but not tough: they will resist changing shape when chewed and fracture suddenly. A tough food such as a badly cooked steak is very chewy and requires you to do a lot of work to break it, but it deforms quite easily so is not hard.

Q 20 (a) As it ages the cheese gets stiffer.

(b) It also becomes stronger with age.

(c) With cumin seeds, the cheese is less stiff and breaks more easily. Maybe the seeds act as small cracks, which spread when the cheese is deformed.

Q 21 (a) It stretches easily, but requires a large force to break it.

(b) It does not stretch much and breaks under a small force.

(c) It does not stretch much and also does not break easily.

(d) It stretches and breaks easily.

Q 22 $n = \dfrac{\text{speed in air}}{\text{speed in material}}$ (Equation 5) so:

$$\text{speed in material} = \frac{\text{speed in air}}{n}$$

$$\text{speed in glass} = \frac{3.00 \times 10^8 \, \text{m s}^{-1}}{1.47}$$

$$= 2.04 \times 10^8 \, \text{m s}^{-1}$$

Similarly:

speed in water = $2.26 \times 10^8 \, \text{m s}^{-1}$

speed in polystyrene = $1.88 \times 10^8 \, \text{m s}^{-1}$

Q 23 (a) Material 1 is air, material 2 is glass. The turn towards the normal indicates that the second material is the denser (i greater than r).

(b) The ray would turn away from the normal as it emerged (r is greater than i). The path is the exact reverse of the one in the diagram. This is an example of the so-called 'reversibility' of light. If you plot the path of light going one way through a blocks it will trace the identical path if the direction is reversed.

(c) It continues in the same direction.

(d) It would get larger.

Q 24 **(a)** $n = \dfrac{\sin i}{\sin r} = \dfrac{v_1}{v_2}$ (Equations 6 and 7)

(b) If light is travelling from a dense material into a less-dense one, the critical angle, C, is the largest possible angle between the ray and the normal that will allow the ray to emerge into the less-dense material; it will emerge at 90° to the normal. At larger angles, the ray will undergo total internal reflection.

Q 25 **(a)** See Figure 2.51

(b) The refractive index increases with concentration, but the relationship is non-linear — the graph curves gently.

(c) About 72% (read from Figure 3.51).

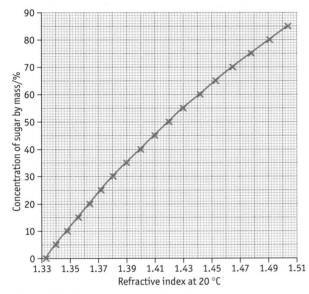

Figure 3.51 The answer to Question 25(a)

Q 26 See Figure 3.52. The graphs go through the origin and appear to be linear, suggesting that the angle, θ, is directly proportional to both concentration, c, and path length, L. $\theta = k c L$ where k is a constant.

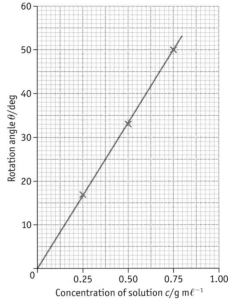

Figure 3.52 The answer to Question 26

Q 27 **(a)** Specific rotation $= \dfrac{\theta}{cL}$

$$= \dfrac{33°}{(0.5 \, \text{g ml}^{-1} \times 1 \, \text{dm})}$$

$$= 66°$$

Note: the specific rotation is, by convention, expressed in degrees alone, although it may appear more sensible to have used ° ml g^{-1} dm^{-1}.

(b) Measure the rotation angle for a much smaller light path and multiply by a suitable factor (say 1 cm and multiply the rotation angle by 10). For even greater rotations, light paths of millimetres could be used.

TECHNOLOGY IN SPACE

Figure 4.1b Space Shuttle Mission STS 117 unfurling the solar arrays for the International Space Station, as reflected in astronaut Suni Williams' visor, June 2007

Why a chapter called *Technology in Space*?

Since the mid 20th century, space technology has played an increasingly important part in our lives, both through satellites orbiting the Earth (Figure 4.1) and through space probes that travel to distant parts of the solar system.

Communications satellites transmit radio signals for telephones and television. Meteorological satellites monitor the atmosphere and the Earth's surface, using remote sensing to provide data for weather forecasting and adding to our understanding of long-term environmental changes. Astronomical satellites provide clearer views of the cosmos than is possible from the ground. Satellites also play a part in locating oil and other mineral deposits and in navigation.

The design, building and operation of a satellite or space probe involves the understanding and application of many areas of physics. In this chapter you will first see how a self-contained renewable electrical power supply can be designed using solar cells, and then how changing temperatures affect the properties of electrical components as a spacecraft moves between sunlight and shadow. In the second year of this course, you will study two more chapters connected with space and communications. *The Medium is the Message* is about modern telecommunications, and *Reach for the Stars* is about the stars and how we study them.

OVERVIEW OF PHYSICS PRINCIPLES AND TECHNIQUES

In this chapter you will begin by using solar cells and revisiting some ideas about current, voltage and resistance in electric circuits. In Part 2 you will meet the idea of internal resistance and you will learn how resistors and power supplies can be combined in circuits to perform particular functions. Part 3 is about the physics behind solar cells, which involves the photon model of light. Finally, in Part 4 you will see how solar radiation input can be measured and then how a simple model of a conductor can be used to explain changes in its resistance with temperature.

In the course of the chapter, you will also be using and developing some key mathematical and ICT skills and techniques – in particular, you will be using algebra and graphs and using a spreadsheet.

Many of the principles and techniques that you meet in this chapter will be picked up and developed further in later chapters. This approach of introducing, revisiting and building on ideas as and when they are relevant to a particular situation is a key feature of this course.

In this chapter you will extend your knowledge of:

- energy conservation and work from *Higher, Faster, Stronger*
- the photon model of light from *The Sound of Music*
- properties of materials from *Good Enough to Eat*.

In other chapters you will do further work on:

- DC electric circuits in *Digging Up the Past* and *Transport on Track*
- material properties in *Spare Part Surgery*
- explanations of why materials behave in certain ways in *Digging Up the Past* and *The Medium is the Message*
- radiation in *Reach for the Stars*.

Figure 4.1b Solar panels on Skylab

1 Satellites in space

1.1 A space engineer

Jeremy Curtis is an engineer who leads the UK Space Agency's space education programme at the Rutherford Appleton Laboratory (RAL) in Oxfordshire. The RAL provides research and technology development, space test facilities, instrument and mission design, and studies of science and technology requirements for new missions. Much of the department's work is in collaboration with UK university research groups and a range of institutes around the world, mostly with European Space Agency (ESA) and NASA missions, but also other countries and organisations including Australia, Japan, Morocco, Pakistan, Russia and the European Union (see Figure 4.2).

Jeremy says, 'I trained as a mechanical engineer, but I find space engineering exciting because I have to work with all sorts of experts such as astronomers, physicists, designers, programmers and technicians working around the world.' He was sponsored by RAL during his university degree and then spent several years on designs for a very large proton synchrotron (a machine for accelerating protons to very high energies) before moving over to space instrument design. In the following passage, he describes some aspects of space engineering.

Figure 4.2 Jeremy Curtis (centre) working on part of a satellite-borne telescope before it is tested at RAL

Why satellites?

Getting spacecraft into orbit is a very expensive activity, with typical launch costs generally measured in tens of thousands of pounds per kilogram. So what makes it worth the bother? There are three key reasons. First, a satellite is at a good vantage point for studying the Earth's surface and atmosphere — just think how many aircraft would be needed to photograph the whole Earth, or how many ships to monitor the temperatures of the oceans. Second, if we want to study most of the radiation coming from distant parts of the universe we have to get above the atmosphere. The Earth's atmosphere absorbs nearly everything that tries to get through it — from X-rays to ultraviolet and from infrared to millimetre waves. Only visible light and radio waves can get through. In fact, even visible light suffers — convection in the Earth's atmosphere makes stars seem to jump about or twinkle, blurring telescope images, so a telescope in space produces sharper images than is possible on Earth.

Finally, and not least, a communications satellite can beam TV pictures across the globe and link telephone users on different continents.

The problem with space

Once you've gone through the huge trouble and expense of launching your satellite, a new set of problems confronts you in space.

Figure 4.3 The Infrared Space Observatory was launched in 1995 by the European Space Agency (ESA) and carries several instruments designed and built in the UK

First, a typical spacecraft may need several kilowatts of power — but where do you plug in? The only convenient renewable source of power is the Sun, so most spacecraft are equipped with panels of solar cells. You can see these on the Infrared Space Observatory (ISO) (Figure 4.3). Unlike on Earth, there is no worry about what to do on cloudy days, but batteries are still needed for periods when the satellite is in the Earth's shadow (usually up to an hour or two per orbit) and the satellite has to be continually steered to keep the panels pointing at the Sun.

So now we have our spacecraft floating in orbit and pointing the same face to the Sun all the time. Although the solar cells provide partial shade from sunlight, this surface starts to heat up, and with no air to convect the heat away the temperature can rise dramatically. To add to the difficulties, the other side of the spacecraft faces cold space (at about 3 K or −270 °C) and so begins to cool down. Unchecked, this would distort the structure, wreck the electronics and decompose the materials that make up the spacecraft. So most surfaces of the spacecraft are covered in 'space blanket' — multilayer insulation made of metallised plastic that reflects the radiation away and insulates the spacecraft. This is the crinkly shiny material you can see in the photo (Figure 4.4).

Figure 4.4 Installing a radiator on the outside of JET-X, an X-ray telescope launched in 1999

1.2 Studying with satellites

FUNcube (Figure 4.5(a)) is a joint project between the Netherlands and UK Radio Amateur Satellites (AMSAT-UK and AMSAT-NL). FUNcube-1 (Figure 4.5(a) is a small satellite measuring just 10 cm × 10 cm × 10 cm, with a mass of less than 1 kg. It is the first spacecraft to have a primary mission of educational outreach to schools and the smallest ever satellite to carry a linear transponder for radio amateurs. FUNcube-1 was successfully launched from Russia on a DNEPR rocket on 21 November 21 2013. More than 500 stations around the world are already receiving and decoding the telemetry and many schools are involved.

Before FUNcube, there were the UoSAT satellites, which were launched in the late 1980s and early 1990s. These were small, relatively low-cost spacecraft each with a mass of typically 50 kg and about 0.5 m across. whose purpose was to test and evaluate new systems and space technology and to enable students and amateur scientists to study the near-Earth environment. They were designed and built by Surrey Satellite Technology Ltd, which is based at the University of Surrey. Figure 4.5(b) shows UoSAT 2, also known as Oscar 11, which is still transmitting signals. Its sensors record the local magnetic field, providing information about solar and geomagnetic disturbances and their effects on radio communications at various frequencies. Instruments on board also measure some sixty items relating to the satellite's operation. These include: the temperatures of its faces, its batteries and other electronic devices; the current provided by its solar arrays; and the battery voltages. UoSAT's orbit takes it over both poles at a height of about 650 km about the surface, and the spinning of the Earth allows us to receive data six times a day. UoSAT 2 has been in operation for over 30 years, which is longer than most satellites.

Even a small spacecraft such as UoSAT or FUNcube needs electricity to run all the on-board systems, from the computer that controls it all to the radio transmitters and receivers that send and receive data to and from ground stations on the Earth's surface.

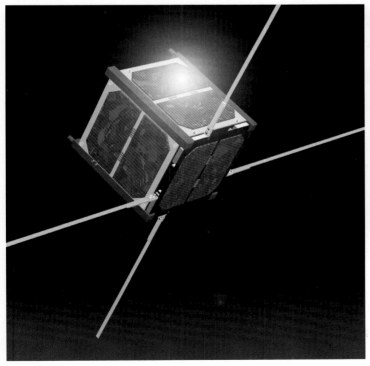

(b)

(a)

Figure 4.5 Small satellites: (a) Artist's impression of FUNcube-1 in orbit (b) UoSAT 2 (the frame at the top of the photo is about 0.5 m across)

For comparison, JET-X (Figure 4.4) is about 540 kg in mass and about 4.5 m long. Communications satellites are larger still, with masses of typically 2 to 5 tonnes. At the top end of the scale is the International Space Station (ISS) (Figure 4.6) – a cooperative venture between 13 nations including the United Kingdom. Construction and testing started in 1995 and completion was finalised in 2011. The completed station has a mass of about 420 tonnes, measures 110 m from tip to tip of its solar arrays, and has pressurised living and working space for its crew of six almost equal to the passenger space on a 747 jet airliner. It has a power demand of over 84 kW.

Figure 4.6 The completed International Space Station (ISS) in 2011. Notice how the solar panels are orientated to capture maximum sunlight.

PRACTICAL SKILLS REFERENCE

Information research

See Practical skills notes 1.2–1.4

⚙ ACTIVITY 1 FINDING OUT ABOUT SPACECRAFT

Use the Internet to find out about the history of space flight. How far have we advanced in the last 50 years? Make a time line and mark on the major advances. You might like to start at the NASA website or Astronaughtix, details of which are provided at www.pearsonhotlinks.co.uk. Search for Salters Horners AS/A level Physics and click on this activity.

⚙ ACTIVITY 2 DATA FROM SPACE

Examine some satellite data (e.g. from FUNcube-1) and see what you can deduce about conditions on board. Depending on the equipment available to you, you might use data stored on a disk, accessed via the Internet or direct from a satellite.

Look particularly for information about current and voltages in power supplies and about the temperature at various locations in the spacecraft.

Print out a sample of records showing how these measurements vary with time. You will be learning more about these aspects of satellite design and operation as you study this chapter.

1.3 Spacecraft power systems

Figure 4.7 shows the three main elements in a spacecraft power system. The *primary source* involves the use of a fuel to produce electrical power. Primary sources include fuel cells in which a chemical reaction between hydrogen and oxygen produces electricity (with drinking water as a useful by-product), and radioisotope thermoelectric generators (RTGs) in which a radioactive decay process produces heating in a thermoelectric module that generates electricity. In spacecraft the most common primary source is the photovoltaic cell, which is powered by solar radiation: here the initial fuel is protons in the Sun that undergo nuclear fusion.

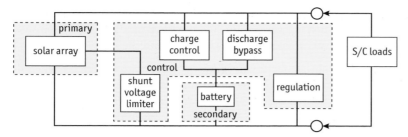

Figure 4.7 Schematic diagram of a spacecraft power system

The *secondary source* is the energy storage system – usually a set of batteries. Sometimes regenerative fuel cells are used in which power from solar arrays electrolyses water to produce hydrogen and oxygen gases during the 'charge' cycle, followed by hydrogen and oxygen recombining to make water during the 'discharge' cycle.

An electronic *power control and distribution system* controls and adjusts the voltage and current inputs and outputs, often using primary and secondary sources together to boost the overall output power.

There are other systems available and these are shown in Figure 4.8. Information on these systems can be found via the Internet using the NASA Educators website (see Figure 4.9) or the Heavens Above website.

QUESTION

Q 1 Using Figure 4.8, decide which would be the most suitable power source(s) for a spacecraft needing:

(a) 1 kW power output for just one week

(b) 10 kW for five years.

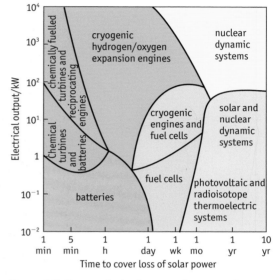

Figure 4.8 Power outputs of spacecraft power systems

Figure 4.9 The NASA Educators website

The most common primary source used in satellites is the photovoltaic cell or solar cell. Many hundreds of thousands of such cells are connected together to make up solar arrays. In Figures 4.5 and 4.6 you can see the arrays of solar cells on UoSAT 2 and the ISS.

Solar cells have one important characteristic: they only generate electricity when illuminated. Each year, orbiting satellites undergo between 90 and 5500 eclipses, moving into the Earth's shadow (Figure 4.10). The former is typical of a geostationary telecommunications satellite, the latter of a satellite in a low orbit, like UoSAT 2. The ISS has sixteen 30-minute periods of shadow a day. The secondary power supply is therefore vital, because during eclipses electrical power has to be supplied by batteries. There are also occasions when the batteries are needed to provide power in addition to that of the solar panels.

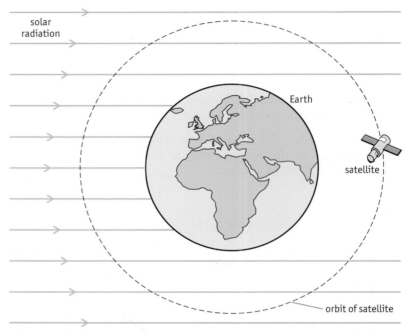

Figure 4.10 A satellite in eclipse

The spacecraft's solar panels are used to recharge its batteries when it emerges into sunlight. To do this they must produce a high enough voltage – higher than the battery's own voltage. (A charger for a 12 V car battery provides about 13 V.) The power system must therefore be carefully designed to ensure that the solar panels can charge the batteries and that the batteries can operate the electrical equipment on board.

So what voltage does a solar cell provide? How does this voltage vary with the brightness of the light? How can we connect up solar cells in order to charge batteries and operate equipment? These are questions that you will be exploring in Part 2 of this chapter.

2 Solar cells and electric circuits

In this part of the chapter you will learn about solar power supplies and electric circuits in order to see what is involved in designing a power supply for a spacecraft. The things that you learn about circuits can be applied to electrical systems operated by other types of power supply – not just to those with solar cells.

2.1 Solar cells

> ### ⚙ ACTIVITY 3 A FIRST LOOK AT SOLAR CELLS
>
> In this short activity, your task is to measure the voltage produced by a solar cell under various conditions of illumination.
>
> Connect a voltmeter across just one of the solar cells, as shown in Figure 4.11. Observe how the voltage across the solar cell changes as you vary the separation between the cell and the lamp. Write a sentence summarising what you have observed.

You should have found that even the highest voltage generated was quite small, so, to charge up the on-board batteries, large numbers of solar cells must be connected together.

> ### ⚙ ACTIVITY 4 SOLAR ARRAY VOLTAGE
>
> Have a look at some satellite data (e.g. from FUNcube) and see how the solar array voltage varies with time. Think how these variations might be explained in terms of the illumination of the satellite.

Figure 4.11 A solar cell connected to a voltmeter and illuminated

How does a solar cell work?

A solar cell (technically, a **photovoltaic cell**) is an electrical power supply. Incoming radiation provides energy that is transferred to an electric circuit via the motion of charged particles. Figure 4.12 shows a schematic diagram of a photovoltaic cell.

> **STUDY NOTE**
>
> In Part 3 of this chapter you will learn more about the physics behind solar cells.

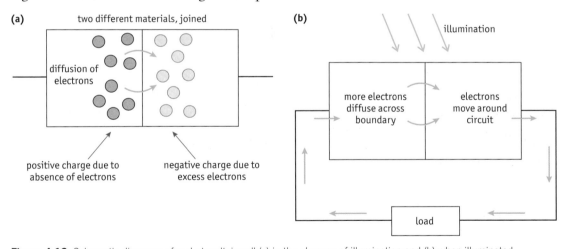

Figure 4.12 Schematic diagrams of a photovoltaic cell (a) in the absence of illumination and (b) when illuminated

The two materials are designed so that electrons spontaneously drift from one to the other, giving one a negative charge and the other a positive charge until drifting is halted by the build-up of electric charge. When the cell absorbs radiation, some of the electrons gain enough energy to move freely. Some move back across the boundary, but most move around the external circuit and are replaced by more electrons drifting across the boundary.

Current and charge, voltage and energy

The continuous flow of charged particles constitutes an electric **current**. Current is defined as the rate of flow of charge past a point in the circuit:

$$\text{current } (I) = \text{charge } (\Delta Q) \div \text{time interval } (\Delta t) \tag{1}$$

The SI unit of charge is the coulomb (C) and the unit of current is the ampere or amp (A):

$$1\,\text{A} = 1\,\text{C s}^{-1}$$

If an amount of charge ΔQ flows past a point in a time interval Δt, then (adapting Equation 1) the current I can be written:

$$I = \frac{\Delta Q}{\Delta t} \tag{1a}$$

Charge is not created or destroyed (it is **conserved**) and there is no build-up of charge anywhere in a circuit, so the rate at which charge flows towards any point in the circuit must be the same as the rate at which it flows away. So in a circuit where all components are joined in **series** (Figure 4.13(a)), the current is the same throughout, and where components are joined in **parallel** (Figure 4.13(b)), the sum of currents flowing into a junction is equal to the sum of currents flowing out of it:

$$I = I_1 + I_2 + I_3 \tag{2}$$

MATHS REFERENCE

Index notation
See Maths note 1.1
Index notation and units
See Maths note 2.2
The delta symbol
See Maths note 0.2

STUDY NOTE

SPC Additional Sheets 1 and 2 are designed to help you get to grips with current and voltage.

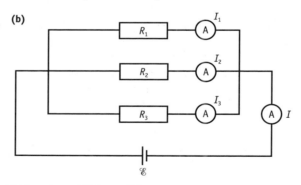

Figure 4.13 Resistors joined (a) in series and (b) in parallel

Energy transfers in electric circuits are often expressed in terms of energy per unit charge. The SI unit of energy is the joule (J) and the unit for energy per unit charge is the volt (V): $1\,\text{V} = 1\,\text{J C}^{-1}$. Energy per unit charge is more usually called **potential difference** (pd) or **voltage** and given the symbol V. Using the symbol W for energy:

$$W = QV \tag{3}$$

STUDY NOTE

Emf stands for electromotive force, however that's rather a misleading term since emf is a measure of energy not a measure of force.

The **emf** of a power supply is a measure of the total energy that it supplies to each coulomb of charge. Energy cannot be created or destroyed (it is conserved) so the energy transferred to the components in a circuit must be equal to the energy transferred from the power supply. In the time that it takes for one coulomb to pass any point in the circuit, the energy transferred by the power supply is numerically equal to its emf $\mathscr{E}$, and the energy transferred in each resistor is equal to the pd, V, across it. So the sum of all the pds across all the components in a series circuit (Figure 4.13(a)) is equal to the emf of the supply:

$$\mathcal{E} = V_1 + V_2 + V_3 \tag{4}$$

Furthermore, when components are connected in parallel (Figure 4.13(b)), each has the same potential difference across it:

$$V_1 = V_2 = V_3 = \mathcal{E} \tag{5}$$

QUESTION

Q 2 A torch battery (chemical cell) has an emf $\mathcal{E}$ of 1.5 V. When it is connected to a bulb, there is a current of 0.5 A in the circuit.

(a) How much charge passed each point in the circuit during a time interval $\Delta t = 2.0$ s?

(b) Use delta notation to write an expression relating the energy ΔW transferred by the cell to a small amount of charge ΔQ.

(c) How much energy does the cell transfer to this amount of charge?

In parts (a) and (c), make sure you show how to manipulate the units as well as the numbers.

(d) Write the units of Equation 3 in terms of SI base units.

> **MATHS REFERENCE**
> Derived units
> See Maths note 2.3

Voltages by design

In designing power supplies for spacecraft, it is not sensible for each to be a one-off. Rather, systems are designed using agreed standards so that items of equipment can be used 'off the shelf' rather than each having to be purpose built. In science and engineering the term 'standard' is used to refer to a particular design specification.

In the early days of space exploration, the spacecraft of the USA and the former Soviet Union (USSR) were very different from each other. However, when it was considered a good idea to be able to dock spacecraft with each other (Figure 4.14), the two countries agreed to have identical docking ports and laid down standards, or specifications, for them.

Large organisations such as NASA (National Aeronautics and Space Administration), the Russian Federal Space Agency (commonly called Roscosmos) and ESA (European Space Agency), which are responsible for the design and construction of spacecraft, lay down standards for equipment design. Spacecraft have a lot of electrical equipment on board and these require specific voltages to operate correctly. To ensure that the required voltages are available, the designers specify a type of circuit, known as a **bus** (Figure 4.15), into which equipment can be connected. It is much like the ring main that connects the main sockets in houses or the wiring harness of a car. In Europe the bus provides voltages of 28 V or 50 V. NASA in the USA has buses supplying voltages in the range 21 V to 35 V.

Figure 4.14 The first international docking of spacecraft, in 1975. The Apollo Soyuz test docking system is shown attached to the final Apollo spacecraft.

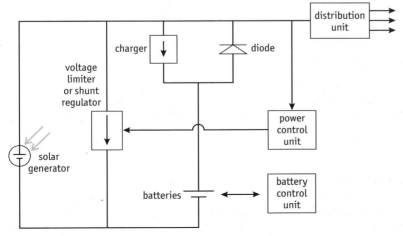

Figure 4.15 A power supply bus

⚙️ **ACTIVITY 5 JOINING SOLAR CELLS**

The bus on an ESA spacecraft needs a voltage far greater than that of a single solar cell. Your task for this activity is to see how solar cells can be joined together to provide high enough voltages. Notice that the circuit symbol for a solar cell (Figure 4.16) is like a dry cell with arrows indicating illumination.

QUESTIONS

Q 3 If a single cell generated a voltage of 0.5 V under specified lighting conditions, what voltage would be produced for each of the circuits shown in Figure 4.16?

Q 4 What is the smallest number of solar cells that would be needed to supply 28 V if a single cell had an output of 0.5 V?

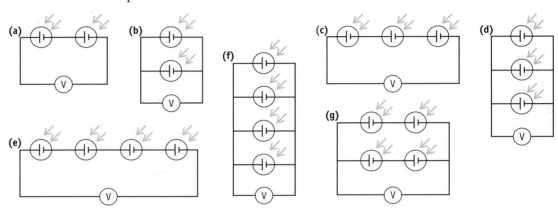

Figure 4.16 Circuits for Question 3

2.2 Cells and circuits

You have seen that instruments on board satellites are designed to use a standard voltage, and you have also seen how to join cells in series and in parallel to produce different voltages. However, there is more to designing a satellite's electrical system than just arranging cells to provide a standard voltage and then connecting up the instruments. The following demonstration illustrates the problem.

⚙️ **ACTIVITY 6 CONNECTING A LOAD TO A POWER SUPPLY**

The voltmeter in Figure 4.17 measures the **terminal potential difference** – the pd between the terminals of the power supply. The purpose of this activity is to show what happens to the voltmeter reading and/or to the brightness of the lamps when first one lamp is connected and then more lamps are added in parallel.

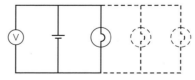

Figure 4.17 Connecting a load to a power supply

Activity 6 raises some important questions that need to be answered in order to design any electrical system:

● Why does the terminal potential difference change when the supply is connected in a circuit?

● How is that change related to the external load?

● What happens when different loads, or combinations of loads, are connected to the supply?

The answers to all these questions relate to electrical resistance, which is discussed in some detail below.

Electrical resistance

The current in an electrical device connected to a power supply (Figure 4.18) depends on the potential difference (voltage) applied between its terminals and on its own internal properties. The more easily charge can flow within it, the lower its **resistance** and the greater the current will be for a given voltage. Resistance is defined by the resistance equation:

resistance (R) = potential difference (V) ÷ current (I) (6)

$$R = \frac{V}{I}$$ (6a)

The SI unit of resistance is the ohm (Ω). $1\,\Omega = 1\,\text{V A}^{-1}$

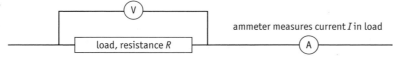

Figure 4.18 Defining resistance

A device (or a material) whose resistance remains constant when measured under constant physical conditions (e.g. constant temperature) over a wide range of voltages is said to obey **Ohm's law** and is often called an **ohmic** device, an ohmic conductor or an ohmic material. Another way to describe ohmic behaviour is to say that potential difference is directly proportional to current under constant physical conditions, i.e. the graph of pd against current is a straight line through the origin (Figure 4.19).

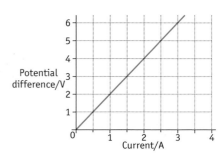

Figure 4.19 A current–voltage graph for an ohmic conductor

QUESTIONS

Q 5 What is the resistance of the conductor in Figure 4.19?

Q 6 Which of the graphs in Figure 4.20 show ohmic behaviour?

Q 7 How can you compare the resistances of two ohmic conductors just by looking at their current–voltage graphs plotted on the same axes (without doing any calculations)?

Q 8 For each of the graphs in Figure 4.20 that does not show ohmic behaviour, describe in words what happens to the resistance as the current increases.

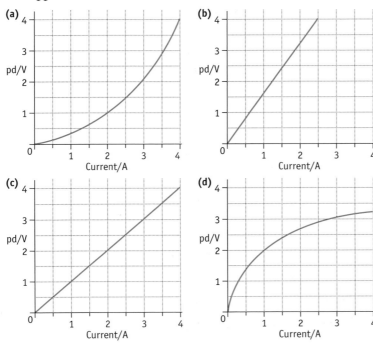

Figure 4.20 Current–voltage graphs for various conductors

STUDY NOTE

For more on using experimental uncertainty and Ohm's Law, see SPC Additional Sheet 3

MATHS REFERENCE

Uncertainties and graphs

See Maths note 7.7

Deciding whether a sample obeys Ohm's law

How can you tell from a set of experimental measurements whether a conductor obeys Ohm's law? The simple way is to plot a graph of voltage and current and see whether you can join the points with a straight line through the origin. Since experimental measurements on an ohmic conductor will rarely lie exactly in a straight line, you need to take account of **experimental uncertainty**: plot **error bars** on the points and use them to draw **error boxes**. If you can draw a straight line through the origin that passes through all the error boxes, then you can say that the conductor obeys Ohm's law *within the limits of experimental uncertainty*.

QUESTION

Q 9 By plotting a graph, decide whether the measurements in Table 4.1 obey Ohm's law within the limits of the experimental uncertainty.

Current (I/A)	Uncertainty $\Delta I = \pm 0.1$ A	Potential difference (V/V)	Uncertainty $\Delta V = \pm 0.1$ V
0.5		0.8	
1.0		1.4	
1.5		1.8	
2.0		2.0	
2.5		2.2	

Table 4.1 Data for Question 9

Combinations of resistors

To answer the questions raised in the points listed below Activity 6, which relate to the designing of a circuit for a particular purpose, we need to think what happens when there is more than one resistor in a circuit. Resistors can essentially be combined in two ways. Figure 4.21 shows some resistors connected in **series** and in **parallel**.

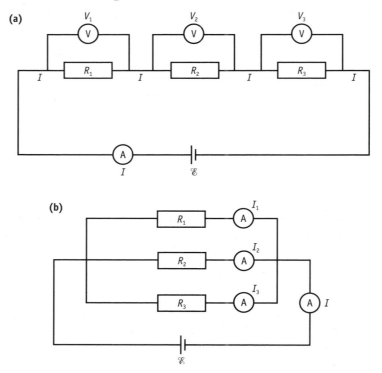

Figure 4.21 Resistors joined (a) in series and (b) in parallel

A single resistor can replace any combination of resistors without changing the currents and potential differences in the rest of the circuit. In a **series** circuit the current is the same throughout the circuit as charge is not created or destroyed (it is conserved). Also, in a series circuit the sum of all the pds across all the resistors is equal to the terminal pd of the supply. This is because energy is transferred via the moving charge from the power supply to the resistors. Energy cannot be created or destroyed (it is conserved) so the energy transferred to the resistors must be equal to the energy transferred from the power supply. Equation 4 can be rewritten as:

$$V = V_1 + V_2 + V_3 \qquad \text{(Equation 4a)}$$

where V is the pd across the power pack. When expressed in terms of current and resistance, Equation 4a becomes:

$$IR = IR_1 + IR_2 + IR_3 \qquad (7)$$

where R is the total resistance of the circuit and R_1, R_2 and R_3 are the individual resistor values. Because current is the same throughout the circuit, the current I is a common factor and will cancel on both sides to give an expression for the total resistance of a series circuit:

$$R = R_1 + R_2 + R_3 \qquad (8)$$

The net resistance of a *series* of resistors is therefore equal to the sum of their separate resistances.

In a **parallel** circuit the potential difference across each branch is the same. Equation 5 can be written as:

$$V_1 = V_2 = V_3 = V \qquad \text{(Equation 5a)}$$

For a parallel circuit, the current flowing through the power supply is equal to the sum of the currents in the individual branches (conservation of charge), as previously presented in Equation 2:

$$I = I_1 + I_2 + I_3 \qquad \text{(Equation 2)}$$

We can use the resistance equation (Equation 6) to obtain an expression for current in terms of the resistance, R, of the whole circuit:

$$I = \frac{V}{R} \qquad (9)$$

Similarly, for the current through the branches of the circuit:

$$I_1 = \frac{V_1}{R_1} = \frac{V}{R_1} \qquad (9a)$$

(and similarly for I_2 and I_3), and so we can rewrite Equation 2 as:

$$\frac{V}{R} = \frac{V}{R_1} + \frac{V}{R_2} + \frac{V}{R_3} \qquad (10)$$

Both sides can then be divided by the common factor V, and so we have a way to replace a set of parallel resistors by a single resistor. Therefore, to find the reciprocal of the net resistance R of several resistors *in parallel*, you need to add their reciprocals:

$$\frac{1}{R} = \frac{1}{R_1} + \frac{1}{R_2} + \frac{1}{R_3} \qquad (11)$$

> **MATHS REFERENCE**
> Reciprocals
> See Maths note 3.3

Then find the reciprocal of the answer to get the net resistance. The net resistance of several resistors in parallel is always less than the smallest individual resistance – use that to check that your answer is reasonable.

⚙ ACTIVITY 7 RESISTORS

Use circuit boards or a circuit simulator such as *Crocodile Physics* to review your knowledge of resistance.

QUESTION

Q 10 Calculate the net resistance of each of the arrangements shown in Figure 4.22. Show your working and include units at each step. (When there is a mixture of series and parallel arrangements, you will need to break down the calculations into stages. Begin by looking for groups of resistors that you can easily replace by a single resistor.)

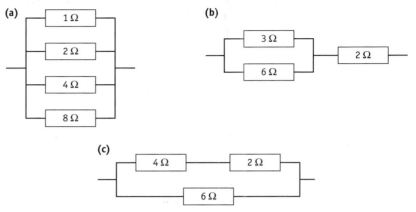

Figure 4.22 Combinations of resistors for Question 10

Internal resistance

The drop in terminal potential difference in Activity 6 can be explained using the idea of **internal resistance**. Any power supply (a photovoltaic cell, a chemical cell, a dynamo) has some electrical resistance due to the materials from which it is made. This resistance cannot be removed from the power supply, but it is normally shown in circuit diagrams as a resistance r in series with the power supply of emf $\mathscr{E}$ (see Figure 4.23). Typically, a dotted line is drawn round $\mathscr{E}$ and r to indicate that they are inseparable.

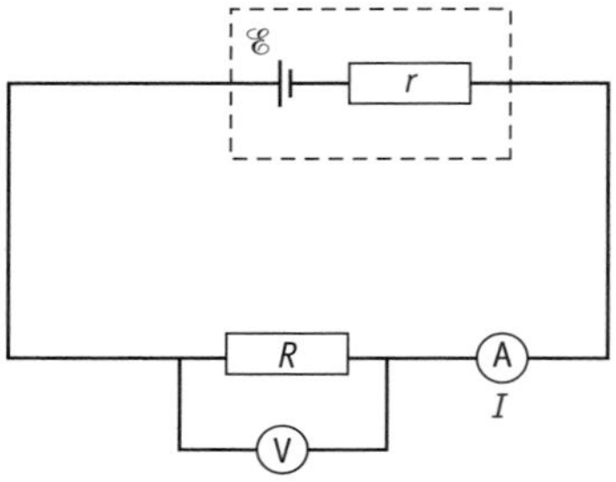

When the power supply is connected to an external load R, there is a current I throughout the circuit – in r as well as in R. Some energy is transferred in the internal resistance of the power supply (it gets warm) as well as in the external load, so the potential difference across the external load (the terminal pd) is less than the full emf of the power supply.

Figure 4.23 Internal resistance

We can apply the resistance equation (Equation 6) to the whole circuit:

$$\mathscr{E} = IR + Ir \tag{12}$$

and to the external load:

$$V = IR \tag{Equation 6}$$

so:

$$V = \mathscr{E} - Ir \tag{12a}$$

The quantity Ir is sometimes called the **lost volts**.

In your GCSE course, you probably treated the terminal pd of a power supply as being fixed. You have now seen that this is not the case. If you are designing a circuit that uses a real power supply rather than an ideal one, you need to take account of the internal resistance.

PRACTICAL SKILLS REFERENCE

Planning and experimental design

See Practical skills notes 2.1–2.2

Carrying out practical work

See Practical skills notes 3.1–3.2

Analysis and interpretation of data

See Practical skills notes 4.1–4.2

Conclusion and evaluation

See Practical skills notes 5.1–5.2

⚙ ACTIVITY 8 HOW DO REAL POWER SUPPLIES BEHAVE?

Explore the behaviour of a power supply that has some internal resistance, using a voltmeter, ammeter and various combinations of resistors.

Predict what will happen to the terminal pd and to the current as the external load is varied, and test your prediction.

Use your measurements of current and terminal pd to deduce values for the power supply's emf and internal resistance.

2.3 Getting the most from your power supply

Space engineers have to design spacecraft power systems that operate as effectively as possible. The following passage discusses what this means.

The output from a power supply depends on what it's connected to, and when we're designing an electrical system for a satellite with limited energy input (from the Sun), we want to make sure it operates as effectively as possible. This raises questions about what we mean by 'output' and 'operate effectively'. I think we can say straight away that simply looking at the current (Figure 4.24) is not a sensible way to measure performance.

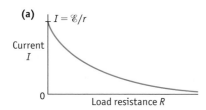 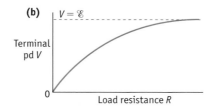

Figure 4.24 (a) Terminal pd and (b) current versus load resistance for a power supply with some internal resistance

*The current is greatest when there is a **short circuit** between the terminals – a connection of low (essentially zero) resistance. The current is certainly large, but all that happens is that the power supply heats up because of its own internal resistance. Not only is that not useful but overheated power supplies have a nasty habit of catching fire or blowing up.*

*The other extreme – going for the greatest possible terminal pd – is equally useless, though less hazardous. The terminal pd is greatest when the supply is on **open circuit** – meaning that there's an extremely large (essentially infinite) resistance between the terminals – in other words, they are not connected via a circuit at all!*

No, to get the best performance out of a power supply, we have to look at maximising the energy transfer to an external circuit, and that involves a trade-off between having a large current on the one hand and a large voltage on the other. It turns out that there is a fairly straightforward way of designing circuits so that they do get the best possible energy transfer from a power supply. You'll come across the terms 'maximum power' and 'impedance matching' in this context – understand those, and you've got it cracked.

Power in electric circuits

Power is the rate at which energy is transferred:

> power P = energy transferred ÷ time taken   (13)

Power has SI units of joules per second ($J\,s^{-1}$) or watts (W); $1\,W = 1\,J\,s^{-1}$. Using ΔW to represent energy transfer, Equation 13 can be written as:

$$P = \frac{\Delta W}{\Delta t} \tag{13a}$$

The symbols ΔE, ΔW, ΔQ are all used to represent an energy transfer and you are likely to see all three if you consult other books. ΔW is sometimes used only for electrical energy and ΔQ for thermal energy – but that is not a hard and fast rule.

In an electrical circuit, power is related to current and to potential difference. The current I is the number of coulombs per second flowing past a point in a circuit, and the potential difference V across a load is the number of joules each coulomb transfers to the load. So the rate of energy transfer in the load, the power P, is given by:

$$P = IV \tag{14}$$

MATHS REFERENCE
Index notation and units
See Maths note 2.2
Algebra and elimination
See Maths note 3.4

WORKED EXAMPLE

If $I = 2\,A\,(= 2\,C\,s^{-1})$ and $V = 3\,V\,(= 3\,J\,C^{-1})$, in each second 2 coulombs flow into the load and each coulomb transfers 3 joules to the load. So, in each second, 6 joules are transferred:

$P = 2\,C\,s^{-1} \times 3\,J\,C^{-1} = 6\,J\,s^{-1} = 6\,W$

Equation 13a and 14 can be combined to give the energy transferred, ΔW, to the load in a given time Δt as:

$$\Delta W = V I \Delta t$$

$$\Delta W \not= \frac{V}{\Delta t} \tag{15}$$

If the load has resistance R, we can use the resistance equation (Equation 6) to eliminate either V or I:

$$P = I^2 R \tag{16}$$

or

$$P = \frac{V^2}{R} \tag{17}$$

QUESTIONS

Q 11 A domestic kettle is marked 230 V, 2000 W. When connected to a 230-volt supply, what is the current in the element?

Q 12 What is the resistance of a light bulb designed to have a power of 60 W when connected to the 230 V mains supply?

Q 13 If a toaster is on for 2.5 minutes and has a current of 0.2 A through the element when connected to a 230 V supply, how much electrical energy is transferred by the toaster?

⚙ ACTIVITY 9 MAXIMISING THE POWER

How can we get maximum power transfer to the external load in a circuit? This activity shows several ways to tackle this question.

Patterns

Calculate the power transferred to various loads by a given power supply, and look for patterns. Try using 'ideal' values that have been made up to give round numbers, and try your own experimental measurements from Activity 8. This may be done on a spreadsheet, as shown in Figure 4.25, or you could use a calculator (which would take much longer).

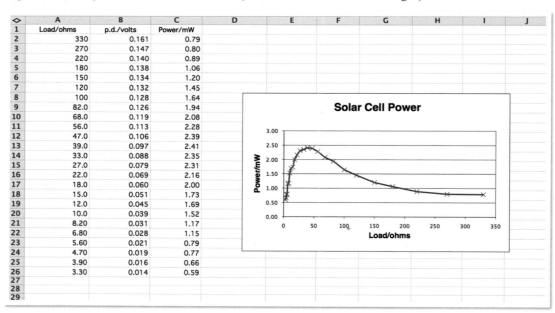

	A	B	C
1	Load/ohms	p.d./volts	Power/mW
2	330	0.161	0.79
3	270	0.147	0.80
4	220	0.140	0.89
5	180	0.138	1.06
6	150	0.134	1.20
7	120	0.132	1.45
8	100	0.128	1.64
9	82.0	0.126	1.94
10	68.0	0.119	2.08
11	56.0	0.113	2.28
12	47.0	0.106	2.39
13	39.0	0.097	2.41
14	33.0	0.088	2.35
15	27.0	0.079	2.31
16	22.0	0.069	2.16
17	18.0	0.060	2.00
18	15.0	0.051	1.73
19	12.0	0.045	1.69
20	10.0	0.039	1.52
21	8.20	0.031	1.17
22	6.80	0.028	1.15
23	5.60	0.021	0.79
24	4.70	0.019	0.77
25	3.90	0.016	0.66
26	3.30	0.014	0.59
27			
28			
29			

Figure 4.25 Using a spreadsheet to calculate power

Algebra

Starting from $\mathscr{E} = IR + Ir$ and $P = VI$, derive an expression for the power in the load resistance R. Eliminate V and I, and end up with an expression that involves only P, $\mathscr{E}$, R and r.

The condition for P to have a maximum value depends on the relationship between the external load R and the internal resistance r. To make this relationship clearer, write $R = fr$ and cancel as many common factors as you can. You should get an expression that involves just P, $\mathscr{E}$, r and f:

$$P = \frac{\mathscr{E}^2 f}{(1 + f)^2 r} \tag{18}$$

For a particular power supply, $\mathscr{E}$ and r remain fixed. Try calculating $f/(1 + f)^2$ for various values of f (0, 0.5, 1, 1.5, 2, …) and see if you can deduce the value of f that gives the greatest value of P. Compare your result with what you found using the spreadsheet.

STUDY NOTE

If you are familiar with calculus, you can derive an expression for maximum power using differentiation. See SPC Additional Sheet 4.

Impedance matching

The introduction to this section mentioned the term **impedance matching**. Impedance is a more general term than resistance that relates current to potential difference – there are some types of electrical device where the relationship between current and pd is more complicated than that described by the resistance equation, particularly when they are connected to an alternating, rather than a direct, supply. However, when dealing with a steady current and pd, impedance can be treated as meaning the same thing as resistance.

Impedance of solar cells

We have been treating the internal resistance (or impedance) of solar cells as though it had a fixed value for any given cell. In fact, the impedance of a solar cell can vary according to conditions, and this needs to be taken into account when designing a power system for a satellite.

✪ ACTIVITY 10 CURRENTS AND VOLTAGES IN SATELLITES

Have a look at some satellite data (e.g. from FUNcube) and see how the battery current and voltage change with time. Think how you might explain any variations in these measurements.

FURTHER INVESTIGATION

When you used solar cells, you ensured (we hope!) that the level of illumination remained the same all the time. If you have an opportunity to carry out more detailed investigative work, you might like to explore what happens to the power output and/or internal resistance of a solar cell as the level of illumination changes. You could try using different light sources, or tilting a cell so that it intercepts different amounts of incoming radiation.

Level of illumination is one factor that could affect the internal resistance of a solar cell. You might be able to suggest other factors and explore them experimentally.

Maximum power – maximum efficiency?

In our work we always try to be efficient, and by that we mean that we make good use of our time and efforts. We also know instinctively what is meant when someone says something is 100% efficient – we know that it cannot be improved. But what does efficiency mean in the context of power supplies?

The **efficiency** of any device or system that transfers energy (such as an electric circuit) has a precisely defined meaning:

$$\text{efficiency} = \frac{\text{energy usefully transferred}}{\text{total energy transferred}} \tag{19}$$

or:

$$\text{efficiency} = \frac{\text{power usefully transferred}}{\text{total power transferred}} \tag{20}$$

MATHS REFERENCE

Fractions and percentages
See Maths note 3.1

Efficiency is often expressed as a percentage. For example, if a system is 20% efficient, then 20% (one-fifth) of the energy supplied by the power source is transferred, usefully in the external load, while the remaining 80% is wasted in heating the power supply and the surroundings.

⚙ ACTIVITY 11 MAXIMUM POWER – MAXIMUM EFFICIENCY?

In an electrical system, is the condition for maximum efficiency the same as that for maximum power? Spend a few minutes discussing the meaning of these two terms, making sure you can distinguish between them. Then try to decide whether the conditions are the same for both. Think what happens to the power output and the efficiency when the load resistance is much greater than the internal resistance, or much smaller, and when the two are equal. You might find it helpful to invent some numerical examples to illustrate what happens.

Designing an electrical system

In Activity 11, you should have convinced yourself that efficiency is greatest when the external load is made as large as possible, which is not the same as the condition for maximum power output. When designing an electrical system, should you go for maximum power or for maximum efficiency? If you want to get as much as possible from a small source of power, you aim for maximum power transfer and match the external load to the internal resistance. This is what is generally done in power systems for spacecraft. A circuit where an amplifier delivers power to a loudspeaker is another example where matched impedances are used to achieve maximum output power (speakers are generally labelled with their impedance). However, if the powers involved are large, it is better to aim for a higher efficiency and to reduce the amount of energy wasted due to the internal resistance of the supply. For example, electric vehicles are designed so that the internal resistance of the power supply is as small as possible and the external load resistance is much larger in comparison.

QUESTION

Q 14 Calculate the output power and the efficiency of the circuit in Figure 4.26. Explain why this arrangement would not be a sensible way to use the power supply.

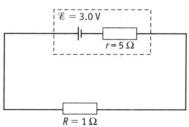

Figure 4.26 Circuit for Question 14

2.4 Summing up Part 2

So far in this chapter, you have reviewed and extended your knowledge of DC electric circuits, learned how cells and resistors can be combined, and learned about the conditions under which a power supply transfers maximum power to a load.

Activity 12 is designed to help you review your progress, and Questions 15 and 16 and Activity 13 are designed for you to reinforce and put into practice what you have been learning.

⚙ ACTIVITY 12 SUMMING UP PART 2

Spend a few minutes checking through your notes – use the following exercises to help you do this.

Skim through Part 2 of this chapter and make sure that your notes include a clear definition or explanation of each of the terms printed in bold type.

Write a short paragraph, illustrated by a circuit diagram, to explain what is meant by impedance matching and why it is important in designing a power system for a satellite. Include *at least five* of the terms that are printed in bold type in Part 2.

QUESTIONS

Q 15 A single 2.0 V cell in a lead-acid battery has an internal resistance, dependent on its state of charge and temperature, of around 0.005 Ω.

(a) If a battery is made up of six cells in series, what is:
   (i) its total internal resistance?
   (ii) its emf?

(b) This battery is then connected to a load resistance of 2.97 Ω. What is:
   (i)   the total resistance of the circuit?
   (ii) the current in the circuit?
   (iii) the terminal potential difference?

(c) A car battery is made up of lead-acid cells, and on starting up a car there may be a current of 200 A. If a car's headlamps are on while a car is being started, they are usually seen to dim appreciably. Explain why.

Q 16 Figure 4.27 shows various arrangements of identical cells.

(a) From (i)–(iv), what can you infer about the way internal resistances combine? (Do they combine like ordinary resistances?)

(b) What load resistance would you use to obtain maximum power transfer from the arrangement of cells in (v)?

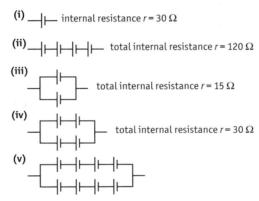

(i) — internal resistance $r = 30\,\Omega$

(ii) — total internal resistance $r = 120\,\Omega$

(iii) — total internal resistance $r = 15\,\Omega$

(iv) — total internal resistance $r = 30\,\Omega$

(v)

Figure 4.27 Combinations of cells for Question 16

⚙ ACTIVITY 13 DESIGN CHALLENGE

This challenge is concerned with designing a solar power supply in order to achieve maximum power transfer to a given load. (It is not intended as a practical activity.)

A single solar cell, under certain conditions, has an emf of 0.45 V and a maximum power output of 0.1 W. An array of identical solar cells, under the same conditions, is required to supply 0.4 W to an external load of 0.506 Ω. If the cells are required each to supply the maximum possible power, how many cells are needed, and how must they be connected? (Hint: start by finding the internal resistance of a single cell, and assume that the internal resistances of these solar cells combine just like ordinary resistances.) Without doing any further calculations, say how many cells would be needed to supply 0.9 W to the same load, and how they must be connected.

3 Solar cells

3.1 Solar cells in space

In the early days of space travel, satellites and spaceships used batteries or fuel cells. However, these had limited lifetimes and reliability. The two-man Gemini spacecraft in 1966 (Figure 4.28) was the first NASA ship powered by fuel cells. However, the accident that crippled Apollo 13 in 1970 was caused by a faulty connection in the service module's fuel cell system (Figure 4.29).

Figure 4.28 Gemini VI and VII rendezvous in orbit

Figure 4.29 The fuel cell system is hidden beneath the exposed section of the interior in this shot of Apollo 15 in lunar orbit in 1971 (photograph courtesy of NASA)

Space scientists and engineers then turned to solar cells to generate their electricity. The Soyuz spacecraft were the first to use solar cells and have been in operation since 1967. Although there were a number of early setbacks, the design has proved robust and reliable, and Soyuz still ferry cosmonauts into orbit. Figure 4.30 shows a modern-day version.

Figure 4.30 A Soyuz spacecraft docking with the ISS in 2005 (photograph courtesy of NASA)

With early solar cell systems, there was still a chance of damage on lift-off. Although the incident sunlight can provide a lot of energy for the spaceship, if the solar panels do not deploy properly then problems can follow. Figure 4.31 shows the space station Skylab in 1973. Note how only one panel is deployed. Astronauts had to spend many hours trying to free the jammed panel in exhausting spacewalks. Note, as well, the improvised heat shield on top of the main module.

Now solar cells are generated on thin metal sheets that can be rolled up for transport into orbit. NASA had to deliver huge trusses of solar arrays to the International Space Station (ISS), which had to be completed before the retirement of the Space Shuttle in 2010. Each mission delivered and installed a 17.5 tonne truss segment to enhance the electrical system of the orbital station. The International Space Station (ISS) requires huge solar panels just to provide enough electricity for its three crew members. The computer-generated picture in Figure 4.32 shows an Orion craft, outward bound for the Moon, approaching the completed ISS. Note how similar the Orion is to the Apollo craft in Figure 4.29.

Figure 4.31 Solar panels on Skylab

When unfurled, the 80-metre arrays provide power for the station (see Figure 4.33). Each of the 82 active array blankets that are grouped into 31 'bays' contains 16 400 silicon photovoltaic cells to generate electricity from sunlight. The truss also contains a rotary joint that rotates through 360°, positioning the arrays to track the Sun.

NASA and its contractor Lockheed-Martin developed a method of mounting the solar arrays on a blanket that can be folded like an accordion. The cells are made from purified crystal ingots of silicon that directly absorbs light to provide electricity for immediate use. These also charge up batteries to provide electricity in emergency.

The complete power system, consisting of US and Russian hardware, generates about 110 kW of total power. Each unit is capable of generating nearly 30 kilowatts (kW) of direct current power. There are two units on each wing module, which together provide power that would meet the electrical needs of about 30 small houses consuming about 2 kW of power each. This does not come cheap – each array wing costs $370 million (about £200 million).

Figure 4.32 Approaching the completed ISS (photograph courtesy of NASA)

Figure 4.33 The International Space Station (ISS) deploying a solar cell truss in 2007 (photograph courtesy of NASA)

A NASA official said, 'Electrical power is the most critical resource for the station because it allows astronauts to live comfortably, safely operate the station, and perform complex scientific experiments. Since the only readily available source of energy for spacecraft is sunlight, technologies were developed to efficiently convert solar energy to electrical power.'

3.2 Explaining solar cells

In order to produce efficient designs for solar panels, scientists and engineers have worked on developing new materials. This requires an understanding of how solar panels use light from the Sun to release electrons within the material, which involves a process known as the **photoelectric effect**. When the photoelectric effect was first discovered in the 19th century, it required a new way of thinking about light to explain what was going on.

The photoelectric effect can be demonstrated by shining light onto a clean metal surface. Under certain conditions, electrons are given off. The electrons released in this way are called **photoelectrons**, and materials that readily release photoelectrons are said to be **photosensitive**.

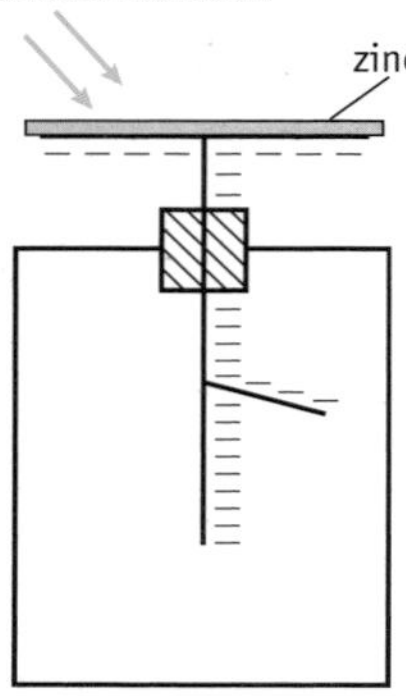

ultraviolet radiation

zinc plate

Figure 4.34 A negatively charged electroscope

ACTIVITY 14 PHOTOELECTRIC EFFECT

Observe the photoelectric effect produced by ultraviolet radiation with zinc or magnesium. One way to do this is to use a zinc plate and a gold leaf electroscope or an electrometer (devices that detect the presence of electric charge – see Figure 4.34). Give the electroscope or electrometer a negative charge. Shine ultraviolet radiation on to the (very clean) zinc and explain what happens to the charge indicated by the electrometer or electroscope. (Think what will happen if electrons can escape from the metal.)

Explaining the photoelectric effect

Experiments show that:

- For any given metal, with radiation below a certain **threshold frequency**, no electrons are released even if the radiation is very intense.

- Provided the frequency is above the threshold, some electrons are released instantaneously, even if the radiation is very weak.

- The more intense the radiation, the more electrons are released.

- The kinetic energy of the individual photoelectrons depends only on the frequency of the radiation and not on its intensity.

These results can only be explained using the photon model of light (see Figure 4.35); a wave model does not predict the observations correctly. In particular, the wave model predicts that weak radiation would eventually allow a large number of electrons to be released, all with low energy, rather than the immediate release of a small number of electrons each with high kinetic energy (see Figure 4.36). The photoelectric effect gave one of the first indications, early in the 20th century, that the wave model of light is not always satisfactory. For explaining the photoelectric effect using a photon model, Albert Einstein was awarded the Nobel Prize in 1905.

STUDY NOTE

See The Sound of Music for an introduction to photons.

We have labelled the photon energy E_{ph} here to distinguish it from other energies also denoted by the letter E.

The release of photoelectrons is initiated by the impact of photons on the target. The energy, E_{ph}, of each photon is related to the wave frequency, f, by:

$$E_{ph} = hf \qquad (21)$$

An electron close to the surface of the target material absorbs the photon. In order to escape, the electron needs to do work against the electrical forces that bind it into the metal. The minimum amount of energy needed for this is called the **work function**, ϕ, of the material. In doing work the electron increases its potential energy by an amount ϕ. Any energy remaining is accounted for as the kinetic energy, E_k, of the escaped electron. Conservation of energy enables us to write the following expression:

$$E_{ph} = E_k + \phi \qquad (22)$$

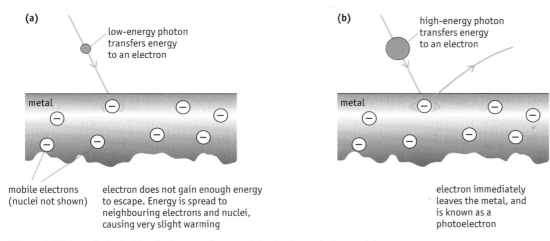

Figure 4.35 The photoelectric effect can easily be explained using a photon model …

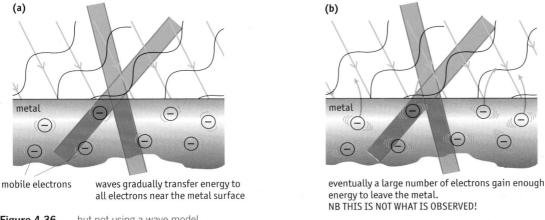

Figure 4.36 … but not using a wave model

Equation 22 describes the following features of the photoelectric effect:

● If $E_{ph} < \phi$ then an electron is unable to do sufficient work and so cannot escape.
● If $E_{ph} = \phi$ then an electron may be released, but with no kinetic energy (i.e. it is free, but cannot move away).
● If $E_{ph} > \phi$ then an electron can escape with kinetic energy up to a maximum of $E_{ph} - \phi$.

The smaller the work function, ϕ, of a material, the more photosensitive the material, i.e. the lower the photon energy needed to release photoelectrons – or, put another way, the lower the threshold frequency. If the threshold frequency is f_0, then:

$$\phi = hf_0 \tag{23}$$

Equations 22 and 23 can be use to derive further equations describing the same situation, for example:

$$hf = E_k + hf_0 \tag{24}$$

or:

$$hf = \frac{1}{2}mv^2_{max} + \phi \tag{25}$$

where, as you saw in *Higher, Faster, Stronger*:

$$E_k = \frac{1}{2}mv^2 \tag{26}$$

This is the kinetic energy of a particle mass m moving at speed v. The label 'max' is a reminder that this is the maximum kinetic energy that an electron can acquire; if it has to do more work than ϕ, then its kinetic energy will be less.

Measuring threshold frequency

A photocell needs to be made from a photosensitive material; if it is to respond to visible radiation, its threshold frequency needs to be lower than that of zinc or magnesium. As you saw in Activity 14, these metals only release photoelectrons when illuminated with ultraviolet radiation. In principle, the threshold frequency can be determined in a single measurement: shine light of a known frequency on to a material, measure the maximum kinetic energy of the photoelectrons, and then use Equation 24 to find f_0.

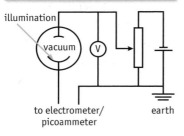

Figure 4.37 Apparatus for determining the threshold frequency of a photosensitive material

Figure 4.37 shows how, in principle, we can measure the electrons' kinetic energy using a photocell and an opposing potential difference that is adjustable using a circuit called a **potential divider**. If photoelectrons are able to move across the gap in the photocell then there will be a continuous flow of charge around the circuit and the electrometer's picoammeter will register a current; this will happen if the applied potential difference, V, is zero. However, if the photoelectrons have to travel towards the negative terminal of the power supply then they lose kinetic energy. Also, the higher the potential difference, the greater the initial kinetic energy the electrons will need to have if they are to reach the other side. If no electrons cross the gap, then the ammeter will read zero.

As you have seen in Part 2 of this the chapter, when charge moves through a potential difference, energy is transferred as described by the relationship:

$$\Delta W = q\Delta V$$

or:

$$\Delta E = q\Delta V \tag{Equation 3}$$

where ΔW or ΔE is the energy transferred, q is the charge and ΔV is the potential difference.

If an electron moved in the opposite direction across the gap, from negative to positive, then the power supply would be transferring energy to the electron; an electron starting from rest would gain kinetic energy:

$$E_k = e\Delta V \tag{27}$$

where e is the electron's charge. Travelling in the opposite direction, an electron would lose this amount of kinetic energy. So, if the applied pd is adjusted so that it just stops the photoelectrons (i.e. so that the meter reading just becomes zero) then Equation 3 can be used to calculate the electron's initial kinetic energy. The potential difference that just stops the photoelectrons crossing the gap is called, unsurprisingly, the **stopping potential**.

Combining Equations 26 and 27, with V now representing the stopping potential, gives:

$$hf = eV + hf_0 \tag{28}$$

Rather than making just one single measurement to determine f_0, it is much better to use several different values of f and record the corresponding stopping potential V. There is a linear relationship between f and V, and a graph of f plotted against V, or V against f, can then be used to determine f_0.

Units: the electronvolt

When we are dealing with individual electrons moving through a potential difference of a few volts, the energies involved are extremely small because the magnitude of the electron charge is only 1.60×10^{-19} C. For example, if an electron moves through a pd of 1 V, the energy transferred is only 1.60×10^{-19} J (see Equation 27). Rather than express such tiny energies in joules, we sometimes use an alternative unit, the **electronvolt** (eV), which is defined as the energy transferred when one electron moves through a pd of 1 V. So, when an electron or a proton is accelerated through a potential difference of V, then the energy transferred is numerically the same as the pd measured in volts.

$$1\,\text{eV} = 1.60 \times 10^{-19}\,\text{J}$$

3.3 Summing up Part 3

In this part of the chapter you have studied an important piece of physics that involves both electricity and light. You have seen that a photon model is needed to explain the photoelectric effect, and you have learnt how the kinetic energy of electrons can be measured using an electrical technique. You have also seen how ideas about charge, potential difference and energy lead to the definition of a convenient unit for expressing very small energies: the electronvolt.

QUESTIONS

magnitude of electron charge, $e = 1.60 \times 10^{-19}\,C$

electron mass, $m_e = 9.11 \times 10^{-31}\,kg$

proton mass, $m_p = 1.67 \times 10^{-27}\,kg$

Planck constant, $h = 6.63 \times 10^{-34}\,Js$

speed of light, $c = 3.00 \times 10^{8}\,m\,s^{-1}$

Q 17 What is the energy transferred when **(a)** an electron and **(b)** a proton is accelerated through a pd of 5000 V? Give your answers in joules and in eV.

Q 18 Calculate the speeds of the electron and proton in Question 17, assuming that the transfer of energy from power supply to the particles is 100% efficient.

Q 19 Light with a wavelength 434 nm shines onto the surface of clean sodium, which has a work function of 2.28 eV. What is the maximum kinetic energy of the photoelectrons? Give your answer in eV and in joules.

Q 20 Explain what would happen if:

(a) the blue light in Question 19 shines on aluminium, whose work function is 4.08 eV?

(b) ultraviolet light shines on sodium?

FURTHER INVESTIGATION

Using light that passes through coloured filters, investigate the frequency response of some photosensitive devices (e.g. photographers' light meters, or light-dependent resistors). Try to determine the lowest frequency (longest wavelength) radiation to which they respond.

4 All under control

So far in this chapter you have dealt mainly with aspects of electrical power system. If you look back at what Jeremy Curtis said in Part 1, you will see that solar radiation is a bit of a mixed blessing for spacecraft: it supplies much-needed energy, but it also gives the engineer more problems to deal with. In this part of the chapter you will consider how heating of electrical components has important implications for designing and operating a spacecraft.

4.1 Facing the right direction

In the summer of 1997, the Russian space station Mir faced a series of problems that began when a docking manoeuvre with a supply module went wrong (rather than docking smoothly, the two vehicles crashed together, damaging part of the outer structure of the space station). While working on repairs, one of the crew accidentally pulled out a cable from the station's main computer. In the words of *New Scientist* magazine (27 July 1997): 'The error left the station almost totally without power and spinning out of control for more than 24 hours.'

Why should disconnecting a *computer cable* leave the station without power? The clue comes in the phrase 'spinning out of control'. The computer controls motors that orient the space station and its solar panels. Unless they are correctly aligned with the Sun, the solar panels do not function effectively.

Figure 4.38 The surface of the comet with one of Philae's feet in the foreground

In November 2014, the European *Rosetta* space mission landed a robotic probe (Philae) on comet 67P Churyumov-Gerasimenko (Figure 4.38). As Philae landed in partial shadow rather than the intended site, the mission controllers had to modify their intended programme of data collection, and used some of the remaining power to nudge the probe so that its solar panels collected more radiation. After sending back about 80% of the planned data, Philae switched to 'hibernation' mode. As comet 67P approaches the Sun, the hope is that the more intense radiation will recharge Philae's batteries so that it can collect and send back more data.

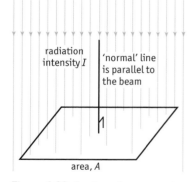

Figure 4.39 A solar cell square-on to a beam of radiation

Power input and radiant energy flux

Figure 4.39 shows a solar cell and a beam of radiation. The 'strength' of the beam is usually described in terms of the rate at which it transfers energy across unit area square-on to the beam. This quantity is called the **intensity**, I, (or radiant energy flux, F) of the beam. (We will use I but you may find F in other books.) The SI units of I (or F) are watts per square metre ($\mathrm{W\,m^{-2}}$). The rate at which energy is transferred to a surface therefore depends on the flux and the area, A, of the surface:

$$P_{\mathrm{in}} = IA \tag{29}$$

If a beam has $I = 10\,\mathrm{W\,m^{-2}}$ and shines square-on to a surface of area $A = 2\,\mathrm{m^2}$ (as in Figure 4.39), then (provided all the incident radiation is absorbed by the surface):

$$P_{in} = 10\,\mathrm{W\,m^{-2}} \times 2\,\mathrm{m^2} = 20\,\mathrm{W}$$

How large a solar array does a spacecraft need?

The size of solar array depends on the spacecraft's power demands. As you can see from Figure 4.40, the average power requirements of various spacecraft have risen appreciably since the 1960s. However, even when the power requirements are known, it is still necessary to have information about how efficiently the solar cells transfer energy. We can adapt Equations 19 and 20 to get:

$$\text{efficiency} = \frac{\text{useful energy output}}{\text{total energy input}} \qquad \text{(Equation 19a)}$$

and:

$$\text{efficiency} = \frac{\text{power usefully transferred}}{\text{power input}} = \frac{P_{out}}{P_{in}} \qquad \text{(Equation 20a)}$$

Here, the input refers to the incoming solar radiation flux and the energy that is transferred by the cell.

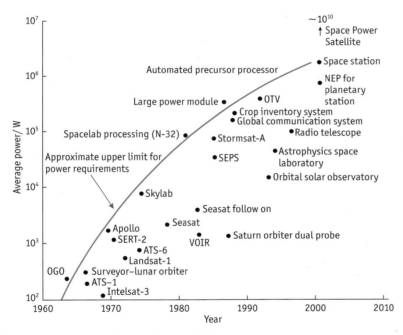

Figure 4.40 Power demands of spacecraft since the early 1960s

The solar arrays on the Hubble Space Telescope have an area $A \approx 20\,\mathrm{m^2}$ and are about 10% efficient, and the solar intensity is $I \approx 1.4\,\mathrm{kW\,m^{-2}}$. To find the maximum possible output power:

$$P_{in} = IA$$
$$\approx 20\,\mathrm{m^2} \times 1.4\,\mathrm{kW\,m^{-2}}$$
$$= 28\,\mathrm{kW}.$$

P_{out} is 10% of P_{in} so:

$$P_{out} = 0.10 \times 28\,\mathrm{kW}$$
$$= 2.8\,\mathrm{kW}$$

QUESTIONS

Q 21 Write a short paragraph, with at least one diagram, to explain why a breakdown in the computer guidance system of the Mir space station resulted in a loss of electrical power.

Q 22 The International Space Station (Figures 4.32, 4.33) has solar arrays that must each produce a peak output power of 16 kW from solar radiation whose intensity is $1.4\,\text{kW}\,\text{m}^{-2}$. If the efficiency of an array is 11%, what must its area be?

The importance of understanding radiation flux is not limited to solar panels on spacecraft. Question 23 uses the same ideas in another situation.

QUESTION

Q 23 In Germany, car manufacturing has incorporated arrays of photovoltaic cells into one of its factories (Figure 4.41). The total area of the arrays is 5000 m² (about that of a soccer pitch). The company states that the peak power output from these arrays is 435 kW. If the peak solar intensity at this location is $600\,\text{W}\,\text{m}^{-2}$, calculate the efficiency of these solar arrays.

Figure 4.41 Solar arrays on a car manufacturing factory

4.2 Temperature changes in spacecraft

So far in this chapter we have been concerned with designing an electrical power supply system for a spacecraft. Temperature control is another important aspect of designing a spacecraft. All spacecraft, no matter what their task or position, have heating and cooling systems on board.

> **⚙ ACTIVITY 19 GETTING WARMER**
>
> Spend a few minutes 'brainstorming' the following questions. Jot down a list of your ideas.
> - Why might the temperature on board a spacecraft vary markedly if it was uncontrolled?
> - What problems might be caused by large changes in temperature on board a spacecraft?
>
> Think about space probes that are designed to study the Sun continuously, such as the Solar Heliospheric Observatory (SOHO), or to explore the outermost regions of the solar system, such as the *Voyager* and *Pioneer* probes. Think about manned space stations and moon landers, and about unmanned satellites of all types orbiting the Earth.

Many spacecraft spin about their own axes and so part, at least, keeps going into and out of the sunlight. Others orbit the Earth and so travel in sunlight on the day side and in the dark (cold) on the night side. While space can be as cold as 3 K (−270 °C), a spacecraft can quickly heat up when facing the Sun or through heating due to its own electrical equipment.

Uncontrolled heating and cooling can cause problems. Mechanical parts can suffer from expansion and contraction, as did the Hubble Space Telescope's first solar arrays, which flexed as they moved in and out of the Earth's shadow, and if electrical components get too hot or too cold then they perform less well. For example, chemical batteries and solar cells tend to function better when they are cool. Table 4.2 shows typical temperature ranges within which various components can operate reasonably well.

Equipment	Temperature range/°C
Electrical equipment	−10 to +40
Chemical batteries	−5 to +15
Fuel (hydrazine)	+9 to +40
Microprocessors	−5 to +40
Mechanical parts	−45 to +65
Solar cells	−60 to +55
Solid state diodes	−60 to +95

Table 4.2 Typical operating temperatures for equipment used in spacecraft

> **⚙ ACTIVITY 20 SOLAR ARRAY TEMPERATURE**
>
> Have a look at some satellite data (e.g. from FUNcube) and see how the temperature of the solar arrays changes with time. Comment on whether the temperatures lie within the ranges given in Table 4.2.

Electrical components in space

Solar radiation is the main source of heating for satellites, but for the Space Shuttle and space probes that enter the atmosphere of the Earth or another planet (or moon), surface heating due to interaction with the surrounding atmospheric gases is also important. The Space Shuttle, for example, is covered with specially designed heat-resistant tiles. In 2005, the Huygens probe (Figure 4.42), carried by the multinational Cassini mission to Saturn, was released into the atmosphere of Titan, Saturn's largest moon. A heat shield protected its instruments from the high temperatures generated as it plunged to the moon's surface, and the probe was the first to land anywhere in the outer solar system. The data that Huygens relayed back to Earth vastly increased our knowledge of Titan's atmosphere and surface.

As you can see from Table 4.2, batteries and solar cells are particularly sensitive to temperature. Questions 24 and 25 illustrate the problem in more detail and indicate the importance of careful choice of materials.

Figure 4.42 The Huygens probe

QUESTIONS

Q 24 Figure 4.43 shows how one type of battery performed with temperature. 'Available capacity' is a measure of the energy that could be transferred from the battery, expressed as a percentage of the maximum transferable energy.

(a) What was the available capacity available at a temperature of:
    (i) 50 °C
    (ii) −20 °C?

(b) By how much does the battery's capacity fall in going from 30 °C to 40 °C?

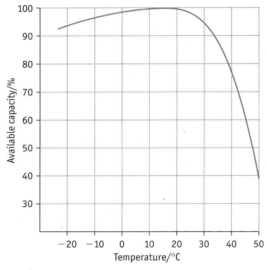

Figure 4.43 The performance of a VARTA RS nickel–cadmium battery

Q 25 Figure 4.44 shows how the efficiency of solar cells made of different materials depends on temperature.

(a) Which material has the highest efficiency at each of the following temperatures?
    (i) 0 °C   **(ii)** 200 °C   **(iii)** 400 °C

(b) Which material(s) would it not be sensible to use for solar cells if their temperatures were likely to rise above 300 °C?

(c) How does the efficiency of a cadmium sulfide (CdS) cell vary when the temperature changes from 0 to 400 °C?

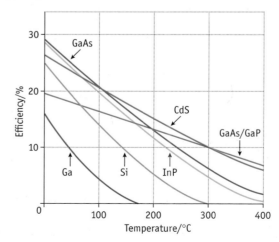

Figure 4.44 The effect of temperature on the efficiency of solar cells of various materials

Q 26 Some proposed space stations of the near future are likely to need 1 MW of power ($1\,MW = 1 \times 10^6\,W$). Suppose such a space station is to have solar arrays made from gallium arsenide (GaAs) and its operating temperature is to be kept below 50 °C. If the incident solar intensity is $1.4\,kW\,m^{-2}$, what is the smallest area that its solar arrays must have?

Resistance and temperature

Not only does temperature affect the performance of solar arrays and batteries, but the resistance of many components also varies noticeably with temperature, as you will see in the following activity.

You will need to use your tables of results and calculations again later, in Activity 22.

 ACTIVITY 21   CHANGING RESISTANCE
You task is to obtain a set of readings for one component, showing how its resistance changes over the range 0 °C to 100 °C, and to write a short report of your findings to exchange with other students who have used a different component. See Figure 4.45.

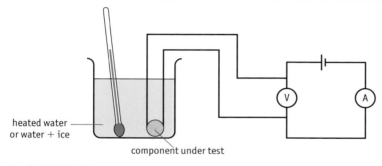

heated water or water + ice

component under test

Figure 4.45 Apparatus for Activity 21

PRACTICAL SKILLS REFERENCE

Planning and experimental design

See Practical skills notes 2.1–2.2

Carrying out practical work

See Practical skills notes 3.1–3.2

Analysis and interpretation of data

See Practical skills notes 4.1–4.2

Modelling current and resistance

The materials used nowadays to make electronic components have been developed to have particular electrical properties. In order to develop 'designer' materials, it is important to describe how particular materials behave and also to understand why. The change in resistance with temperature is one such aspect of material behaviour that can be explored with the help of scientific modelling.

Scientific modelling

The variation of resistance with temperature raises two questions: *Is there a simple relationship between resistance and temperature?* And: *Why does resistance change with temperature?* The second question is of interest when we are trying to understand the behaviour of the natural world and perhaps develop new materials whose resistances change in particular ways. The first question is of particular interest to anyone wanting to know how an electrical system is going to behave. Both these questions involve the important scientific idea of **modelling**.

One of the main goals of science is to describe and understand the natural world – partly for the satisfaction of knowing for its own sake, and partly in order to make use of that knowledge through technology. Exploring the natural world in this way involves the use of **scientific models**. A scientific model is a way of thinking about and visualising objects or processes, often involving a mathematical description. A model in this sense does *not* normally mean a small- or large-scale replica.

Models that represent attempts to understand the world at a fundamental level often need to be adapted and refined depending on what we are using them for and as our knowledge of the world develops. For example, if you picture atoms and molecules as small spheres as in Figure 4.46, you are using a model that can explain some large-scale behaviour of materials (differences between solids, liquids and gases, for example). However, it does not explain electric currents nor does it explain how atoms combine chemically (a model of an atom consisting of a small nucleus

Graphite

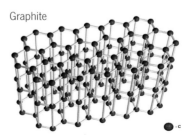

Figure 4.46 A simple model explains some of the properties of matter

surrounded by orbiting electrons would be more helpful for this). In turn, the nucleus-plus-electrons model has to be refined in order to explain radioactive decay. During this course, you will meet several examples of scientific models being developed and refined.

Other models are empirical – that is, they are based on observation and experiment rather than on any fundamental thinking about the underlying processes. Ohm's law ($V \propto I$) is an **empirical model** that describes mathematically the way that some materials behave. Sometimes empirical relationships give clues to something deeper. For example, Isaac Newton observed that all falling objects have the same gravitational acceleration, which led him to an understanding of gravitational force without which we would not be able to launch satellites into orbit.

Even where they do not directly reveal fundamental insights into the laws of nature, empirical models are extremely useful to scientists and engineers. Ohm's law is just one example of such an empirical relationship. The relationship between resistance and temperature is another.

Model making and model fitting

In principle, making an empirical mathematical model is straightforward. It simply involves collecting some experimental measurements and looking for a mathematical way to describe them – ideally, a fairly simple relationship between two measured quantities. In practice, this can turn out to be less simple than it sounds.

More commonly, you are likely to be concerned with **model fitting**, where you start off with a model and see whether experimental measurements agree with it. You met this in Questions 6–8, where you had to decide whether a given material obeyed Ohm's law. Plotting a graph is often a good way to see whether measurements fit a given model – particularly if the expected graph is a straight line, and the experimental values are plotted complete with error bars.

Matching experimental measurements to a mathematical model can help you to find the values of unknown quantities. If a set of current and voltage measurements fit Ohm's law, then you can determine the conductor's resistance. In Section 2.3 you used a mathematical model to describe the behaviour of a power supply with internal resistance, and in this way you were able to determine the internal resistance and the emf of the supply.

Is there a simple relationship between resistance and temperature?

Some conductors have a resistance that increases uniformly with temperature. This behaviour can be described by a mathematical model:

$$R_\theta = R_0 (1 + \alpha\theta) = R_0 + \alpha R_0 \theta \tag{30}$$

where:

R_θ = resistance at temperature θ

R_0 = resistance at $0\,°\mathrm{C}$

α is the **temperature coefficient of resistance**

The coefficient α can be described as 'the fractional increase in resistance compared with the value at $0\,°\mathrm{C}$'. The units of α are $°\mathrm{C}^{-1}$, so that the units of $\alpha\theta$ are $°\mathrm{C}^{-1} \times °\mathrm{C}$, i.e. $\alpha\theta$ has no units – it is just a number.

The value of a can be positive or negative, depending on whether resistance increases or decreases with rising temperature. Resistors that are designed to have a large variation with temperature (**thermistors**) are often referred to as NTC (negative temperature coefficient) or PTC (positive temperature coefficient) thermistors, depending on the way their resistance changes.

Table 4.3 lists some very precise values for the resistance of five different material samples, all designed to have a resistance of $1.00000\,\Omega$ at $0\,°\mathrm{C}$ (i.e. $R_0 = 1.00000\,\Omega$). By looking at the numbers in each column, you can see that the change in resistance with temperature is linear in each case.

Temperature/°C	Resistance/Ω				
	Carbon	Copper	Constantan	Steel	Tungsten
0	1.00000	1.00000	1.00000	1.00000	1.00000
20	0.99000	1.08000	1.00002	1.06600	1.10400
40	0.98000	1.16000	1.00004	1.13200	1.20800
60	0.97000	1.24000	1.00006	1.19800	1.31200
80	0.96000	1.32000	1.00008	1.26400	1.41600
100	0.95000	1.40000	1.00010	1.33000	1.52000

Table 4.3 Temperature data for five resistors

WORKED EXAMPLE

Figure 4.47 shows a graph of resistance R_θ plotted against temperature θ for copper. The graph is a straight line and cuts the vertical axis at $R_0 = 1.00000\,\Omega$. The gradient of the line is equal to αR_θ. From Figure 4.47:

$$\Delta R = 0.40\,\Omega,\ \Delta\theta = 100\,°C$$

$$\text{gradient} = \frac{\Delta R}{\Delta\theta}$$

$$= \frac{0.40\,\Omega}{100\,°C}$$

$$= 0.0040\,\Omega\,°C^{-1} = 4.0 \times 10^{-3}\,\Omega\,°C^{-1}$$

$$\alpha = \frac{\text{gradient}}{R_0}$$

$$= \frac{4.0 \times 10^{-3}\,\Omega\,°C^{-1}}{1.0\,\Omega}$$

$$= 4.0 \times 10^{-3}\,°C^{-1}$$

STUDY NOTE

In this example the gradient is numerically the same as α, but that will not in general be the case.

MATHS REFERENCE

Linear relationships
See Maths note 5.2
Gradient of a linear graph
See Maths note 5.3

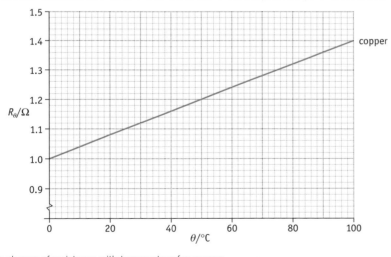

Figure 4.47 The change of resistance with temperature for copper

QUESTIONS

Q 27 The temperature coefficient of resistance of copper is $4.28 \times 10^{-3}\,°C^{-1}$. A piece of copper connecting wire has a resistance of $0.50\,\Omega$ at $0\,°C$. What will be its resistance at $80\,°C$? In the light of your answer, say whether you think that the connecting wires in a circuit can be ignored when taking account of changes in electrical properties with temperature.

Q 28 (a) Which of the materials listed in Table 4.3 have a positive temperature coefficient of resistance, and which have a negative coefficient?

(b) Suggest a reason why constantan is so called.

(c) Choose one material from carbon, tungsten or steel. Plot a graph, similar to Figure 4.47, to show its behaviour. Calculate its temperature coefficient of resistance.

ACTIVITY 22 MODEL FITTING

Your task is to determine whether your experimental measurement of resistance and temperature from Activity 21 match the mathematical model discussed above, and then to communicate your findings to students who have discussed other components.

Your graph of R_θ against θ that you plotted in Question 28 (c) will enable you to decide whether a particular set of measurements fits the model, and to find the values of R_0 and α.

4.3 Why does resistance change with temperature?

You will have seen that different components behave very differently on being heated. Why is this? We can explain the main features using a simple model for current and a so-called classical model of materials.

Modelling current

Within a conductor, there are some charged particles that are free to move. When a pd is applied, the particles that have negative charge (e.g. electrons) move towards the positive terminal, and those with positive charge (e.g. positive ions in a solution) move towards the negative terminal. This movement forms an electric current as described by Equation 1a:

$$I = \frac{\Delta Q}{\Delta t}$$

(Equation 1a)

As the current is a measure of the rate at which charge passes a point, it will depend on the speed at which the particles move and on their individual charge. By thinking about what happens when the charged particles move, we can set up a model that relates these small-scale quantities to the current that we measure with an ammeter.

Figure 4.48 shows a section of conductor that contains freely moving particles, each with charge q, moving along at speed v. There are n particles per unit volume – that is, their **number density** is n – and the conductor's cross-sectional area is A. We can use this model to derive an expression for I in terms of n, q, A and v.

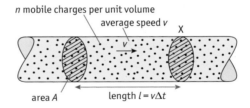

area A length $l = v\Delta t$

Figure 4.48 Charged particles in a conductor

In a time interval Δt, all the particles in a length l will pass a reference point X, where:

$$l = v\Delta t$$

(31)

The number of particles, N, in this length of conductor is found by multiplying the volume, V, of the conductor by the particles' number density:

$$V = Al$$

(32)

so:

$$N = nAl$$

(33)

The charge ΔQ passing point X in time Δt is given by:

$$\Delta Q = Nq = nAlq$$

(34)

Substituting for l from Equation 32 gives:

$$\Delta Q = nAqv\Delta t$$

(35)

Dividing both sides by Δt and comparing with Equation 1a, we get:

$$I = nAqv$$

(36)

⚙ ACTIVITY 23 MOVING CHARGES

How fast do you think the charged particles move in a current-carrying conductor? Write down your guess then use the apparatus in Figure 4.49 to observe mobile coloured ions.

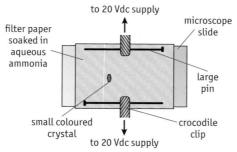

Figure 4.49 Apparatus for Activity 23

The results of Activity 23 may have surprised you. The speed v is known as the **drift speed** (or **drift velocity**) and in most conductors is quite small. The following questions explore the relationship between the various quantities in Equation 36.

QUESTIONS

Electron charge $e = 1.60 \times 10^{-19}\,C$

 Q 29 (a) Using SI base units, show that the right-hand side of Equation 36 has the correct units for current.

(b) Referring to Equation 36, explain why increasing the pd across a conductor increases the current.

Q 30 In a **semiconductor**, the number density of free-moving charges is much less than in a metal. If a sample of semiconductor is joined in series with a metal sample of the same cross-sectional area, and a pd is connected across the arrangement, what can you say about the drift speeds in the two samples?

Q 31 (a) Suppose each atom in a metal occupies a cube of side $5 \times 10^{-10}\,m$ and each contributes one electron that is free to move. What is the number density of the free electrons?

(b) Suppose also that there is a current of 0.2 A in a wire made from the metal, with a square cross-section of side 0.5 mm. What must be the electrons' drift speed?

Modelling resistance

The model of current introduced above can be used when we try to explain changes in resistance with temperature. To reduce the resistance, we must do something that either increases the number density of free-moving charged particles, or increases their drift speed for a given applied pd.

Our model for resistance starts with the ideas that materials are made up of atoms that are constantly vibrating. As the temperature rises, the atoms vibrate more vigorously. At the same time, a rise in temperature can result in the release of more electrons from atoms. It is the flow of these free electrons that forms an electric current.

As the electrons move through the material, they 'collide' with the vibrating atoms and are scattered, which disrupts their flow. As the atoms vibrate more vigorously, so the frequency of 'collision' or interaction between the atoms and the electrons also increases. This reduces the rate of flow of the electrons and so the current falls. In other words, the resistance increases (Figure 4.50(a)). However, if more electrons are released from the atoms as the temperature rises, then there is a greater rate of flow of charge – the current increases. In other words, the resistance falls (Figure 4.50(b)).

The change in resistance with temperature, as illustrated in Question 29, depends on which of these two effects 'wins'. In a metal, the temperature has virtually no effect on the number of electrons that can move freely through the material, so the dominant effect is that of atomic vibrations. However, in a semiconductor a small rise in temperature leads to the release of a large number of electrons, and this effect now outweighs that of atomic vibrations.

(a)

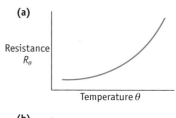

(b)

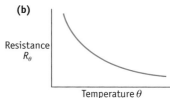

Figure 4.50 Schematic diagrams showing the change in resistance with temperature due to (a) thermal vibrations and (b) the release of electrons

4.4 Electronic materials and components

Space technology relies heavily on 'designer' materials that have been developed to have particular electrical properties. Such materials are essential for the solar cells and the components in communication and control systems on board a spacecraft – just as they are for familiar Earth-based electronic devices.

'Designer' electronic materials are usually based on semiconductors (conductors in which the number density of free-moving charges is much less than in a metal). Silicon (Si) and germanium (Ge) are semiconducting elements that are widely used in electronics, along with others such as gallium (Ga) and indium (In). The properties of a pure semiconductor can be altered in a controllable way by **doping**, which involves adding small amounts of another semiconductor (about 1 part in 10 million). The presence of the impurity distorts the atomic structure of the lattice, which changes the amount of energy needed to release an electron and hence alters the way in which the material's electrical properties depend on factors such as temperature.

We have already mentioned thermistors, which are usually designed to have a negative temperature coefficient – their resistance falls as temperature rises and so more electrons are released to move through the material.

In some semiconductors, electrons can be released from atoms when they absorb a photon. This is similar to the photoelectric effect, only now the electrons remain within the material and move around freely. The number density of free electrons depends on the intensity of the illumination, and this property is exploited in a **light-dependent resistor** (LDR).

Joining different semiconductors together can make other electronic devices. The simplest is a **diode**, made from two different semiconductors chosen so that current can flow easily in one direction but not the other. As electrons flow across the junction in the 'forward' direction, they lose energy. By carefully controlling the properties of the semiconductors, the diode can be designed so that this energy loss can lead to the emission of a photon of visible or infrared radiation. The diode is then known as an LED (light-emitting diode) or IRED (infrared-emitting diode).

4.5 Summing up Part 4

In this part of the chapter you have learned why it is important to control the temperature on board a spacecraft, and you have seen how and why electrical resistance changes with temperature and with illumination.

> ⚙ **ACTIVITY 24 SUMMING UP PART 4**
> Look through Part 4 and make sure that you know the meaning of each of the terms printed in bold.
> Write a short paragraph explaining why the resistance of copper increases with temperature whereas that of carbon decreases.

QUESTIONS

Figure 4.51 shows the voltage–current graphs for an ohmic conductor, a filament lamp, a thermistor and a diode, together with their circuit symbols.

Q 32 Explain why the lines are present in both the top right and bottom left quadrants of all the graphs except the one for a diode.

Q 33 Using ideas about free electrons and lattice vibrations, explain:

(a) how the resistance of an LDR changes as the intensity of illumination is increased

(b) the shapes of the graphs for the thermistor and the filament lamp.

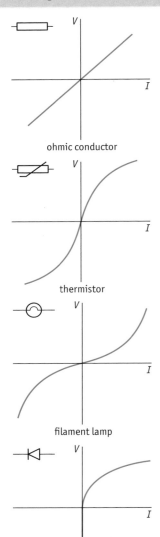

ohmic conductor

thermistor

filament lamp

diode

Figure 4.51 Voltage–current graphs for an ohmic conductor, filament lamp, thermistor and a diode

LINK THE LEARNING

5 Mission accomplished

In this chapter you have studied some aspects of electric circuits and power supplies, and some aspects of energy transfer processes. You have also studied the photoelectric effect that underlies the operation of solar cells. This concluding section is intended to help you look back over the whole chapter and consolidate your knowledge and understanding.

5.1 Conservation of ...

In studying this chapter you have learned some fundamental pieces of physics that all relate to the important idea of conservation. In everyday language, conservation is often used to mean keeping something as it is: not damaging it, not wasting it, not using it up. For example, you might talk of conserving the countryside or conserving fuel.

In its scientific sense, conservation means when some measurable quantity remains unchanged. One example is the conservation of mass. For example, if you are dealing with a complex network of pipes (such as in a water or gas supply system) then conservation of mass is important to bear in mind when considering rates of flow through various parts of the system.

The conservation of charge is another example: no situation or process has ever been found in which the total amount of charge changes. You are probably used to the idea of positive and negative charge, and that removing electrons (negatively charged) from an initially uncharged object leaves behind an equal amount of positive charge. The total amount of charge (found by adding up individual positive and negative charges with their correct signs) is always unchanged. We used this fundamental law of nature earlier in this chapter, when we said that the rate of flow of charge (i.e. the current) into a point in an electric circuit must be equal to the rate of flow of charge away from that point. You will probably also have used charge conservation in balancing nuclear and chemical equations.

The conservation of energy is another fundamental law of nature. Even through energy is not 'stuff', nor is it an easily measurable property of matter, it is still possible to define and measure amounts of energy transferred or stored, and no process has ever been found in which energy is either created or destroyed. The law of energy conservation underlies much of the work of this chapter. For example, in looking at energy in an electric circuit in Part 2, we used the fact that the energy supplied by a power source to each coulomb of charge must be equal to the energy delivered to the circuit by each coulomb.

> ⚙ **ACTIVITY 25 CONSERVATION RULES – OK!**
>
> Many of the activities, diagrams and questions in this unit illustrate and use the conservation laws discussed above. By copying and completing Table 4.4, which lists several of these examples, you will make a chart showing conservation laws in use. Some of the rows of the table have been filled in to give you the idea – but you might decide to design your own chart in a different way, and perhaps to add sketch diagrams and extra notes.

Reference	Illustrates/uses conservation of ...	Notes
Section 2.1, Figure 4.12 How does a solar cell work?	charge	Electrons drift across boundary leaving positive charge. Overall charge is still zero.
Activity 4	energy	Emf (energy supplied to each coulomb) by cells connected in series is equal to sum of emfs of individual cells
Resistors in series and parallel	charge	
Resistors in series and parallel	energy	
Activity 7		
Maximising the power	energy	Total power supplied by cell = power in external circuit + power in internal resistance
Activity 15, Q16–Q18	energy	
Energy and temperature change: Activity 20, Q25	energy	
Activity 20	energy	

Table 4.4 Conservation laws in use

5.2 Modelling light

In Part 3 of this chapter you used a photon model to explain the photoelectric effect, but in *The Sound of Music* refraction and polarisation were explained using waves. In some situations the behaviour of light (and other electromagnetic radiation) can best be explained using the photon model, and sometimes a wave model works better. The nature of light has puzzled and intrigued scientists for many centuries, with sometimes one model being favoured and sometimes the other, depending on the experimental evidence available. Looking at the way ideas about light have changed over time illustrates an important aspect of how science works: theories and models are only as good as the experimental evidence that supports them, and may change over time as new evidence becomes available. Nowadays, we accept that we need two ways of modelling light, and that which one is considered the better model varies. However, this view has only come about because of careful experiment and observation accompanied by deep thinking, with quite a bit of controversy along the way (as you will see in Activity 26).

PRACTICAL SKILLS REFERENCE

Information research

See Practical skills notes 1.2–1.4

STUDY NOTE

You also used both the wave and photon model in *The Sound of Music*.

ACTIVITY 26 A BRIEF HISTORY OF LIGHT

Use the Internet and other resources to find out how ideas about light have changed over time, and something about the people involved in investigating and publicising them. Try to include the following:

- ancient Greek and ancient Roman ideas about light (e.g. Democritus, Lucretius, Augustine of Hippo)
- Arab scientists' ideas and work on the nature of light (e.g. ibn Al-Haytham)
- Isaac Newton's theory of corpuscles
- Thomas Young's experiments
- the photoelectric effect (Planck, Einstein).

Summarise your findings on a timeline that can be displayed as a poster.

5.3 Questions on the whole chapter

Q 34 A set of similar, but not identical, components was tested in a class experiment. The different groups each used an ammeter, a voltmeter, a constant-voltage power pack and a variable resistor in their testing circuit.

The results for five different groups of students are shown in Figure 4.52. Each group found an equation to fit their results that could be written in the form:

$$y = mx + c$$

with:

$$x = I \text{ and } y = V:$$

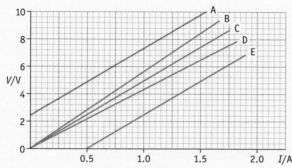

Figure 4.52 *V–I graphs obtained by five groups of students*

(a) Which graph(s) have:
   (i) a positive *c* value?   (iii) zero *c*?
   (ii) the largest *m* value?   (iv) the same *m* value?

(b) Using the graphs in Figure 4.52 to help you decide which component(s), A to E:
   (i) obeys Ohm's Law
   (ii) might have been tested using a meter with a zero error
   (iii) has *V* directly proportional to *I*
   (iv) could contain a fixed resistor in series with an extra source of emf.

Q 35 Electric vehicles were first introduced in the late 19th century. At the end of that century, around 40% of all motor vehicles were powered by electricity, far more than by petrol. Recent years have seen a revival of interest in entirely battery-powered vehicles.

(a) The Elcat Cityvan 2000, a minivan developed in Finland, has a set of six lead-acid batteries of emf 12.0 V connected to provide 72.0 V. Draw a diagram to show how the batteries must be connected together.

(b) The vehicle is powered by a DC motor which, when under the greatest load, draws a current of 300 A from the batteries.
   (i) Given that each lead-acid battery has an internal resistance of 0.0065 Ω, calculate the voltage (terminal potential difference) across all six batteries under this condition.
   (ii) Calculate the power transferred by the resistance of each battery while there is a current of 300 A in the circuit.
   (iii) What effect will this power transfer have on the batteries?

(c) The set-up described here does not maximise the power transferred by the batteries. Explain why it would in practice be unwise to design the van circuit to maximise the power transfer.

Q 36 Figure 4.53 shows approximately how the current in a filament lamp and an LED varies over time after they are connected in a circuit.

(a) (i) What does the area under each of the curves represent?
   (ii) Calculate the charge passing through the filament lamp in the first second after it has been turned on.
   (iii) Calculate the charge passing through the LED in the first 1 ms.

(b) The filament lamp current rises to 0.4 A, but soon falls to a steady value of 0.2 A. Explain why this rise and fall happens in the filament lamp but not the LED.

(c) Use Figure 4.53(a) to explain why filament bulbs are most likely to fail when they are first turned on. With reference to Figure 4.53(b), explain whether this is the case for an LED.

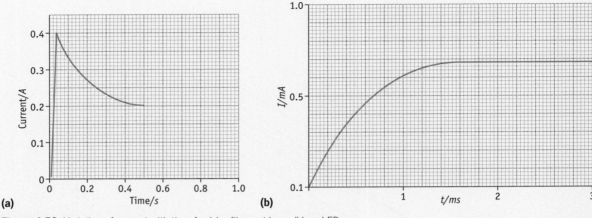

Figure 4.53 Variation of current with time for (a) a filament lamp (b) an LED

Q 37 The internal resistance of a dry cell often increases with age, which can be partly due to the growth of crystals within the cell itself or to deposits on the electrodes within the cell. A cell that originally has an emf of 12.0 V and an internal resistance of $0.5\,\Omega$ supplies a toy racing car that has a motor of resistance $8.0\,\Omega$.

(a) What is the current in the circuit when the cell is new?

The cell needs to be recharged or recycled if the terminal pd drops below 80% of its original value.

(b) What is the pd across the motor **(i)** when the cell is new and then **(ii)** when it is ready for recycling?

(c) Assuming that the emf remains constant, what is the current in the circuit when the cell is due for recycling, and so what is the internal resistance of the cell? Comment on this result.

Q 38 The total electrical power generated in the world today is about $10^9\,\text{kW}$. In the rich countries this works out at roughly $1\,\text{kW}$ per person. During the next century the world's population is likely to grow to about 10^4 million. To provide everyone with the 'energy standard' of $1\,\text{kW}$, some $10^{10}\,\text{kW}$ of electricity will need to be produced.

One possible way to achieve this large increase in power might be to build Space Power Satellites (SPS) – a concept first conceived in the 1960s. This would involve building very large solar arrays in geostationary orbit and beaming the power developed by their solar cells to Earth by microwaves (see Figure 4.54).

(a) Calculate the power that could be provided by an SPS array of area $5 \times 10^7\,\text{m}^2$ (50 km²) if the combined efficiency of the array, transmitter and receiver is 8%, and the solar radiation intensity is $1400\,\text{W m}^{-2}$.

(b) How many such arrays would be needed to provide $10^{10}\,\text{kW}$?

Q 39 If a photoelectron is released from a layer of photosensitive material with no kinetic energy and then accelerated through 100 V, what will be its final kinetic energy? Give your answer in eV and in joules.

Q 40 Suppose light produces a current of $6.5 \times 10^{-11}\,\text{A}$ in a solar cell. How many electrons must be released every second?

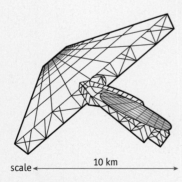

scale ⟷ 10 km

Figure 4.54 Artist's impression of a Space Power Satellite

Q 41   In an incandescent light bulb, a thin piece of tungsten wire (the filament) is connected in series to the thick copper connecting wires. Two students are discussing the situation. Student A says 'the electrons must be moving at the same speed in all the wires'. Student B says 'the copper probably has a greater number density of electrons because it's a good conductor'. Write a few sentences to explain whether you agree with what they are saying.

5.4 Achievements

Now you have studied this chapter you should be able to achieve the outcomes listed in Table 4.5.

TABLE 4.5 ACHIEVEMENTS FOR THE CHAPTER *TECHNOLOGY IN SPACE*

	Statement from Examination Specification	Section(s) in this chapter
1	know and understand the distinction between base and derived quantities and their SI units	2.1, 2.2, 2.3
2	demonstrate their knowledge of practical skills and techniques for both familiar and unfamiliar experiments	2.2, 3.2, 4.2
4	understand the limitations of physical measurement and apply these limitations to practical situations	2.2, 4.2
5	be able to communicate information and ideas in appropriate ways using appropriate terminology	2.4, 5.1, 5.2, 4.2
8	understand the ways in which society uses science to inform decision making	3.1
30	be able to use the equation $\text{efficiency} = \dfrac{[\text{useful energy (or power) output}]}{[\text{total energy (or power) input}]}$	2.3, 4.1
31	understand that electric current is the rate of flow of charged particles and be able to use the equation $I = \dfrac{\Delta Q}{\Delta t}$	2.1, 4.3
32	understand how to use the equation $V = \dfrac{W}{Q}$	2.1, 2.2
33	understand that resistance is defined by $R = \dfrac{V}{I}$ and that Ohm's law is a special case when $I \propto V$ for constant temperature	2.2
34	understand how the distribution of current in a circuit is a consequence of charge conservation	2.1, 2.2
35	understand how the distribution of potential differences in a circuit is a consequence of energy conservation	2.1, 2.2
36	be able to derive the equations for combining resistances in series and parallel using the principles of charge and energy conservation, and be able to use these equations	2.2
37	be able to use the equations $P = VI$, $W = VIt$ and be able to derive and use related equations, e.g. $P = I^2R$ and $P = \dfrac{V^2}{R}$	2.3
38	understand how to sketch, recognise and interpret current-potential difference graphs for components, including ohmic conductors, filament bulbs, thermistors and diodes	2.2
45	know the definition of electromotive force (emf) and understand what is meant by internal resistance and know how to distinguish between emf and terminal potential difference	2.2
46	CORE PRACTICAL 3: Determine the emf and internal resistance of an electrical cell	2.2
47	understand how changes of resistance with temperature may be modelled in terms of lattice vibrations and number of conduction electrons and understand how to apply this model to metallic conductors and negative temperature coefficient thermistors	4.2
48	understand how changes of resistance with illumination may be modelled in terms of the number of conduction electrons and understand how to apply this model to LDRs	4.4
70	be able to use the equation intensity of radiation $I = \dfrac{P}{A}$	4.1
92	understand that the absorption of a photon can result in the emission of a photoelectron	3.2
93	understand the terms threshold frequency and work function and be able to use the equation $hf = \phi + \dfrac{1}{2}mv^2_{max}$	3.2
94	be able to use the electronvolt (eV) to express small energies	3.2
95	understand how the photoelectric effect provides evidence for the particle nature of electromagnetic radiation	3.2

Answers

Q 1   **(a)** Fuel cells, with or without the addition of cryogenic engines (the point representing 1 kW, 1 week, lies more or less on the line between these two regions of the graph).

      (b) Solar and nuclear dynamic systems (notice that $10^1 \, \text{kW}$ means 10 kW).

Q 2   **(a)** $\Delta Q = I\Delta t = 0.5 \, \text{C s}^{-1} \times 2.0 \, \text{s} = 1.0 \, \text{C}$

      (b) $\Delta W = \mathscr{E}\Delta Q$

      (c) $\Delta W = 1.5 \, \text{J C}^{-1} \times 1.0 \, \text{C} = 1.5 \, \text{J}$

      (d) units of W (energy) = units of force × distance

$$= \text{N} \times \text{m} = \text{kg m s}^{-2} \times \text{m}$$
$$= \text{kg m}^2 \, \text{s}^{-2}$$

        or

units of energy = units of $\frac{1}{2}mv^2 = \text{kg} \times (\text{m s}^{-1})^2$
$$= \text{kg m}^2 \, \text{s}^{-2}$$

units of Q (charge) $= \text{C} = \text{A s}$

units of V (pd) $= \text{J C}^{-1} = \text{kg m}^2 \, \text{s}^{-2} \div \text{A s} = \text{kg m A}^{-1} \text{s}^{-3}$

Q 3   In circuits (a), (c) and (e) the cells are in series so their voltages add: (a) 1.0 V, (c) 1.5 V (e) 2.0 V. Circuits (b), (d) and (f) all give 0.5 V as the cells are joined in parallel.

In (g) each pair of cells in series gives 1.0 V. The two pairs are joined in parallel so the net output would also be 1.0 V.

Q 4   A single row of 56 cells joined in series gives an output of 28 V. (Several rows of 56 cells could be connected in parallel to give the same output voltage.)

Q 5   2 Ω. Read any pair of values from the graph, for example, when $I = 3 \, \text{A}$, $V = 6 \, \text{V}$.

$$R = \frac{V}{I} = \frac{6V}{3I} = 2 \, \Omega$$

Q 6   Graphs (b) and (c) show ohmic behaviour – they are straight lines through the origin.

Q 7   The steeper the graph, the higher the resistance. (Graph (b) shows a higher resistance than graph (c).)

Q 8   In (a) the resistance increases at large currents and voltages, and in (d) the resistance decreases as the current is increased. You can check this by reading values from the graphs and calculating resistance. For example, in (a), when $I = 2 \, \text{A}$, $V = 1 \, \text{V}$ and so $R = 0.5 \, \Omega$; when $I = 3 \, \text{A}$, $V = 3 \, \text{V}$ so $R = 1 \, \Omega$ (an increase). In (d), when $I = 1 \, \text{A}$, $V = 2 \, \text{V}$ so $R = 2 \, \Omega$, and when $I = 3 \, \text{A}$, $V = 3 \, \text{V}$ and $R = 1 \, \Omega$ (a decrease).

Q 9   Figure 4.55 shows a graph of the measurements. It is not possible to draw a straight line through the origin that also passes through all the error boxes, so the material does not obey Ohm's law. (Its resistance decreases as current and voltage increase.)

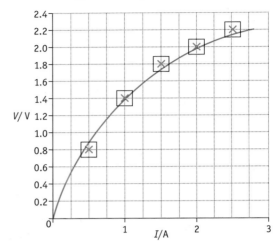

Figure 4.55 The answer to Question 9

Q 10   **(a)** $\dfrac{1}{R} = \left(\dfrac{1}{1} + \dfrac{1}{2} + \dfrac{1}{4} + \dfrac{1}{8}\right)\Omega^{-1} = 1.875 \, \Omega^{-1}$

$$R = \frac{1}{1.875} \, \Omega = 0.53 \, \Omega$$

      (b) First replace the 3 Ω and 6 Ω combination:

$$\frac{1}{R} = \left(\frac{1}{3} + \frac{1}{6}\right)\Omega^{-1} = 0.5 \, \Omega^{-1}, \; R = 2 \, \Omega$$

The complete arrangement is then equivalent to two 2 Ω resistors in series, giving a total resistance of 4 Ω.

      (c) First replace the series of 4 Ω + 2 Ω by a single 6 Ω resistor. The complete arrangement is then equivalent to two 6 Ω resistors in parallel.

$$\frac{1}{R} = \left(\frac{1}{6} + \frac{1}{6}\right)\Omega^{-1}, \text{ and so } R = 3 \, \Omega$$

Q 11 $P = IV, \; I = \dfrac{P}{V} = \dfrac{2000 \, \text{W}}{230 \, \text{V}} = 8.7 \, \text{A}$

Q 12 $P = \dfrac{V^2}{R}, \; R = \dfrac{V^2}{P} = \dfrac{(230 \, \text{V})^2}{60 \, \text{W}} = 882 \, \Omega$

Q 13 $\Delta W = VI\Delta t = 230 \, \text{V} \times 0.2 \, \text{A} \times 2.5 \times 60 \, \text{s} = 6.9 \times 10^3 \, \text{J}$

Q 14 Current $I = \dfrac{\mathscr{E}}{R + r} = \dfrac{3.0\,\text{V}}{6\,\Omega} = 0.50\,\text{A}$

$P_{\text{out}} = (0.50\,\text{A})^2 \times 1\,\Omega = 0.25\,\text{W}$

Total power is:

$P_{\text{in}} = (0.50\,\text{A})^2 \times 6\,\Omega = 1.50\,\text{W}$

Efficiency $= \dfrac{0.25\,\text{W}}{1.50\,\text{W}} = 0.17 = 17\%$

(Alternatively, efficiency $= \dfrac{I^2 R}{I^2(R + r)} = \dfrac{R}{R + r}$

$= \dfrac{1\,\Omega}{6\,\Omega} = 0.17 = 17\%$)

This would not be a sensible arrangement for several reasons. The output power is less than it would be under conditions for maximum power (0.25 W compared with over 0.45 W when $R = r$), but the total power transferred by the battery is greater than it would be if $R = r$ (1.5 W compared with 0.9 W), so the battery would run down more quickly. Most of the battery power (80% of it) is wasted due to internal heating in the battery.

Q 15 **(a)** The cells are in series so the total emf and the total internal resistance are found by adding the separate emfs and internal resistances.
   (i) $6 \times 0.005\,\Omega = 0.03\,\Omega$
   (ii) $6 \times 2.0\,\text{V} = 12.0\,\text{V}$

(b) **(i)** The internal resistance and the load form a series circuit, with resistance $R + r = (2.97 + 0.03)\,\Omega = 3.00\,\Omega$
   (ii) $I = \dfrac{\mathscr{E}}{R + r} = \dfrac{12.0\,\text{V}}{3.00\,\Omega}$
   $= 4.0\,\text{A}$ (Equation 12)
   (iii) Terminal pd $V = IR = 4.0\,\text{A} \times 2.97\,\Omega = 11.9\,\text{V}$

(c) If the current in the battery is 200 A then the 'lost volts' $Ir = 200\,\text{A} \times 0.03\,\Omega = 6\,\text{V}$. The terminal pd must therefore fall to $12\,\text{V} - 6\,\text{V} = 6\,\text{V}$. If the headlamps are designed to be connected to a pd of 12 V they will dim noticeably.

Q 16 **(a)** Internal resistances combine just like ordinary resistances in series and parallel, as the following calculations for arrangements (ii) – (iv) show.
   (ii) Total resistance $r = 4 \times 30\,\Omega = 120\,\Omega$
   (iii) $\dfrac{1}{r} = \left(\dfrac{1}{30} + \dfrac{1}{30}\right)\Omega^{-1} = \dfrac{1}{15}\,\Omega^{-1}$, so
   $r = 15\,\Omega$
   (iv) Each pair of cells in series has resistance $60\,\Omega$.
   $\dfrac{1}{r} = \left(\dfrac{1}{60} + \dfrac{1}{60}\right)\Omega^{-1} = \dfrac{1}{30}\,\Omega^{-1}$, so
   $r = 30\,\Omega$

(b) Power transfer will be maximum when the external load resistance is equal to the total internal resistance. Each set of four solar cells has a total internal resistance of $120\,\Omega$. The two sets in parallel have a total resistance of $60\,\Omega$, so the external load must be $60\,\Omega$.

Q 17 **(a)** Energy transferred $= 5000\,\text{eV}$

$= 5000 \times 1.60 \times 10^{-19}\,\text{J}$

$= 8.00 \times 10^{-16}\,\text{J}$

(b) The answer is the same as (a) because the same amount of charge has been accelerated through the same pd.

Q 18 Rearranging Equation 26, $v = \sqrt{\dfrac{2E_k}{m}}$. To be sure of getting speeds in m s^{-1}, you need to express the energies in joules, not eV.

Electron: $v = \sqrt{\dfrac{2E_k}{m_e}}$

$= \sqrt{\dfrac{2 \times 8.00 \times 10^{-16}\,\text{J}}{9.11 \times 10^{-31}\,\text{kg}}}$

$= 4.19 \times 10^7\,\text{m s}^{-1}$

Proton: $v = \sqrt{\dfrac{2E_k}{m_p}}$

$= \sqrt{\dfrac{2 \times 8.00 \times 10^{-16}\,\text{J}}{1.67 \times 10^{-27}\,\text{kg}}}$

$= 9.79 \times 10^5\,\text{m s}^{-1}$

Q 19 Using Equation 21:

Photon energy

$E_{\text{ph}} = hf$

$= \dfrac{6.63 \times 10^{-34}\,\text{J s} \times 3.00 \times 10^8\,\text{m s}^{-1}}{434 \times 10^{-9}\,\text{m}}$

$= 4.58 \times 10^{-19}\,\text{J}$

$= \dfrac{4.58 \times 10^{-19}\,\text{J}}{1.60 \times 10^{-19}\,\text{J eV}^{-1}}$

$= 2.86\,\text{eV}$

Then using Equation 22 for the maximum kinetic energy:

$E_k = E_{\text{ph}} - \phi$

$= 2.86\,\text{eV} - 2.28\,\text{eV}$

$= 0.54\,\text{eV}$

$= 0.54 \times 1.60 \times 10^{-19}\,\text{J}$

$= 0.864 \times 10^{-19}\,\text{J}$

$= 8.64 \times 10^{-20}\,\text{J}$

Q 20 **(a)** The photon energy is less than the work function so no photoelectrons will be released. (The absorbed radiation will just produce a slight heating of the metal.)

(b) Ultraviolet radiation has a shorter wavelength than visible light, therefore a higher frequency and higher-energy photons. The photoelectrons released from sodium will therefore have more kinetic energy than those released by blue light.

Q 21 Your answer should make the point that input power to solar panels varies with angle. In order to intercept as much radiation as possible, the panels must point directly at the Sun – a change of angle will result in a loss of power. You could go on to say that, provided the panels are within a few degrees of being square-on, the loss of power will not be great. However, once the misalignment is more than, say, 20°, the power drops by a large fraction. A diagram similar to Figure 4.39 would be suitable.

Q 22 $P_{out} = 0.11 \times P_{in}$

so:

$$P_{in} = \frac{P_{out}}{0.11}$$

$$= \frac{16\,kW}{0.11}$$

$$= 147\,kW$$

$$= 1.47 \times 10^5\,W$$

$P_{in} = IA\ (\theta = 0°)$

so:

$$A = \frac{P_{in}}{I}$$

$$= \frac{147\,kW}{1.4\,kW\,m^{-2}}$$

$$= 105\,m^2\ (\approx 10^2\,m^2)$$

or:

$$A = \frac{P_{in}}{I}$$

$$= \frac{1.47 \times 10^5}{1400\,W\,m^{-2}}$$

$$= 105\,m^2\ (\approx 10^2\,m^2)$$

(Notice that you can either use W or kW, but you must be consistent and not use a mixture.)

Q 23 Input power is greatest when the arrays are square-on to the incident radiation.

$P_{in} = IA$

$$= 600\,W\,m^{-2} \times 5000\,m$$

$$= 3.00 \times 10^6\,W$$

$$= 3.00 \times 10^3\,kW$$

$$\text{Efficiency} = \frac{P_{out}}{P_{in}}$$

$$= \frac{435\,kW}{(3.00 \times 10^3\,kW)}$$

$$= 0.145$$

$$= 14.5\%$$

Q 24 **(a)** **(i)** about 38%
(ii) about 94%

(b) From about 95% to about 75%, i.e. by about 20% of the maximum available capacity

Q 25 **(a)** **(i)** gallium arsenide (GaAs)
(ii) cadmium sulfide (CdS)
(iii) gallium arsenide/gallium phosphide (GaAs/GaP)

(b) It would not be sensible to use gallium and silicon as their efficiencies have already fallen to zero and so no energy transfer would take place.

(c) At 0 °C cadmium sulfide cell's efficiency is near 29%, but this falls to about 6% at 400 °C.

Q 26 From Figure 4.45, a GaAs array would have an efficiency of about 25% at 50 °C. If P_{out} is to be 1×10^6 W, and P_{out} is 25% of P_{in}, then $P_{in} = 4 \times 10^6$ W.

If the entire array is square-on to the incident solar flux, then $\theta = 0°$ and $P_{in} = IA$ so $A = \dfrac{P_{in}}{I}$

$$\frac{P_{in}}{I} = \frac{4 \times 10^6\,k}{(1.4 \times 10^3\,W\,m^{-2})} = 2.8 \times 10^3\,m^2$$

Q 27 $R_\theta = R_0(1 + \alpha\theta) = R_0 + \alpha R_0\theta$

$R_{80} = 50.0\,\Omega\ (1 + 4.28 \times 10^{-3}\,°C^{-1} \times 80\,°C)$

$$= 0.50\,\Omega \times 1.324 = 0.67\,\Omega$$

The percentage change in resistance is quite large:

$$\frac{0.17\,\Omega}{0.50\,\Omega} \approx 34\%$$

However, the resistance of the connecting wires in a circuit is likely to be much less than that of other components, so can usually be ignored. In a circuit that contained a large amount of copper (in coils of electromagnets, for example) the effect of temperature would need to be considered.

Q 28 (a) Copper, constantan, steel and tungsten all have positive temperature coefficients. Carbon is the odd one out with a negative coefficient.

(b) Its resistance is near coefficient over a fairly wide temperature range.

(c) Figure 4.56 shows a plot of all the data from Table 4.3. The temperature coefficients are: carbon $5.0 \times 10^{-4}\,°C^{-1}$, steel $3.3 \times 10^{-3}\,°C^{-1}$, tungsten $5.2 \times 10^{-3}\,°C^{-1}$.

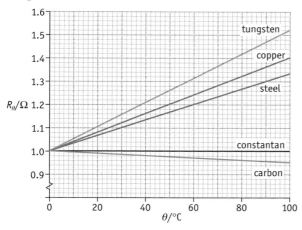

Figure 4.56 The answer to Question 28

Q 29 (a) n is a number per m^3 so has units m^{-3}. A is an area, with units m^2. q is charge, so its SI base units are As. v is a speed, with units $m\,s^{-1}$.

units of $nAqv = m^{-3} \times m^2 \times As \times m\,s^{-1} = A$ which is the SI unit of current.

(b) Increasing the pd supplies more kinetic energy to each charged particle. The drift speed increases so the current increases.

Q 30 The samples are in series so there is the same current, I, in each. As each has the same area, A, and (we can assume) particles with the same charge, q, the drift speed, v, in the semiconductor must be much greater than in the metal to compensate for the much smaller number density, n.

Q 31 (a) Volume occupied by each atom:

$$V = (5 \times 10^{-10}\,m)^3 = 1.25 \times 10^{-28}\,m^3$$

Number density $n = \dfrac{\text{number of free charges}}{\text{volume occupied by that number}}$

$$= \frac{1}{1.25 \times 10^{-28}\,m^3} = 8.00 \times 10^{27}\,m^{-3}$$

(b) $A = (0.5 \times 10^{-3}\,m)^2 = 2.5 \times 10^{-7}\,m^2$

From Equation 36:

$$v = \frac{I}{nAq}$$

$$= \frac{0.2\,A}{8.00 \times 10^{27}\,m^{-3} \times 2.5 \times 10^{-7}\,m \times 1.60 \times 10^{-19}\,C}$$

$$= 6.25 \times 10^{-4}\,m\,s^{-1}$$

Q 32 The lines in the top right quadrant are when currents and voltages are in the forward direction through the component, whereas the line in the bottom left quadrant represents the characteristics of the voltages and currents when they are reversed.

Q 33 (a) Increasing the illumination on an LDR provides energy to release electrons, so the number density of free electrons increases and the current for a given pd increases. Therefore, the resistance of the LDR become less as the intensity of illumination increases.

(b) In any component that has resistance, an electric current produces heating. As the current in a resistor is increased, its temperature rises.

Increasing the current in a metal filament produces more vigorous lattice vibration as temperature rises, and makes little or no difference to the number density of free electrons, so the resistance increases. At high voltages and currents, the resistance of a metal filament is therefore greater than would be predicted by Ohm's law and the current at a given voltage is lower.

Increasing the current in a thermistor leads to the release of many more electrons and the increase in number density of free electrons outweighs the effect of lattice vibrations, so the resistance decreases. At high voltages and currents the resistance is less than that predicted by Ohm's law and the current at a given voltage is greater. (This can lead to a runaway situation: increasing the current raises the temperature, which reduces the resistance, which increases the current …)

DIGGING UP THE PAST

Why a chapter called *Digging Up the Past*?

Imagine the scene: it is a frosty Sunday morning in the middle of the English countryside. From a collection of parked cars and bikes emerge a group of people in warm clothing, their breaths dissipating as clouds through the blazing sunlight as they proceed to pace purposefully around a field of grass. This is an archaeological team at work. And who is that person in the middle? Well, believe it or not, it is a physicist! Modern physics now finds a place at the heart of historical research. This chapter will reveal how archaeologists use physics to locate, date and investigate.

The story starts with some non-destructive investigations that use electrical measurements to locate likely areas with buried features. You will discover how the secrets of England's greatest battle, the Norman invasion, are being revealed in Sussex using physics. Resistance, resistivity and electric potential can all be understood in the context of probing beneath the soil.

Figure 5.1 shows three artefacts from archaeological finds. Consider the recent history of each.

● How did anyone know it was under the ground and how did they know where to look?

● How can we be sure about its age?

● What about the structure and material composition?

● How could we answer these questions?

These are the very questions that require an understanding of physics. History and physics meet in these three photographs.

Figure 5.1a Archaeological artefacts: ceremonial iron dagger

Figure 5.1b Archaeological artefacts: stone wall

Figure 5.1c Archaeological artefacts: terracotta urn

The story concludes with techniques used to investigate and analyse artefacts that have emerged from an archaeological site. The passage of X-rays through objects uncovers secrets of material content and hidden structure, and electron microscopy reveals information about the composition and origin of specimens.

OVERVIEW OF PHYSICS PRINCIPLES AND TECHNIQUES

In this chapter you will build on earlier work to learn more about electric circuits and the physics of electromagnetic radiation and diffraction. In doing so, you will be developing your skills in devising and carrying out experimental work and in using mathematical techniques to display and analyse data. There are also opportunities to use spreadsheets and the internet.

In this chapter you will extend your knowledge of:

● properties of waves and light from *The Sound of Music* and *Good Enough to Eat*
● electrical properties of materials, resistance and DC circuits from *Technology in Space*
● energy and using graphs from *Higher, Faster, Stronger*.

In other chapters you will do more work on:

● resistance and DC circuits (in *Transport on Track*)
● properties of materials (in *The Medium is the Message*)
● waves (in *Build or Bust?*)
● using graphs (in *The Medium is the Message* and *Probing the Heart of the Matter*).

Let's start by going back to the beginning: the interesting objects are under the soil somewhere, but where? Locating the correct site is the challenge that awaits us. You are now a geophysicist with an interest in archaeology – so read on.

1 The secrets of resistance

The trained forensic scientist will look for clues at the scene of the crime, and these clues will be readily available on the surface. A hair on a table or a bloodstain on a carpet might well be minute fragments of evidence, but they are visible and they are accessible. The archaeologist has a much harder task. Time erases surface traces. The clues to the past often lie buried under layers of soil. The only indications that something might lie below the surface are aerial photographs showing perhaps a hint of a ditch or a wall and of course historic records from the day.

When such historical research does hint that there might be something interesting below your feet, it is not a signal to grab your spade and dig. Careless digging may disturb valuable hidden artefacts, and anyway, all the land in the UK is owned by somebody. Your local archaeological society is your first port of call if you are interested in delving deeper.

1.1 Resistive surveying

Digging is an invasive activity. It changes the site permanently, rather like the destructive testing of a car just to test if the air bag works in the event of a crash. There are other preliminary techniques that archaeologists will use before picking up their spades and trowels. One of the most common is a resistive survey (Figures 5.2 and 5.3).

The water content of soil helps it to conduct an electric current. Rocks are poorer conductors (more resistive). By sinking two metal probes into the soil and measuring the resistance between them, archaeologists can make a tentative guess at where buried rocks and stone, and so walls, are likely to be. Later in this chapter you will see just how this technique helped reveal the truth about the exact landing site for William the Conqueror's invading army of 1066, perhaps the most important event in the history of England.

Figure 5.2 Carrying out a resistive survey

Figure 5.3 A physicist advises an archaeologist where to dig

PRACTICAL SKILLS REFERENCE

Scientific questions and information research

See Practical skills notes 1.1–1.4

⚙ ACTIVITY 1 ARCHAEOLOGY ON THE INTERNET

Use the Internet to find out about archaeological survey techniques and for background information on archaeology in general.

⚙ ACTIVITY 2 PROBING RESISTANCE

Use a resistance meter (an ohm meter), or an ammeter and voltmeter, to explore the resistance of various conducting objects. Include some non-uniform conductors such as that shown in Figure 5.4. Discuss your results in a group and create a summary that describes how resistance depends on the length and cross-section of a conductor.

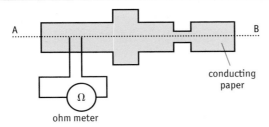

Figure 5.4 Probing the resistance of a non-uniform conductor

The search for the site of the Norman invasion

Local Hastings historian Nick Austin has used soil resistance measurements to uncover what he believes to be the site of the first Norman encampment and landing site prior to the famous Battle of Hastings. His survey was carried out between 1993 and 1994 and covered an area 560 m by 320 m; his research led him to believe that this was the site of the main Norman fort. Aerial photographs of the area indicated a possible fort outline but gave no clue to subsoil details.

Austin used a resistance meter to measure soil resistance at 1 m spaces and displayed the results on a computer. Dark patches indicate areas of high resistance, i.e. the likely presence of walls, and light patches indicate low resistance, i.e. the likely presence of damp ditches. Figure 5.5 shows some of his results.

Nick Austin's interpretation of the results identifies a series of ditches and sections of the fort perimeter. The survey corroborates the aerial photographs and Nick's own dowsing results. However, the major finding was the square structure at the centre of the area. This is clearly a man-made structure and is most likely to be the keep of the original Norman fort.

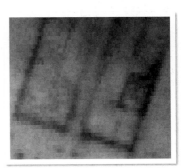

Figure 5.5 Results of a resistance survey

Activity 3 uses a simple model to help you appreciate how resistance measurements can give information about hidden structures. In place of soil you will use conducting Teledeltos paper.

⚙ ACTIVITY 3 MODELLING A RESISTIVE SURVEY

In each of two practical challenges you will be presented with the task of saying something about what lies below the surface by probing the resistance between pairs of points. The conducting paper has been shaped to represent places of lower and higher resistance. Your task is to locate the hidden structure simply by taking resistance measurements.

In real fieldwork a system of four probes can be used. The outer two supply an emf to drive current through the soil and the inner two measure the potential difference across a standard distance. The measured pd depends on the resistance of the subsoil.

Resistance surveys can be seen in action on *Time Team* DVDs (Channel 4 and in several YouTube videos). They help to confirm the speculation about subsoil structures that aerial surveys and historic document research indicate might be present. Only when three, or more, indicators point towards a definite structure will the diggers start their work.

However, even if there is something hidden mysteriously below the topsoil, it is not always easy to predict its shape. As you saw in Activity 2, different shapes will give different resistances. So how does shape affect resistance?

1.2 Resistivity

Activity 4 uses conducting putty as a material with a shape that can be easily changed. It will help you to focus your attention on the factors influencing the resistance of a conductor.

> **⚙ ACTIVITY 4 SIZE AND SHAPE**
>
> Investigate how the resistance of a piece of conducting putty with a fixed area of cross-section depends on its length. Combine your results with those of other students who have used a different area. Use a spreadsheet to plot graphs showing how the resistance varies with length and with area of cross-section.

Resistivity defined

Gathering results from Activity 4, you can show that for a piece of material of length l and cross-sectional area A, resistance is directly proportional to the length of the conductor:

$$R \propto l \tag{1}$$

and is inversely proportional to the cross-sectional area:

$$R \propto \frac{1}{A} \tag{2}$$

Combining these two gives:

$$R \propto \frac{1}{A} \tag{3}$$

Provided we assume that temperature is constant, the only other variable is the type of material itself. For a given size and shape of sample, some materials have higher resistance than others. The number describing this property of the material is called its **resistivity**, and it is given the symbol ρ (the greek letter rho). Equation 3 then becomes:

$$R = \frac{\rho l}{A} \tag{4}$$

If you rearrange Equation 4, it becomes:

$$\rho = \frac{AR}{l} \tag{4a}$$

Resistivity therefore has units of resistance × area ÷ length, $\Omega\,\text{m}^2/\text{m}^{-1}$. This simplifies to resistance × length, so its SI units are $\Omega\,\text{m}$. The numerical value of a material's resistivity is the same as the resistance between opposite faces of a 1 m cube.

Note that the resistivity of a material is a property of that type of material. It is a quantity like density in that it doesn't depend on the particular size or shape of material. It is pointless looking up the resistance of copper in a data book; you might as well look up the mass of copper. These answers will not be listed because the answer depends on the size and shape of the sample. However, you will be able to look up a value for the resistivity of copper as well as its density. No other information is required, just the name of the material.

The other side of the resistivity coin is **conductivity**, symbolised σ (the Greek letter sigma). A good conductor will have a high conductivity and a low resistivity. Resistivity and conductivity are simply the reciprocals of each other:

$$\sigma = \frac{1}{\rho} \tag{5}$$

The SI units of conductivity are $\dfrac{1}{\Omega\,\text{m}}$, or $\Omega^{-1}\text{m}^{-1}$.

Resistors in circuits

You have studied DC circuits and will know something about resistors connected together either in series or in parallel. We can relate an understanding of resistivity to such combinations.

Figure 5.6 shows how four blocks of conducting material (resistive putty perhaps), each with resistance R, might be combined. In Figure 5.6(b) the four blocks are in series and can be considered as one long block. By increasing the length, we know the resistance increases, and this is in keeping with the resistor combination formula:

$$R = R_1 + R_2 + R_3 \dots \qquad (6)$$

Figure 5.6(c) shows how four blocks are equivalent to a single block with four times the cross-sectional area of the original. The four blocks are placed in parallel. We know from experience that the total resistance is reduced. We would expect the resistance to be divided by four, and this is in keeping with the parallel resistance formula:

$$\frac{1}{R} = \frac{1}{R_1} + \frac{1}{R_2} + \frac{1}{R_3} \dots \qquad (7)$$

STUDY NOTE

The chapter *Technology in Space* included expressions for combinations of resistors.

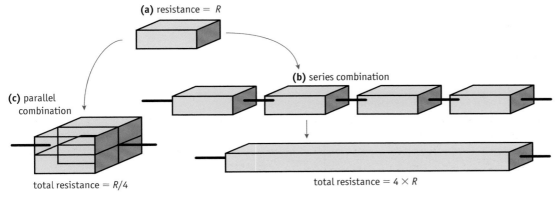

(a) resistance = R

(b) series combination

(c) parallel combination

total resistance = $R/4$

total resistance = $4 \times R$

Figure 5.6 Combining four blocks of resistive material

✪ ACTIVITY 5 MEASURING RESISTIVITY

Determine an accurate value for the resistivity of a metal made into a wire. Use a micrometer to measure its diameter and take electrical measurements when it is connected in a circuit.

QUESTIONS

Q 1 A student found the resistance of a 20 cm length of cable to be 8 Ω. What would you expect the resistance of a metre of the cable to be? What assumption have you made?

Q 2 (a) An archaeologist found that two probes placed in soil 0.5 m apart showed a resistance of 300 Ω. What would you expect the resistance to be if you increased the separation of the probes to 5 m?

(b) The probe spacing in archaeology is typically 0.5 m rather than 5 m. Suggest a reason for this.

Q 3 (a) The resistance of a 10 cm length of resistive putty was found to be 48 Ω. The putty was then rolled to twice its length. Suggest a value for the resistance between its ends and explain your answer.

(b) The original cross-sectional area of the putty in part **(a)** was 1 cm². Use this and the data from part **(a)** to calculate a value for the resistivity of the putty.

Q 4 Derive an expression for the resistance R of a material sample in terms of its length l, area of cross-section A and conductivity σ.

PRACTICAL SKILLS REFERENCE

Scientific questions and information research

See Practical skills notes 1.1–1.4

Planning and experimental design

See Practical skills notes 2.1–2.2

Carrying out practical work

See Practical skills notes 3.1–3.2

Analysis and interpretation of data

See Practical skills notes 4.1–4.2

Conclusion and evaluation

See Practical skills notes 5.1–5.2

Q 5 The resistance readings in Table 5.1 were taken from an archaeologist's notebook. She suspected that a salt-water ditch and a stone wall crossed the path of her linear resistance readings but lie buried beneath the topsoil. Suggest a place for the location of each feature.

Distance from gate to probes/m	Ohm meter reading of resistance between probes/kΩ
1	0.35
2	0.33
3	0.35
4	0.37
5	0.22
6	0.34
7	0.35
8	0.36
9	0.77
10	0.80
11	0.34
12	0.30

Table 5.1 Resistive survey data for Question 5

Comparing resistivities

Table 5.2 lists the resistivities of some materials, and Figure 5.7 is a partially completed bar chart displaying the data.

Material	Resistivity, $\rho/\Omega\,\mathrm{m}$
copper	1.7×10^{-8}
glass	1.0×10^{12}
carbon	1.4×10^{-5}
perspex	1.0×10^{16}
lead	2.1×10^{-7}

Table 5.2 Resistivities of some materials

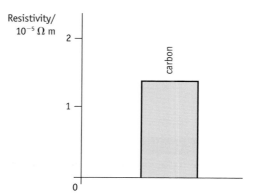

Figure 5.7 A bar chart to display the data from Table 5.2

QUESTION

Q 6 The bar in Figure 5.7, for carbon, is 1.4 cm long. On the same scale, how long would be the bars representing glass and copper? Comment on your answers.

As your answers to Question 6 have shown, there are problems using a linear scale to represent data that range over several orders of magnitude. To compress the range of the numbers, such data are often plotted using a **logarithmic scale** (often shortened to log scale); the logarithm of the value is plotted rather than the value itself.

MATHS REFERENCE

Combining powers
See Maths note 1.3

MATHS REFERENCE

Logs and powers of 10
See Maths note 8.1

Logs on a calculator
See Maths note 8.2

⚙ ACTIVITY 6 PLOTTING ON A LOG SCALE

Copy Table 5.2 and add another column headed '$\log_{10}$ of resistivity'. Use your calculator to find the values of $\log_{10}$ resistivity. Now display these values on a bar chart. Select your own scale factor so that the chart fits into a half page of your notes.

Explaining resistivity

A good electrical conductor, such as the metal wire you used in Activity 5, has a low resistivity. Electrical insulators have much higher resistivities. **Semiconductors**, as their name implies, are a group of materials in the middle of the resistivity spectrum. Table 5.3 lists some typical resistivities of each of these types of material.

Category	Material	Resistivity/$\Omega\,$m
Good conductors	Copper	1.7×10^{-8}
	Lead	2.1×10^{-7}
Semiconductors	Silicon	2.3×10^{3}
	Germanium	4.7×10^{-1}
Insulators	Glass	1.0×10^{12}
	Perspex	1.0×10^{16}

Table 5.3 Conductors, semiconductors and insulators

In the chapter *Technology in Space* you used an equation for the current in a conductor of cross-sectional area A, with n mobile charges per unit volume, each with charge q, drifting with an average speed v:

$$I = nAvq \tag{8}$$

We can relate this equation to the material's resistivity (and conductivity). Start by thinking about the drift speed, v. It must depend on the potential difference, V, applied between the ends of the sample, and it turns out that:

$$v = \frac{kV}{l} \tag{9}$$

where l is the length of the conductor and k is a constant (sometimes known as the **mobility**) that depends on the material. Substituting this expression for v, Equation 8 then becomes:

$$I = \frac{nAkVq}{l} \tag{10}$$

We can compare this with the resistance equation:

$$I = \frac{V}{R} \tag{11}$$

to deduce that:

$$R = \frac{l}{nAkq} \tag{12}$$

Then using Equations 4 and 5 we can write new expressions for resistivity and conductivity:

$$\rho = \frac{1}{nkq} \tag{13}$$

$$\sigma = nkq \tag{14}$$

A simplified model enables us to explain these vast differences in resistivity. The model involves electrons being free from atoms and available to move through the lattice. Figure 5.8(a) illustrates the difference between conductors and insulators.

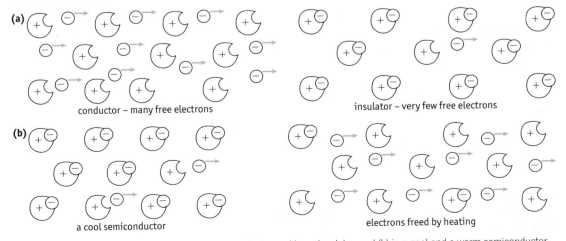

Figure 5.8 Sketches illustrating electrons (a) in a conductor and in an insulator, and (b) in a cool and a warm semiconductor

To explain why some electrons are free to move and others are bound in atoms demands a deep appreciation of the energetics of atoms and is beyond this course. However, it is not difficult to appreciate that, given enough extra energy, a bound electron can become a free electron. The most common example of this effect occurs in semiconductor materials, where a small increase in temperature can have the effect of releasing a large proportion of electrons, vastly increasing their number density n, and so reducing the resistivity of a material dramatically. Semiconductors are very temperature-sensitive (Figure 5.8b) and so find a use in thermistors and temperature-sensing circuits. LDRs (light-dependent resistors) free their electrons through energy supplied by light. The result is the same: better conduction.

QUESTIONS

Q 7 Look back at Section 4.2 of *Technology in Space*, then refer to Equations 9, 13 and 14 above and explain in terms of n, k and q, why heating a metal conductor leads to an increase in its resistance.

Q 8 A length of copper wire is connected to a power supply so that the initial current flowing through it is measured to be 0.70 A. The diameter of the wire is 0.40 mm and the free electron density for the copper is $8.48 \times 10^{28}\,\text{m}^{-3}$.

  (a) Calculate the drift velocity of the free electrons.

  (b) If the wire is 500 mm in length, calculate the resistance of the wire using the resistivity from Table 5.3.

  (c) Calculate the value of the pd applied between the ends of the wire.

1.3 Potential difference and potential dividing

Resistance surveying essentially involves measuring the potential difference between parts of an electric circuit, as described below. This section looks more closely at the meaning of a voltage and involves estimating and calculating potential differences in simple circuits.

Multi-probe techniques

To introduce you to the idea of a resistive survey, the earlier work in this section was restricted to the simple case of two resistance probes sunk into the soil. A more advanced technique, pioneered by Frank Wenner in 1916, uses a voltmeter to probe positions along a line of soil in which there are two other probes connected to a power supply. Figure 5.9 shows a simplified version of the arrangement.

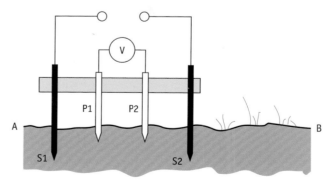

Figure 5.9 Multi-probe resistance surveying

STUDY NOTE

For more on the Hog's Back survey, see *Digging Up the Past* Additional Sheet 1.

Probes S1 and S2 are the electrodes connected to the supply. (In the field, an alternating supply is used to avoid problems of gaseous build up at the electrodes due to electrolysis.) P1 and P2 are a second pair of probes at a fixed separation that are connected to a voltmeter. By using the voltmeter probes along the line AB, a map of potential differences can be built up. As the pd between fixed points is related to the resistance between the points, the voltmeter readings indicate patches of high and low resistance.

The Wenner arrangement was used in 1971 to probe the site of a prehistoric ditch on the Hog's Back in Surrey. The results are shown schematically in Figure 5.10, together with a sketch of the ditch.

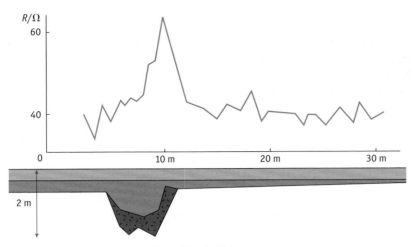

Figure 5.10 A survey of the Hog's Back revealed a prehistoric ditch

Resistive tomography

The availability of fast computer sampling has made possible a technique in resistive surveying known as 'resistive tomography' (Figure 5.11). This uses a linear array of probes, 14 in this example. The probes are placed in location and the potential differences between all possible probe combinations are sampled using an interfaced field computer. The computer will then generate a resistive map of the ground in a vertical plane immediately below the row of probes. As the array of probes is advanced across a site, the computer can eventually generate a three-dimensional resistive image of the entire area to a depth of a few metres. This can be done 'live' on site.

STUDY NOTE

The word 'tomography' means 'drawing a slice'; the same word is used in some types of medical imaging, e.g. computerised tomography (CT) scanning.

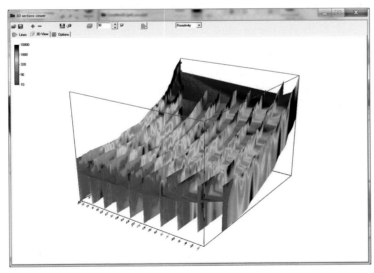

Figure 5.11 Resistive tomography survey showing vertical 'slices'

Beyond archaeology

Resistive surveying has many applications beyond archaeology. As far back as the 1920s, resistivity measurements were proposed as a method for locating coal reserves, and it is now one of a range of techniques used to map the rocks and minerals that lie beneath the ground. The practice of drilling a small borehole vertically downwards in order to extract samples of material for testing is still an important stage of the process. However, thanks to the development of inexpensive data logging equipment and computing power, what was once a very time-consuming, laborious survey process, usually involving relatively coarse measurements, has become much more efficient, allowing for more intricate and complex resistivity maps to be drawn. Figure 5.12 shows the resistivities of various materials that are commonly found on Earth (note the logarithmic scale).

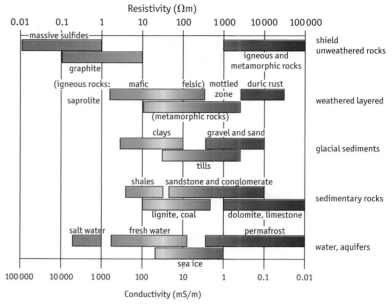

Figure 5.12 Resistivity ranges for different material types

Figure 5.13 shows a cross-section produced using resistive tomography in an area of Pennsylvania, USA, where an abandoned coal mine is known to exist. The mined-out regions from which coal has been extracted are indicated by regions of low resistivity, possibly due to the presence of water. Erecting buildings above voids such as these, which exist at shallow depths below the surface, can pose a safety risk, with buildings potentially subsiding and in extreme cases ground giving way.

(MSL is mean sea level. Note the use of ohm-ft as the unit for resistivity here; this is not uncommon practice in the USA, but is very unusual in other parts of the world (1 ft = 0.3048 m).)

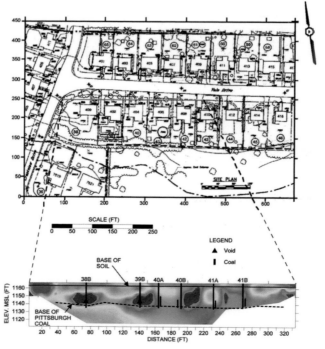

Figure 5.13 Resistivity survey of a former coal mine

Resistive measurements are also used on the human body; they provide a very cost-effective way of determining the proportion of body fat. Bathroom scales can be made so that when someone stands on them, they effectively connect themselves into a simple circuit. A pd is applied between their feet and an ammeter within the scales detects the current. This is the principle behind 'Bioelectrical Impedance Analysis' (which will often utilise alternating current). Fat contains little water in comparison to lean tissue and so will have a higher resistivity. A drawback of this method is that the user's level of hydration affects the reading. However, by measuring the person's resistance, the instrument can produce an estimate of the proportion of fat within the body.

Dividing the potential

Before going any further, you would be advised to recall that voltmeters are connected 'across' components and that a voltage represents the energy transferred as electric charges pass through a component.

⚙ ACTIVITY 7 ENERGY IN CIRCUITS

Consider the two circuits shown in Figure 5.14. Discuss with a friend whether each circuit diagram makes sense. Consider in particular the conservation of energy.

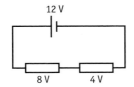
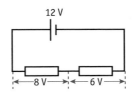

Figure 5.14 Two circuit diagrams for Activity 7

Your discussion in Activity 7 ought to have identified that in the second circuit there appears to be more energy 'transformed' by the charges as they pass through the resistors than the cell could supply (remember that $1\,V = 1\,J\,C^{-1}$). If the cell supplies each coulomb of charge with $12\,J$ of energy, then no more than $12\,J$ can be transferred by each coulomb. A simple statement that summarises this conservation of energy is to say that, in such a circuit, the sum of pd values across the resistors in a series circuit must match the pd from the cell. Activity 8 explores this idea further.

⚙ ACTIVITY 8 SPLITTING THE POTENTIAL DIFFERENCE

Use circuits such as those in Figure 5.15 to explore the relationships between resistances and potential differences. Look in particular at the ratios of the resistances and of the potential differences.

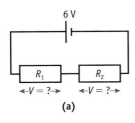
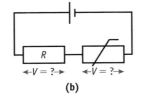
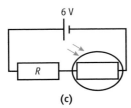
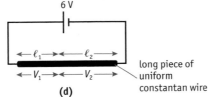

Figure 5.15 Circuit diagrams for Activity 8

Potential divider circuits

The type of circuit you have used in Activity 8 is known as a **potential divider**: the terminal potential difference of a supply is divided between series resistors in the ratio of their resistances or, in the case of a uniform wire, the ratio of the distances from the contact point to the ends.

This type of circuit is widely used in a variety of applications that range far beyond archaeology. There are two important ways in which potential dividers are used.

Variable voltage supply

You are probably familiar with low-voltage power supply units where you can adjust the output voltage by turning a knob. Inside the unit, a fixed (low) voltage is applied between the ends of a coil of resistance wire, and by turning the knob you move a sliding contact along the coil so that the output voltage varies between zero and the maximum possible value. You can replicate this arrangement in the laboratory using a rheostat (variable resistor) with three terminals and by connecting a battery between the two outer terminals (Figure 5.16). The output can be used as the voltage supply for another circuit. The resistor inside the unit provides the internal resistance of the variable-voltage power supply.

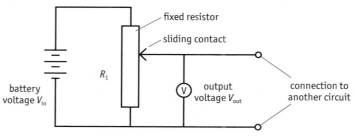

Figure 5.16 Variable voltage supply

Sensors

Many electrical devices are designed to respond to changes in conditions such as temperature or illumination; for example, street lamps that switch on when it gets dark, and ovens that stop heating up when they reach a given temperature. The sensors in such devices usually contain a potential divider circuit made up of a fixed resistor in series with one whose resistance changes, such as a thermistor or an LDR as shown in Figure 5.17. The output from the potential divider is used to control a switching circuit. Usually, if the potential divider output voltage falls below a certain threshold voltage, the switch turns on the power in another circuit; if the potential divider output rises above the threshold, the power is turned off.

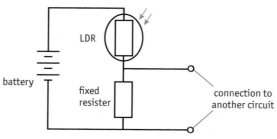

Figure 5.17 Light-sensing circuit

What difference?

Have you ever wondered why voltage is called potential *difference*? The difference between what and what? Consider the simple arrangement of two resistors in Figure 5.18. Without setting up the circuit, you ought to be able to identify the value of the pd across each resistor.

The answer is 4 V and 8 V. The values 4 V and 8 V are potential differences. The word 'difference' implies a subtraction of two values. What two values could you use to produce 8 V? Obviously 8 V and 0 V come to mind. But also 9 V and 1 V, or 15 V and 7 V. They will each produce a difference of 8 V.

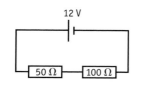

Figure 5.18 Two resistors in a circuit

These pairs of numbers suggested are known as **potentials**. Their difference is naturally enough called a **potential difference**. It is conventional to label the negative terminal of a battery or cell as having a potential of zero. If the battery provides a potential difference of 12 V, then the positive terminal will be labelled +12 V, so a potential difference of 12 V.

STUDY NOTE
For more about potential, see *Digging Up the Past* Additional Sheet 2.

⚙ ACTIVITY 9 POTENTIAL

Consider the two circuits shown in Figure 5.19. The circuit in Figure 5.19(a) has a number of places labelled with potentials. The potential differences are also shown. Look over this circuit so that you can follow the reason for the potential values.

Copy the circuit in Figure 5.19(b) and label the places marked X with suitable potentials. Take the cell negative terminal as zero. One of the potential differences is included as a clue.

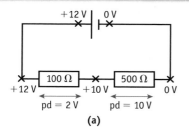 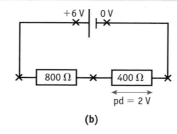

Figure 5.19 Circuit diagrams for Activity 9

In resistive surveying, the surveyor is mapping potential and potential differences in a three-dimensional object (the ground) so the situation is somewhat harder to analyse theoretically than that in Activity 9. Activity 10 is an extension activity in which you can explore variations of potential in two dimensions.

⚙ ACTIVITY 10 POTENTIAL IN TWO DIMENSIONS

Use an arrangement such as that shown in Figure 5.20 to explore the variation in potential in a two-dimensional object. Plot a map of potential on a piece of graph paper. Look for points that have the same potential; you can link these with a line called an **equipotential** line.

1.4 Summing up Part 1

In this section you have reviewed and extended your knowledge of electric circuits and learned how the idea of resistivity is used in archaeological surveys. You have also considered some ethical issues relating to archaeological investigation. Activity 11 is designed to help you consolidate what you have learned and also to develop your communication skills.

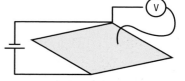

Figure 5.20 Diagram for Activity 10

⚙ ACTIVITY 11 SUMMING UP PART 1: SURVEYING THE FIELD

Imagine that you are a member of an archaeological team – perhaps a friend has dragged you along to a summer vacation 'holiday' site for company. The historical evidence suggests that a nearby field belonging to a local farmer, Mr Muncastle, is a likely site for the location of a Roman villa. The team you are working with want to carry out a resistive survey of the field. They have persuaded you to write to the farmer asking permission to gain access to his field for a survey, lasting about a day. (He will have to usher his bull into another field and is not too sure what damage you might do.)

Write a letter to Mr Muncastle to explain the non-destructive nature of the test in a language that he will appreciate and to also explain what will happen during the day.

Prepare for a meeting with Mr Muncastle to do a deal with him in the event that the survey is positive and the team wants to spend four days excavating a corner of his field. What do you anticipate he will say? How will your team respond?

FURTHER INVESTIGATION

If you have an opportunity for further practical work, you might consider the following suggestion:

Use Teledeltos paper to explore the equipotentials and electric field around conductors with a variety of shapes. In particular, look at the potential gradient around sharp points. Think how this might relate to the operation of a lightning conductor and to guidelines on safe behaviour during thunderstorms.

QUESTIONS

Q 9 For the circuits shown in Figure 5.21:

    (a) calculate the value of the pd when the voltmeter is attached as shown by the broken lines

    (b) state the potential at each of the places marked X.

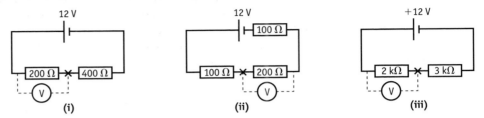

Figure 5.21 Circuit diagrams for Question 8

Q 10 Heavy vehicles can distort older steel and iron bridges. To monitor these distortions, scientists use an instrument called a strain gauge. A strain gauge is a thin strip of metal (Figure 5.22). When it stretches it gets longer and thinner, and this changes its resistance. You can monitor this change using a potential divider circuit.

    (a) If a strain gauge is stretched, in what way will its resistance change? Will it increase or decrease?

    (b) If the length of a strain gauge increases by 10%, by what factor will the resistance change? Explain your answer.

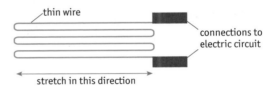

Figure 5.22 Schematic diagram of a strain gauge

The gauge shown in Figure 5.22 has a total uncoiled length of 28 cm. The thin strip is 0.6 mm wide and 0.002 mm thick. The resistivity of the metal used is $2.6 \times 10^{-6}\,\Omega\,\text{m}$.

    (c) Calculate the resistance of the strain gauge.

The gauge is connected in series with a fixed resistor to form a potential divider. A 6 V supply is used to provide the pd across the divider. The fixed resistor, R, must be chosen so that the pd across the strain gauge is 1.2 V when it is unstretched.

    (d) Calculate the value of the fixed resistor, R.

Q 11 Overhead power lines are constructed of aluminium strands wrapped around one or more steel core cables (Figure 5.23). Aluminium is a very good conductor, but is very ductile and so long cables are prone to stretch under their own weight when spanning large distances. The steel core is used to provide the composite cable with increased stiffness and strength.

A typical cable is constructed of 88 aluminium strands, each with a diameter of 3 mm, wrapped around seven steel core wires of diameter 5 mm.

    (a) Calculate the resistance of one aluminium strand of length 1.1 km, given that the resistivity of the aluminium is $2.9 \times 10^{-8}\,\Omega\,\text{m}$.

    (b) Repeat part (a) for one of the steel strands of resistivity $4.1 \times 10^{-7}\,\text{m}$.

    (c) What would be the overall resistance of a 1.1 km length of the multi-strand cable?

    (d) What would be the advantages and disadvantages of using polymer core strands in place of the steel strands?

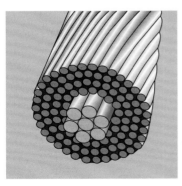

Figure 5.23 A power cable

Q 12 **(a)** A uniform wire has a resistance of 50 Ω and is connected to cell so that it has 6 V across its length, *l*, as shown in Figure 5.24. Sketch a graph to show how the reading on the voltmeter will change as the probe separation *d* is increased by sliding the right-hand probe along the test wire. Your graph should show pd on the *y*-axis and probe separation (*d*) on the *x*-axis.

(b) Two pieces of conducting paper (Teledeltos) are now connected to the 6 V cell as shown in Figure 5.25, using connecting wires with negligible resistance. Each piece has a total resistance of 100 Ω between the points where it is connected. Sketch a graph to show how the pd measured by the voltmeter will change as the right-hand probe of the voltmeter is moved from left to right across the arrangement.

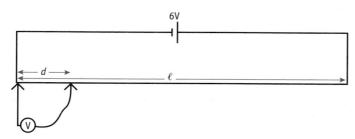

Figure 5.24 Diagram for Question 12(a)

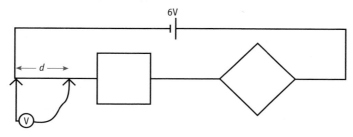

Figure 5.25 Diagram for Question 12(b)

2 The inside story

2.1 X-rays

Once artefacts have been recovered, the real investigation begins. **X-rays** are invaluable in probing the finds, both to discover what lies hidden within and to determine from what materials they are made and how best to conserve them.

MATHS REFERENCE

Logs and powers of 10
See Maths note 8.1

Logs on a calculator
See Maths note 8.2

⚙ ACTIVITY 12 THE ELECTROMAGNETIC SPECTRUM

Table 5.4 lists the typical wavelengths of the radiation that makes up the electromagnetic spectrum. Use these values to produce a labelled 'number line' showing the various regions of the spectrum. First, try plotting the wavelengths on a linear scale and note any problems this creates. Then copy Table 5.4 and add another column, headed 'log$_{10}$ of wavelength'. Complete this column (you should be able to do most of this without using a calculator) and then plot the values of log$_{10}$ of wavelength on a number line. Choose a scale so that the entire spectrum fits across the page in your notes.

Type of radiation	Approximate wavelength range/m
γ-rays	10^{-14} (or less) $- 10^{-11}$
X-rays	$10^{-11} - 10^{-8}$
Ultraviolet	$10^{-8} - 4 \times 10^{-7}$
Visible	$4 \times 10^{-7} - 7 \times 10^{-7}$
Infrared	$7 \times 10^{-7} - 10^{-3}$
Microwaves	$10^{-3} - 10^{-1}$
Radio	$10^{-1} - 10^3$ or more

Table 5.4 The electromagnetic spectrum

In Activity 12 you used a wave model for X-rays. In *The Sound of Music* and *Technology in Space* you used a photon model for electromagnetic radiation. An X-ray photon has higher energy than a photon of visible light, which explains why X-rays are so penetrating and cause ionisation.

STUDY NOTE

For more on X-rays, see *Digging Up the Past* Additional Sheet 3.

What's inside?

Soon after Wilhelm Röntgen discovered X-rays in 1895, the archaeologist Sir Flinders Petrie obtained the first X-ray of a mummified leg. A little later, Elliot Smith and Howard Carter told of their experience transferring the rigid mummified Pharaoh Tithmosis VI by taxicab to a private X-ray unit in Cairo Hospital. Today, conservators routinely use X-rays to assess the condition of archaeological finds (Figure 5.26); one of the greatest benefits of X-radiography is that it is a non-destructive technique.

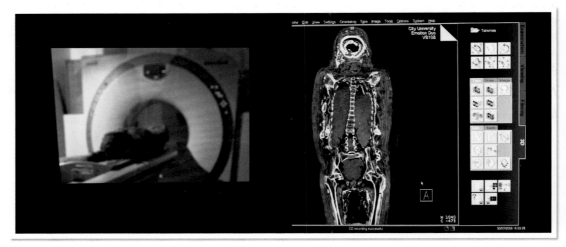

Figure 5.26 A mummy being scanned

'Pete Marsh', the Iron Age human body found in Lindow Moss in Cheshire, was X-rayed using the technique of computer-aided tomography (CAT), whereby images of 'slices' of the body can be studied. Such scans have been invaluable in investigating pathological changes and the process of mummification.

In 1976 a major archaeological dig of a Viking settlement in York produced such a wealth of finds that it was decided to build the now world-famous Jorvik Centre on the site. Many Anglo-Saxon artefacts were later unearthed, including an almost-intact helmet, known as the Coppergate helmet (after the area where it was found). The helmet was lifted carefully form the ground and eventually X-rayed and CAT-scanned at York District Hospital. The X-rays (Figure 5.27) revealed the presence of corroded chain mail and one of the cheek pieces inside the helmet, which helped archaeologists with the painstaking process of conservation.

The spot where the Coppergate helmet was found is marked by a plaque in the entrance of the Jorvik Centre in Coppergate, York. The helmet itself can be seen at the nearby Castle Museum.

QUESTIONS

Q 13 Explain why the term 'shadow radiograph' is appropriate for a conventional X-ray image.

Q 14 Explain the difference between conventional X-ray images and X-ray tomography.

Q 15 Suggest why there was concern that the York hospital CAT scanner might not give satisfactory images of the Coppergate helmet and its contents.

Q 16 Explain, using diagrams if necessary, how taking both horizontal and vertical radiographs enabled the archaeologists to pinpoint the precise location of the items inside the helmet.

Q 17 In addition to determining the nature and location of the contents of the helmet, what other information did archaeologists obtain through using X-rays?

2.2 X-ray diffraction

As well as using X-rays to probe the content of artefacts, another technique – X-ray diffraction – is a powerful tool in determining the precise composition of the materials that make up the object. This can lead archaeologists to a better understanding of the sources of the materials used, the methods used in manufacturing objects and how best to prevent further corrosion.

The archaeologist's view of X-ray diffraction

As well as using X-rays to 'see' what an artefact consists of, it is possible to use X-rays to analyse precisely what materials were used to create it. X-ray diffraction is a technique that use **monochromatic** (i.e. single-wavelength) X-rays to identify which crystalline minerals are present, and it will reveal not only whether an element is present as an oxide or other compound but also the proportions of each mineral present and the phases of the minerals (i.e. the forms of crystal lattice; see Figure 5.28). It can be applied to metal, ceramic or stone artefacts and the pigments used to decorate them.

Archaeologists use X-ray diffraction for various purposes, including the following:

● Conservators are interested in the corrosion products present. This allows them to know more about the burial history of the artefact, for example its exposure to water or oxides present in the soil surrounding it. This helps them to determine the best conservation techniques to prevent further deterioration of the object.

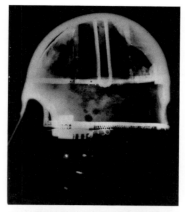
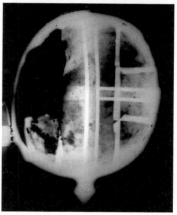

Figure 5.27 Some of the original radiographs of the Coppergate helmet

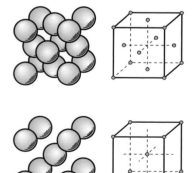

Figure 5.28 Different phases of a mineral

● Archaeologists can determine the raw materials used to create the object. This may give an indication of the sources of these raw materials, which is helpful in determining ancient trade routes and other aspects of ancient economy and society. More importantly, the precise composition of alloys, often determined by investigation of the slags and residues left in metal workshops, can indicate the techniques used to manufacture them.

● X-ray diffraction analysis will provide information on the thermal treatments to which metal artefacts were subjected during their fabrication. For example, cold working a metal results in fragmentation and distortion of the crystal grains, whereas annealing results in the growth of large, undistorted crystal grains that give very distinctive X-ray diffraction patterns.

● Study of the pigments used to decorate objects can provide an insight into the techniques of manufacture of the pigment and its application to the surface of the object. Different oxides were used to produce a particular colour in different places across the ancient world at different times. A study of similarities and differences in techniques for producing pigments can indicate whether groups were developing in isolation or influenced each other. The same technique can identify the true colours used in, for example, 17th-century works of art (Figure 5.29) to aid accurate restoration.

Figure 5.29 A seventeenth-century work of art

How does X-ray diffraction work?

The simplest version of X-ray diffraction takes a thin slice of material and allows the X-rays to pass through it, or else passes the X-rays through a powdered sample of the material. You can simulate this using a fine powder sandwiched between two microscope slides. Another simulation uses a diffraction grating (a regular array of very narrow lines ruled on transparent plastic or glass) in front of the laser – this produces a very different pattern.

⚙ ACTIVITY 13 SIMULATING X-RAY DIFFRACTION

Observe the patterns produced on a screen when a laser shines through some fine powder and through one or more diffraction gratings (Figure 5.30). Try using two gratings together, crossed at various angles to one another. With other students, brainstorm your ideas about how these different patterns are produced.

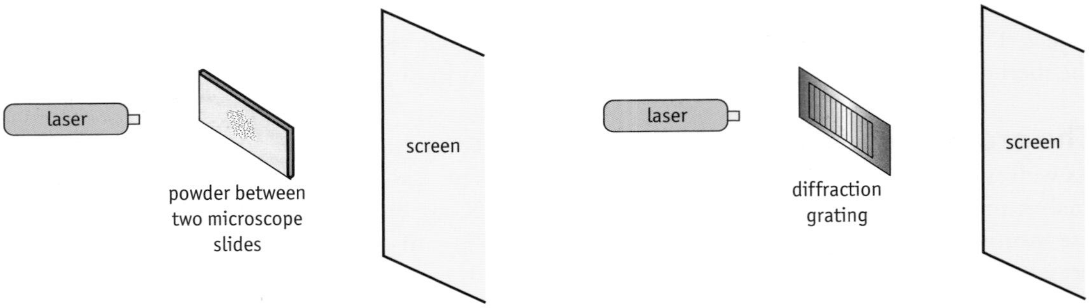

STUDY NOTE

To review your knowledge of diffraction and superposition, see *Digging Up the Past* Additional Sheets 4 and 5.

laser — powder between two microscope slides — screen

laser — diffraction grating — screen

Figure 5.30 Diagrams for Activity 13

To explain the two effects you have just seen you will need to understand three phenomena: **diffraction**, **superposition** and **interference**.

Diffraction (the spreading of waves) and interference (when coherent waves undergo superposition and reinforce or cancel each other) combine to give the effects seen when you shine a laser through a single crystal or a powdered polycrystalline sample to give intense points of light at certain well-defined points (as seen in Activity 13). If we know more about the precise mechanisms involved, we can use this phenomenon to find out more about the sample.

ACTIVITY 14 DOING DIFFRACTION – INVESTIGATING INTERFERENCE
Explore the effects of diffraction and interference of different waves through a series of three experiments: a ripple tank, a laser and microwaves.

Activity 14 illustrates diffraction – the spreading of waves into unexpected areas. For significant diffraction to take place, the gap or obstacle must be comparable in size to the wavelength of the waves used. If coherent waves travel through different distances and then meet up again, superposition produces an interference pattern. If waves pass through a regular array of gaps or obstacles, such as a diffraction grating, then diffraction gives rise to many sets of overlapping waves that produce a **diffraction pattern** when they superpose. You can demonstrate that by shining a laser through fine gauze (Figure 5.31); the finer the gauze, the greater the spacing of the dots in the pattern. The spacing of the dots also depends on the wavelength of the light: the longer the wavelength, the greater the spacing – you can demonstrate this if you have lasers of different colours e.g. red and green.

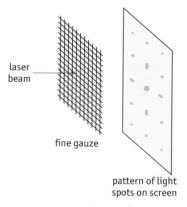

Figure 5.31 Producing an optical diffraction pattern

Von Laue's experiment
The use of X-rays to analyse materials is based on an experiment performed early in the 20th century by the German physicist Max von Laue (1879–1960).

After X-rays were discovered in 1896, their nature was the subject of much speculation and experiment. They were found not to be charged particles because they were not deflected by electric or magnetic fields, unlike electrons (whose deflection was discovered and explained by J.J. Thomson in 1897). In 1912 von Laue succeeded in showing that X-rays were electromagnetic waves by obtaining an interference effect. All attempts had so far failed, as the gap size used was far greater than the wavelength of the X-rays. Then a crystal was used to diffract the X-rays and cause interference patterns. Figure 5.32 shows the basic set up of von Laue's experiments.

The central bright spot surrounded by fainter pattern of surrounding spots (as in Figure 5.33) confirmed that X-rays were waves, and measurements showed that their wavelength was of the order 10^{-10} m. It is precisely this effect that you saw with the laser shone through crossed gratings in Activity 13.

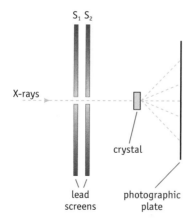

Figure 5.32 Von Laue's experimental set up

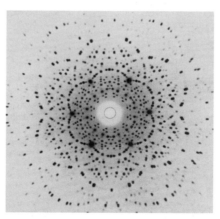

Figure 5.33 A modern X-ray diffraction photograph

2.3 Diffraction grating

Huygens' principle
We can explore the principles underlying von Laue's experiment by analysing what happens when light passes through a **diffraction grating**. A diffraction grating consists of a regular array of narrow slits, so we can think of it as a very simple one-dimensional crystal that produces noticeable diffraction with visible light, rather than X-rays. Diffraction gratings are usually made with a few hundred slits per mm, so the slit size and separation (about 10^{-6} m) are comparable with the wavelengths of visible light.

Each slit can diffract light through a large angle. Diffraction occurs at all the slits and, in certain directions, the waves interfere constructively and give a beam of light that produces a bright spot on a screen.

To understand how this works, we use **Huygens' principle** (or **Huygens' construction**), named after Dutch physicist Christiaan Huygens (1629–1695), who was one of the earliest people to suggest that light travels as waves. According to this principle, each point on a wavefront is the source of a new spherical wavefront known as a **secondary wavelet**. The new wavefront is the tangent to all the secondary wavelets.

Figure 5.34 shows Huygens' principle used to construct a plane wave travelling at constant speed and how the shape of the wavefront changes as it passes through a slit. In these diagrams, only a few secondary wavelets are shown, but you need to imagine that every single point on the wavefront produces a secondary wavelet.

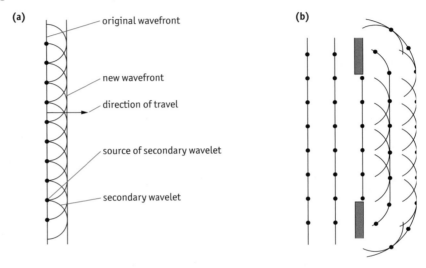

Figure 5.34 Huygens' principle applied to a plane wave (a) unobstructed (b) passing through a slit

QUESTIONS

Q 18 Use Huygens' principle to construct the shape of a wave spreading out from a point source at constant speed.

Q 19 Figure 5.35 shows plane wavefronts in a beam of light crossing a boundary from air to glass. Use Huygens' principle to construct the wavefronts within the glass and show the direction of the refracted beam.

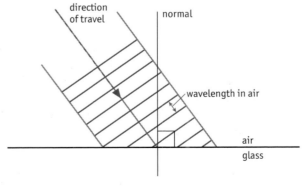

Figure 5.35 Diagram for Question 19

The grating equation

Figure 5.36 shows Huygens' principle applied to a diffraction grating. The distance marked d is called the **spacing** of the grating; it is the distance from the centre of one slit to the centre of the next. Each slit is a source of secondary wavelets, and since there are no wavelets from points between the slits, there are now several different tangents that can be drawn across all the secondary wavefronts. These tangents are new plane wavefronts that emerge from the grating; there are light beams travelling in several different directions as well as the straight-through direction.

Figure 5.36 shows that beams of light emerge only in directions where the secondary wavelets are in phase; that is, where the path difference between waves from one slit and its neighbour is a whole number of wavelengths. Figure 5.37 shows the direction of waves travelling at an angle θ. The path difference between neighbouring slits is marked p, and it is one side of a right-angled triangle with hypotenuse d:

$$p = d\sin\theta \qquad (15)$$

STUDY NOTE

You met path difference and phase difference in *The Sound of Music*.

MATHS REFERENCE

Sine, cosine and tangent of an angle

See Maths note 6.2

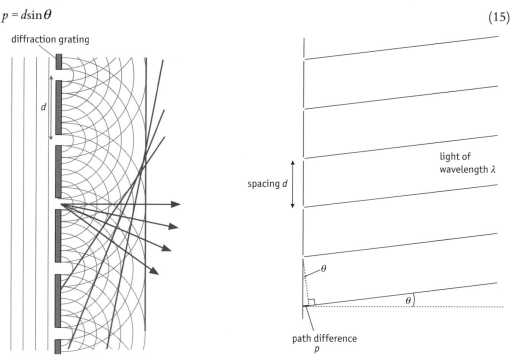

Figure 5.36 Huygens' principle applied to a diffraction grating

Figure 5.37 The paths of waves emerging from part of a diffraction grating

The condition for a bright beam to emerge from the grating is therefore described by the **diffraction gating equation**:

$$d\sin\theta_n = n\lambda \qquad (16)$$

where n is a whole number (including zero) and θ_n is the angle of the nth bright beam counting round from the centre. The number n is known as the **diffraction order**. If $n = 0$ there is no path difference, the waves are all in phase and we see the central bright beam (called the zero-order beam) shining straight through the grating. For $n = 1, 2$, etc., there is a bright beam on each side of the centre; these are less bright than the central beam because the light diffracted by each slit decreases in brightness at larger angles. The beam with $n = 1$ is called the first order beam, $n = 2$ is the second order and so on.

The number of diffraction orders is limited by the wavelength of the light and the grating spacing. The value of $\sin\theta$ can be no greater than 1. This corresponds to light emerging at $\theta = 90°$, so that the path difference between light emerging from neighbouring slits is equal to the spacing, d. The path difference cannot be any greater than d.

STUDY NOTE

For analysis of another situation involving diffraction by narrow slits, see *Digging Up the Past* Additional Sheet 6.

QUESTIONS

Q 20 A diffraction grating has 300 lines per mm. Light from a sodium lamp, wavelength 589 nm, shines through the grating.

    (a) What is the grating spacing expressed in metres?

    (b) What is the angle of the first-order diffracted beam?

    (c) What is the highest diffraction order possible with this light and this grating?

Q 21 Explain what happens if a beam of white light shines through a diffraction grating onto a white screen.

Using diffraction

When analysing crystals and archaeological artefacts, radiation (X-rays) of known wavelength is used to probe the structure and to deduce the arrangements of atoms and their spacing. Yet experiments 'the other way round' are very widely used: in other words, using a grating of known spacing to determine an unknown wavelength. This is what you will do in Activity 16.

✿ ACTIVITY 15 DIFFRACTION GRATING
Use a diffraction grating to determine the wavelength of light from a laser or other light source.

Powder photos

The diffraction grating equation describes a relatively simple situation: diffraction by a one-dimensional array of slits. Diffraction by a crystal is more complex to analyse. One approach is to treat a crystal as a combination of several gratings, all with different spacings and orientations; this quickly becomes very complicated. Another approach is the one devised by crystallographer Lawrence Bragg (1890–1971), who realised that the planes of atoms in a crystal can be regarded like mirrors that reflect X-rays, and that strong reflected beams only shine out when the radiation reflected from successive layers is in phase, as shown in Figure 5.38.

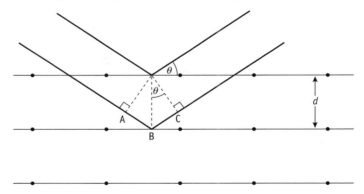

Figure 5.38 X-rays are reflected from successive layers of a crystal

✿ ACTIVITY 16 DIFFRACTION BY CRYSTALS
Use a ripple tank to see the diffraction effects produced by a two-dimensional 'crystal'. Then use microwave apparatus to see the same effect in three dimensions.

QUESTION

Q 22 Use Figure 5.38 to derive an equation for the angles at which strong beams will emerge from the crystal.

Most X-ray diffraction studies of archaeological (and other) materials use a technique known as **powder photography**, which is based on Bragg's analysis. A sample of the material is ground to a powder (this is a destructive technique, unlike radiography), which is then turned into a rod-shaped specimen either by mixing it with an adhesive or by sealing it in a glass capillary tube. The rod is placed in a cylindrical X-ray camera and illuminated with a beam of monochromatic X-rays (Figure 5.39). As the X-rays are reflected off successive layers of atoms, they undergo interference, and the film in the camera records a number of bright lines (areas of constructive interference; see Figure 5.40). The distances between these lines give information on the crystal lattice spacing of the crystals present, which is then used to identify the actual composition of the object by comparing the patterns of lines with the lines formed by known substances. (This powder technique cannot be used to determine the crystal form of metals, as the powdering distorts the crystal lattice; instead, a thin slice of the artefact has to be used.)

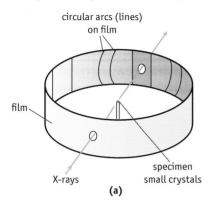
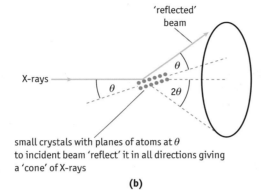

(a)   **(b)**

Figure 5.39 An X-ray powder camera

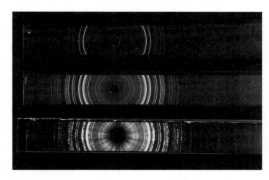

Figure 5.40 Typical X-ray powder photos

> ⚙ **ACTIVITY 17 WHERE HAS IT BEEN?**
> The Coppergate Helmet was subjected to X-ray diffraction analysis in order to determine what it was made from and the likely conditions in which it was buried. Study the relevant X-ray diffraction spectra and write a short report on the deductions that can be made.

2.4 Summing up Part 2

In this section you have seen how the composition of artefacts can be analysed using X-rays. You have also had several opportunities to develop skills of communication.

> ⚙ **ACTIVITY 18 SUMMING UP PART 2**
> Spend a few minutes checking through your notes and make sure you understand all the terms printed in **bold**. Then add notes on diffraction to your summary of wave properties from MUS Activity 25.

QUESTIONS

Q 23 Explain why a sound from the far side of a doorway can be heard in all parts of a room but light passing through the same doorway casts a sharp shadow.

Q 24 Light shining through a grating with 500 lines per mm produces a second-order beam at an angle of 35°. What is the wavelength of the light expressed in nm?

Q 25 Steel components corrode (rust) in various ways when exposed to air, rain and heating. The compounds FeO (iron oxide), Fe_2O_3 (iron(III) oxide), Fe_3O_4 (tri-iron tetroxide) and $Fe_2O_3H_2O$ (hydrated iron(III) oxide) can be formed, depending on the type of steel and its situation. Knowledge of which oxide(s) are present can help the manufacturer and the user of the steel.

X-ray diffraction is frequently used to analyse the corrosion products. The corroded surface layer of the steel component is scraped off, ground into a powder, placed in the X-ray camera and exposed to X-rays.

A drawing of an X-ray diffraction photograph for one particular sample is shown in Figure 5.41, together with those of pure iron and some known oxides. The original photographs were all negatives and so the dark lines indicate a high exposure to X-radiation.

Using the images in Figure 5.41, state which oxide was present in the corroded surface layer (in addition to iron itself).

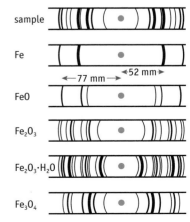

Figure 5.41 X-ray diffraction images for Question 25

3 Taking a closer look

When an artefact is uncovered at an archaeological dig, one of the first investigations may be to use an optical microscope to look at it in more detail. This can be done on the site, as optical microscopes are very portable. However, optical microscopes have their limitations, so artefacts are sometimes taken to a laboratory for more detailed examination using an electron microscope. This part of the chapter is about how optical and electron microscopes are used in archaeology.

3.1 Seeing the detail

A typical human eye can only **resolve** (distinguish between) two point-like objects if they are separated by at least 0.1 mm when viewed from 25 cm away. The **resolution** of the eye is limited by diffraction. As light waves pass through the pupil of the eye, they are diffracted, so the image is slightly blurred. The wavelength of visible light is very much smaller than the width of the pupil, so the amount of diffraction is very small. However, if the two images are very close together on the retina, they merge together and it is impossible to distinguish between them. Figure 5.42 shows this effect with light passing through a much smaller aperture than the pupil of the eye, and Activity 19 illustrates the limits to the resolution of your own eyes.

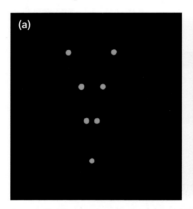 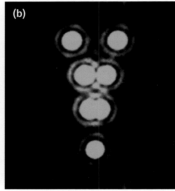 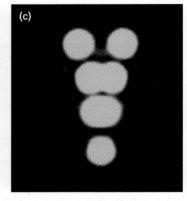

Figure 5.42 (a) A set of light sources; (b) the sources viewed through an aperture (the two closest sources are barely resolved); (c) the same sources viewed through a smaller aperture (the two closest sources are not resolved)

> **⚙ ACTIVITY 19 SEEING THE DETAIL**
>
> Use a fine dark-coloured pen to draw two parallel lines a few mm apart on a piece of white card. Place the card several metres away and walk slowly towards it. Record the distance at which you are first able to see the two lines separately. From these measurements, calculate the smallest separation that you would be able to resolve from a distance of 25 cm.

An optical microscope with a magnification of 500 can be used to observe detail down to a scale of 0.2 μm (200 nm). A feature 0.2 μm wide will have an image 0.1 mm wide, which you can resolve when you observe it from a distance of about 25 cm using the microscope.

> **⚙ ACTIVITY 20 OPTICAL MICROSCOPE**
>
> Use an optical microscope to look at some artefacts.

Figure 5.43 shows optical microscope pictures of some archaeological specimens. If archaeologists could see smaller objects clearly, such as details of pollen grains, this would give them more information to help work out, for example, the age of the site and whether it has been disturbed. A grain of pollen is about 40 μm in size (though they vary between about 10 μm and 100 μm).

A feature that is 0.1 μm wide and magnified 1000 times would give the same size image as an object 0.2 μm wide and magnified 500 times, yet there is a problem. The wavelength of visible

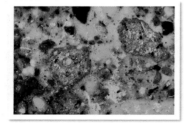

Figure 5.43 An optical microscope image of a fragment of the material used to construct a Roman bath. The sample is dated 450 BC showing the longevity of building materials from this period. Magnification ×7.

light is between about 750 and 400 nm, so features of about 750 nm and smaller will themselves produce noticeable diffraction of the light waves. This will blur the image produced by the microscope. As you saw in Activity 14, an object that is much smaller than the wavelength will not cast a shadow, so this limits the size of objects that can be seen with an optical microscope; objects smaller than 200 nm (0.2 μm) simply do not produce an image.

Furthermore, there is a limit to the detail that can be seen within a larger object: the smaller the feature the greater the blurring, and magnifying the image makes no difference to its clarity. For detail on a scale of a few hundred nm, the blurring is considerable, and below the 200 nm limit it is no longer possible to distinguish features at all.

A design brief for a microscope similar to an optical microscope but with a greater magnification would say that it needed to use radiation with a shorter wavelength than visible light. The obvious choice would ultraviolet or X-rays, but there are difficulties in designing lenses for these regions of the electromagnetic spectrum. Fortunately another solution is available – the electron microscope, which uses different waves and can be used to study pollen grains (Figure 5.44) and other minute objects.

Figure 5.44 Electron micrographs of pollen grains

3.2 Electron waves

Beams of electrons can be diffracted. You probably find this quite surprising since diffraction is something that waves do, whereas you have probably always thought of electrons as particles.

The wave-like side of the electron's character was discovered in the 1920s, and the discovery came about in two ways. First came a theoretical prediction by the French scientist Prince Louis de Broglie (1892–1987). Louis de Broglie knew that light can behave as either waves or 'particles' (photons), and in 1924, in his doctoral thesis, he put forward the idea that electrons (and other particles) might have a similar dual nature and sometimes behave as waves. He predicted that the wavelength, λ, of a particle of mass m moving at speed v would be given by:

$$\lambda = \frac{h}{mv} \quad (17)$$
$$= \frac{h}{p}$$

where p is the particle's momentum and h is the Planck constant. This wavelength is sometimes known as the **de Broglie wavelength** of a particle.

Experimental support for this revolutionary idea was obtained within the next three years by American scientists Clinton Davisson and Lester Germer, and independently by British scientist George Thomson, who produced diffraction patterns using electron beams directed at metals and crystals. All these scientists received Nobel prizes for their work. George Thomson was the son of J.J. (Joseph) Thomson who, a generation earlier, had received a Nobel Prize for demonstrating conclusively that electrons were particles.

STUDY NOTE
You met momentum in *Higher, Faster Stronger*.

STUDY NOTE
You met the Planck constant in *The Sound of Music* when dealing with atomic energy levels.

Electron diffraction can be demonstrated using the apparatus shown in Figure 5.45. In the electron gun (Figure 5.46), electrons are 'boiled off' a heated filament by a process called **thermionic emission**. They are then attracted towards a positive anode, accelerated by a potential difference of a few hundred volts. The glass tube containing the gun and target has a near-vacuum inside, so there are few air molecules to impede the motion of the electrons. Most of the electrons pass straight through the anode and fly straight on to hit the graphite target. The electron beam passes through the thin layer of graphite and hits the fluorescent layer inside the rounded end of the tube, transferring energy to it and making it glow. Graphite consists of layers of carbon atoms arranged in regular hexagonal patterns (Figure 5.47), and so produces a diffraction pattern with waves whose wavelength is comparable to the atomic spacing.

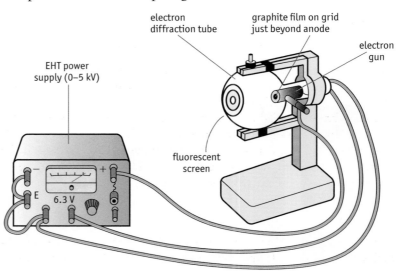

Figure 5.45 An electron diffraction tube

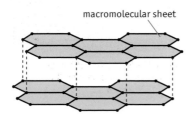

Figure 5.47 The arrangement of carbon atoms in graphite

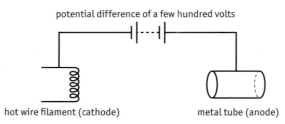

Figure 5.46 An electron gun

⚙ ACTIVITY 21 ELECTRON DIFFRACTION

Use the apparatus shown in Figure 5.45 to observe electron diffraction. Predict and observe what happens to the electrons' speed, and therefore to their wavelength and the spacing of the diffraction pattern, as the accelerating voltage is increased.

Hold a magnet close to the tube and observe what happens to the beam.

As you have seen in *Technology in Space* and in Part 1 of this chapter, when charge moves through a potential difference, energy is transferred as described by the relationship:

$$\Delta E = q\Delta V \tag{18}$$

where ΔE is the energy transferred, q is the charge and ΔV the potential difference.

If an electron moved in the opposite direction across the gap, from negative to positive, then the power supply would be transferring energy to the electron; an electron starting from rest would gain kinetic energy:

$$E_k = e\Delta V \tag{19}$$

where e is the electron's charge.

QUESTION

electron charge $e = 1.60 \times 10^{-19}\,\mathrm{C}$

electron mass $m_e = 9.11 \times 10^{-31}\,\mathrm{kg}$

Planck constant $h = 6.63 \times 10^{-34}\,\mathrm{J\,s}$

Q 26 Electrons are accelerated in an electron gun by a potential difference, V, of 100 V.

(a) What is each electron's maximum kinetic energy? Give your answer in units of joules and in eV.

(b) Calculate the speed of the electrons.

(c) What is the electrons' de Broglie wavelength?

(d) Using SI base units, show that h/p has units of length

The very small wavelength of electrons with energies of a few hundred eV is comparable with X-rays, which explains why the electrons are diffracted when they are passed through crystals. X-ray diffraction patterns rely on X-rays being scattered by relatively heavy atoms, whereas electrons are diffracted by light elements such as carbon, nitrogen and hydrogen, so electron diffraction patterns are used to analyse materials made of lighter elements (Figure 5.48). Furthermore, there is another very big, and useful, difference between X-rays and beams of electrons: electrons are deflected by magnetic and electric fields whereas X-rays are unaffected. This is made use of in the design of electron microscopes.

3.3 Electron microscopes

Nowadays there are several types of microscope that make use of electron beams. Two widely used designs are the Transmission Electron Microscope (TEM) and Scanning Electron Microscope (SEM).

TEM

The first type of electron microscope to be developed, and still widely used, is the transmission electron microscope (TEM). A TEM can be used to look at samples that are very thin (typically less than 1 μm thick). The electrons pass through the sample and form an image.

Some samples have to be specially prepared to withstand being placed in a vacuum and bombarded by high-energy electrons. Biological samples are particularly difficult to prepare as they contain water (which does not diffract electrons) and the conditions in the microscope would damage them. Methods include embedding them in plastic, freezing with liquid nitrogen and staining with heavy metal stains to provide image contrast. Very thin slices can then be shaved off to look at with the TEM. Figure 5.49 shows a TEM image.

How does passing a beam of electrons through a thin sample of material result in an image? The technique depends on the fact that not all of the electrons pass through the sample unaffected. There are three possibilities:

● electrons pass through undeflected

● electrons are deflected (scattered) without losing energy

● electrons lose energy, and most of these are also scattered.

If all of these electrons continued on through the microscope and were focused on a fluorescent screen, there would be no contrast in the image formed. An aperture placed in the beam allows only the electrons that are either undeflected or scattered through small angles to pass through. Areas of the sample that cause a lot of scattering will appear dark.

In many ways the TEM is like an optical projection microscope. The parts are compared in Figure 5.50. Instead of a lamp, the electron microscope has an electron gun, as described in Section 3.1. This requires a high-voltage supply. The smaller the detail to be observed,

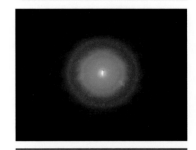

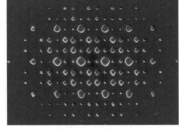

Figure 5.48 Electron diffraction patterns of (a) graphite and (b) titanium-nickel alloy

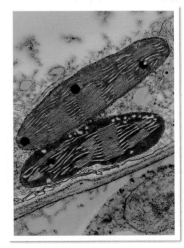

Figure 5.49 TEM image of microbial consortia within a degraded archaeological hair shaft

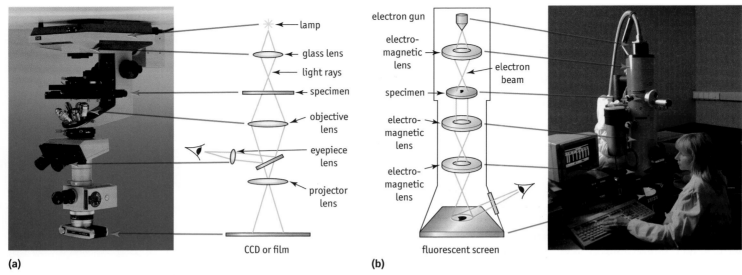

(a)   (b)

Figure 5.50 Schematic diagrams of (a) an optical microscope (upside down) (b) a Transmission Electron Microscope (TEM)

the smaller the wavelength required, and so the higher the energy of the electrons used in the beam. The whole microscope is enclosed in a vacuum, which requires vacuum pumps to maintain the very low pressure.

STUDY NOTE

For some notes on websites with information about using microscopes in archaeology, see *Digging Up the Past* Additional Sheet 7.

⚙ ACTIVITY 22 TEM

Use a computer simulator to try out a TEM, or explore YouTube to find out more about the design and operation of a TEM. Find out more about its design and operation and sample preparation, and look at some images.

In the optical microscope light is focused onto the sample and onto a ground glass screen using glass lenses. The electron microscope uses magnetic 'lenses'. Electromagnets can be used to focus the electron beam because electrons are deflected as they pass through a magnetic field – as you saw in Activity 22. To focus the electron beam, you can change the strength of the magnetic field by altering the current in the electromagnets. Electrons can't be seen, so the electron microscope has a fluorescent screen to reveal the image. When the electrons strike the screen it glows. If a CCD camera is used to produce pictures and store them on computer, 'false colour' pictures can be produced in which different intensities are given different colours to enhance the contrast of the image.

SEM

Not all materials can be made into the very thin samples needed to get a TEM image. The scanning electron microscope (SEM) uses the beam of electrons in a different way (Figure 5.51). The electrons that are back-scattered from the sample are collected and used to build up the image (these are sometimes called secondary electrons). The scanning coils are supplied with a varying electric current to produce a varying magnetic field. This sweeps the electron beam across the sample repeatedly to build up an image, in the same way that an old TV or PC monitor sweeps an electron beam across the screen to build up the picture.

⚙ ACTIVITY 23 SEM

Use a SEM computer simulator or explore YouTube to find out more about how an SEM operates. Find out what information a SEM can give about the surface composition of a specimen.

3.4 Summing up Part 3

In this part of the chapter you have seen how artefacts can be examined in more detail using microscopes to magnify a specimen. You have learned that:

● there is a minimum size feature that can be seen with a microscope, because of diffraction effects

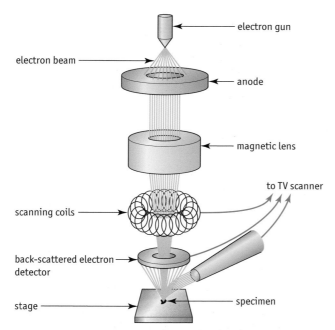

Figure 5.51 Schematic diagram of an SEM

- beams of electrons can behave as waves (you have seen electron diffraction patterns that are evidence of this)
- electrons have a wavelength that is related to their speed
- electron microscopes can be used to see much smaller features than an optical microscope.

You have looked at the design and operation of transmission electron microscopes (TEMs) and at scanning electron microscopes (SEMs).

⚙ ACTIVITY 24 SUMMING UP PART 3

Spend a few minutes checking through your notes, making sure you know all the meanings of the key terms printed in **bold**. If you are developing a summary of key terms, ensure that it is up to date. In particular, look at some of the terms that you met in earlier chapters and see whether you need to refine or extend your definitions.

⚙ ACTIVITY 25 MICROSCOPES

Write a paragraph explaining the advantages of using an electron microscope rather than an optical microscope. Use the following terms in your explanation:

- de Broglie wavelength
- resolution (or resolve)
- diffraction
- image

QUESTION

electron charge $e = 1.60 \times 10^{-19}\,\mathrm{C}$
electron mass $m_e = 9.11 \times 10^{-31}\,\mathrm{kg}$
Planck constant $h = 6.63 \times 10^{-34}\,\mathrm{J\,s}$

Q 27 A particular electron microscope is designed to study objects down to about 50 nm in size. For the images to provide useful information, the electron wavelength should be no more than twice the size of the objects.

(a) Derive an expression relating the accelerating voltage, V, to the electron wavelength λ and the charge and mass of the electron.

(b) Calculate the accelerating voltage that should be used.

(c) Explain what will happen to the electron wavelength and the resolution of the microscope if you double the accelerating voltage.

4 Archaeologists at work

Many years ago archaeology was considered to be closely related to history and to require a lot of time spent cataloguing artefacts. The help that science could offer a 19th-century archaeologist was limited. Today, science – and especially physics – provides many useful tools for locating and identifying objects. In addition to this, one of the key facts we want to know about an artefact is how old it is, and here physics can help in many ways.

In this section you will learn about how the community of archaeological scientists interacts with society and how it regulates itself to ensure that the evidence it presents can be trusted.

4.1 The dating game

In Parts 1 to 3 of this chapter you saw how archaeologists can locate ancient remains and how they can determine the composition of artefacts. However, *when* historical items were made is also of vital concern. By dating artefacts, the archaeologist can begin to build up the time sequence of events, which can then be used to provide an accurate analysis of the past.

Before the application of scientific methods and techniques, the dating of archaeological sites and artefacts was pretty much a hit and miss affair. For example, if one item was found at a deeper level in the dig than another, it was assumed to be older. Yet there are hidden assumptions here. What if the site had been disturbed, mixing up the artefacts?

Over the past half century or so, archaeological dating has become more sophisticated. Archaeologists now regularly use measurements that involve a deep understanding of nuclear physics, magnetism in materials and chemical analysis (among others). As a result, a much greater understanding of the relationships between past events has emerged, though even these modern methods have their limitations. Fluorine testing, for example, is used for relative dating. It is useful for testing whether bones were buried at the same site at the same time, but cannot be used to compare bones from different sites or to give a definite age. It relies on the fact that fluorides are found in most groundwater and are absorbed by bones. The amount of fluoride absorbed depends on the water, the soil and the time the bone has been buried, which allows a modern bone to be distinguished from an ancient one.

4.2 Is it genuine?

Hoaxes have been quite common in archaeology, as people used them to seek fame and financial gain. However, with better testing and authentication techniques, hoaxes tend to be less common today than they were in the past. Previous archaeological hoaxes have often involved burying an artefact and then 'discovering' it. In Japan in 2000, the archaeologist Shinichi Fujimura was photographed digging the holes to bury the artefacts. One of the most famous hoaxes involved a skull found in Sussex in 1911.

Figure 5.52 (a) A timber frame house dated by dendrochronology; (b) a skull dated by radiocarbon dating

> ⚙ **ACTIVITY 26 DATING TECHNIQUES**
>
> Prepare a poster on a sheet of A3 paper that describes dendrochronology or radiocarbon dating (Figure 5.52).
>
> What is the point of developing several methods of dating? Isn't just one sufficient?
>
> In a group, spend a few minutes brainstorming possible responses.

Piltdown Man

Charles Dawson, an amateur archaeologist, was involved in the discovery of a human skull and jaw alongside some animal bones. The find was of great importance at the time, as it seemed to confirm Darwin's theory of evolution. The jaw was ape-like, fitting predictions of how our ancestors had looked, and was believed to be 500 000 years old (Figure 5.53). Arthur Woodward, a respected palaeontologist (fossil expert), named the skull Dawson's Dawn Man or *Eoanthropus dawsoni*, and it subsequently became known as the 'Piltdown Man' after the location of the gravel pits where it was found.

 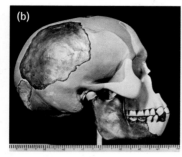 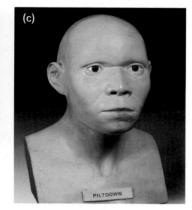

Figure 5.53 (a) Working on the Piltdown site; (b) the Piltdown Man skull; (c) a reconstruction based on the skull

Despite some doubts being raised (for example, someone said it was an orang-utan skull), for the next forty years the skull was widely believed to be authentic. It supported the developing theory that linked apes to humans: an ape-like jaw but a skull containing a brain the size of a human brain. Further finds near the site seemed to confirm the authenticity of the find, and the Natural History Museum accepted it. However, by 1953, evidence from other parts of the world did not fit the find. Fossils found elsewhere in Europe and Africa were dismissed as they didn't match Piltdown Man and had a much smaller skull. One find in South Africa, 'Taung's child', was initially dismissed but was later recognised as a member of the human family tree.

With the advent of new dating methods and more rigorous analytical techniques, Piltdown Man was re-assessed by the Natural History Museum. From these tests, it became clear that the skull was made up of two parts – a chimpanzee jaw and a human skull. To make them look old, the bones had been stained brown. In fact, all the bones from Piltdown had undergone similar staining. More detailed analysis also revealed that the teeth of the skull had been filed down to remove the dental patterns of the female ape. Dating techniques contributed further important evidence, and Piltdown Man was exposed as a hoax.

 **ACTIVITY 27 PILTDOWN MAN**

Use the Internet to find out more about the Piltdown Man hoax. Find out which dating techniques were used and what they revealed, then summarise the scientific evidence that led to Piltdown Man being declared a hoax.

PRACTICAL SKILLS REFERENCE

Scientific questions and information research

See Practical skills notes 1.1–1.4

4.3 Peer review

Scientists communicate their work by publishing reports (usually known as papers) in specialist journals, which can be either paper-based or electronic. One way the scientific community tries to prevent hoaxes is by using the **peer review** process. 'Peer' means 'equal', and a key feature of the process is that scientists, in this case archaeologists, review each other's research work before it is published.

The reviewers are expected to comment on the work in light of their own experience in the same area. They are asked to say whether:

- the science is correct
- the observations or experimental results appear to be authentic
- the conclusions are justified by the results
- the work is original
- other people's relevant work is acknowledged
- the findings are communicated clearly.

If a journal editor receives unfavourable reports from peer reviewers, the paper is usually sent back to the authors for revision or, in extreme cases, may be rejected. Magazines and journals that are peer reviewed declare this, so that their readers know how much weight to give the information they are reading (Figure 5.54). Scientists use the published information to devise their own investigations, and if their results are not consistent with what's reported then questions are asked. This is what eventually led to the Piltdown hoax being uncovered – the find did not fit in with all the other finds and discussions eventually led to more rigorous tests, which proved that the skull was not genuine.

Some journals publish **review papers**. These do not necessarily report original research but they are written by an expert in the field to give a full and up-to-date account of recent work in a particular area of research. Such papers are peer reviewed to check that the science is correctly reported and clearly communicated to the intended readers.

The peer review process is also used when allocating research funds. In the UK, there are seven research councils that are responsible for allocating some £3 billion of government money to a range of research projects. This money is used to fund the best research as judged by independent expert peer reviews. The research funding covers the medical and biological sciences, physics, chemistry, engineering, social sciences and the arts and humanities.

An archaeologist who wanted funding for a project would put forward a detailed written proposal to the relevant research council. The proposal would then be peer reviewed, along with other proposals, to decide which projects should be funded.

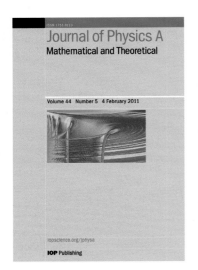

Figure 5.54 The *Journal of Physics A: Mathematical and Theoretical* is a peer-reviewed journal. (http://dx.doi.org/10.1088/1751-8113/44/5/055201)

⚙ ACTIVITY 28 PEER REVIEW

Using the checklist given above, review a write-up of a piece of experimental practical work that has been carried out by another student following this course.

LINK THE LEARNING

5 Reconstruction

5.1 Putting the pieces together

An archaeologist collects and uses diverse pieces of evidence that provide information about a site – these might include survey results, physical objects (from walls to minute fragments of bone or pottery) and written historical evidence. These then need to be pieced together to construct a coherent and self-consistent story.

Rather in a similar way, this chapter has contributed several pieces to your study of physics, some of which need to be brought together with things you have learned, or will be learning, in other chapters. In Activity 29, you will bring together some pieces from separate parts of this chapter, and in Activity 30 you will collect together information from this and some other chapters.

⚙ ACTIVITY 29 USING ELECTROMAGNETIC RADIATION

In this chapter and in *Technology in Space* and *The Sound of Music*, you have seen several uses for various types of electromagnetic radiation. Using a copy of Table 5.5, make a summary listing at least two uses of radiation in each part of the spectrum given in the table. Look back through your work on all these three units, and use books or the Internet to find some additional information.

Type of radiation	Approximate wavelength range/m	Examples of uses
γ-rays	10^{-14} (or less) $- 10^{-11}$	
X-rays	$10^{-11} - 10^{-8}$	
Ultraviolet	$10^{-8} - 4 \times 10^{-7}$	
Visible	$4 \times 10^{-7} - 7 \times 10^{-7}$	
Infrared	$7 \times 10^{-7} - 10^{-3}$	
Microwaves	$10^{-3} - 10^{-1}$	
Radio	$10^{-1} - 10^{3}$ or more	

Table 5.5 Using electromagnetic radiation

⚙ ACTIVITY 30 PUTTING THE PIECES TOGETHER

You learned something about each of the following in at least two parts of this chapter. Look back through your work and make brief notes under each heading, listing the examples that were used in different parts of the chapter and noting any ways in which the ideas were developed or refined. You could also add cross-references to other chapters where you have studied these same areas.

- DC circuits: resistance, resistivity, potential difference, potential divider, charge and energy
- Waves: electromagnetic spectrum, diffraction, superposition
- Electrons: particle and wave models
- Ethical issues in science
- Logarithmic scales

5.2 Questions on the whole chapter

 Scientists planned to stretch a length of steel wire, 12.35 m long with diameter 1.0 mm, between two rocks either side of a geological fault line in order to detect small changes in the movement of the Earth. As the fault moved, the wire would extend and its resistance change.

(a) The resistivity of the wire chosen was $1.5 \times 10^{-8}\,\Omega\,\text{m}$. Calculate the resistance of the length of wire used.

(b) The scientists were interested in changes in length greater than 5%. For such a change:
  (i) What would be the new length of the stretched wire?
  (ii) What would its new resistance be?

(c) In practice the 'noise' inherent in the experiment prevented meaningful results. Suggest what might be the cause of 'noise' in this case.

Q 29 Some electronic devices need connections to −4.5 V, 0 V and +4.5 V. To achieve this, they are operated from so-called *split rail supplies*. Figure 5.55 shows how a 9 V battery can be used for such a supply.

(a) (i) Match the labels −4.5 V, 0 V and +4.5 V to the points A, B and C.
  (ii) What name is given to this type of arrangement of resistors and battery?

(b) To check that the 25 kV overhead supply has been disconnected before starting work, railway engineers use a device consisting of a probe of resistance R_p and a voltage detector of resistance R_d. One end of the device is hooked on to the power line and the other end is attached to Earth (usually the rail). (See Figure 5.56.) If the 25 kV supply is left on, the detector registers a voltage of 25 V.

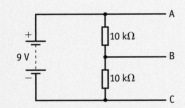

Figure 5.55 A 9 V battery used to provide a split rail supply

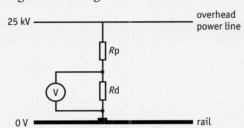

Figure 5.56 A device for checking overhead power lines

(i) If the resistance of the whole arrangement is 39 MΩ, what are the resistances of the detector, R_d, and the probe, R_p?
  (ii) If there was poor contact with the rail or overhead cable (for example, due to rust), explain the effect this would have on the voltage across the detector.

 A novel proposal for a system to sense the angular position of a telescope consists of a circular metal track with one probe of an ohmmeter attached to a fixed point on the ring. The other probe is attached to the telescope and slides around the ring as the telescope rotates.

The metal rod used to form the ring has resistivity ρ and a cross-sectional area. It is used to form a closed ring of radius r (Figure 5.57).

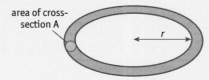

Figure 5.57 Metal rod used to form a ring

(a) In terms of r, what is the length, l, of the rod used to form the track?

(b) Write down an equation for the resistance measured between the two ohmmeter probes when they are diametrically opposite one another on the track, as shown in Figure 5.58(i).

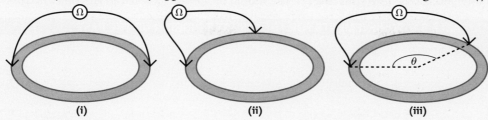

Figure 5.58 Diagram for Question 30

(c) What would be the resistance when the probes are a quarter of the track length apart (Figure 5.58b)?

(d) Sketch a graph showing how the total resistance between the probes, R_{total}, varies with angle θ.

(e) Suggest some practical limitations to this proposed scheme for determining the orientation angle of the telescope.

(f) Write down a general equation for R_{total} in terms of the angle θ (Figure 5.58c). Hint: if you express the angles in radians rather than degrees, the two parts have length $r\theta$ and $r(2\pi - \theta)$, and the algebra involved in the expression for R is slightly simpler.

Q 31 Some artefacts from an archaeological site need to be investigated in more detail. The features the archaeologists want to study are:

A pollen grains with features 0.1 μm in size

B weevil holes in grains of flour, which are 0.5 mm in size

C microfossils with features 1 μm in size

D ships' timbers with features 150 nm in size

E damage to bones with features 0.002 mm in size.

(a) Which features can be resolved with an optical microscope?

(b) Which features can only be resolved with an electron microscope?

(c) Explain why the electron microscope can resolve smaller features than the optical microscope.

Q 32 In an electron microscope, the electrons are accelerated through a potential difference of 10 kV.

(a) What is the kinetic energy of the electrons in eV and in joules?

(b) Calculate the speed of the electrons.

(c) What is the electrons' de Broglie wavelength?

$e = 1.60 \times 10^{-19}$ C

$m = 9.11 \times 10^{-31}$ kg

$h = 6.63 \times 10^{-34}$ J s

Q 33 A group of people are speculating about the finds on an archaeological site, and suggest hiding an artefact – a bone from another site – for archaeologists to find. One of them speculates whether this may have been done in the past, and whether you can believe anything you read about archaeological finds.

(a) Write a paragraph for the local paper explaining some of the different tests that could be done on a bone found at an archaeological site and at the site where it is found to check that evidence is consistent.

(b) Write a paragraph to explain how journals use the peer review process to check on the material they are publishing, and how a reader could tell whether a journal uses the process or not.

5.3 Achievements

Now you have studied this chapter you should be able to achieve the outcomes listed in Table 5.6.

TABLE 5.6 ACHIEVEMENTS FOR THE CHAPTER DIGGING UP THE PAST

	Statement from Examination Specification	*Section(s) in this chapter*
1	know and understand the distinction between base and derived quantities and their SI units	1.2
2	demonstrate their knowledge of practical skills and techniques for both familiar and unfamiliar experiments	1.2, 1.3, 2.3
4	understand the limitations of physical measurement and apply these limitations to practical situations	1.2, 2.3
5	be able to communicate information and ideas in appropriate ways using appropriate terminology	1.4, 2.1, 2.3
7	understand the role of the scientific community in validating new knowledge and ensuring integrity	4.2, 4.3
39	be able to use the equation $R = \dfrac{\rho l}{A}$	1.2
40	CORE PRACTICAL 2: Determine the electrical resistivity of a material	1.2
41	be able to use $I = nqvA$ to explain the large range of resistivities of different materials	1.2
42	understand how the potential along a uniform current-carrying wire varies with the distance along it	1.2
43	understand the principles of a potential divider circuit and understand how to calculate potential differences and resistances in such a circuit	1.3
44	be able to analyse potential divider circuits where one resistance is variable including thermistors and Light Dependent Resistors (LDRs)	1.3
83	understand what is meant by diffraction and use Huygens' construction to explain what happens to a wave when it meets a slit or an obstacle	2.3
84	be able to use $n\lambda = d\sin\vartheta$ for a diffraction grating	2.3
85	CORE PRACTICAL 8: Determine the wavelength of light from a laser or other light source using a diffraction grating	2.3
86	understand how diffraction experiments provide evidence for the wave nature of electrons	2.3
87	use the de Broglie equation $\lambda = \dfrac{h}{p}$	3.2

Answers

Q 1   A metre length would be five times longer, so its resistance would be $5 \times 8\,\Omega = 40\,\Omega$. This assumes that the cable cross-section area is uniform throughout and so resistance is proportional to length.

Q 2   **(a)** The separation of 5 m is ten times greater, so you would expect a resistance about ten times greater, i.e. about $3000\,\Omega$.

     (b) A 5 m separation would not detect small-scale structures, such as a 1 m-wide door opening or a 0.5 m wall. Probes separated by 5 m would be unwieldy.

Q 3   **(a)** If the length is doubled then the area of cross-section is halved (to keep the same volume). On its own, doubling the length doubles the resistance, as does halving the area; both of these together multiply the resistance by four.

$$4 \times 48\,\Omega = 192\,\Omega$$

     (b) $l = 10\,\text{cm} = 0.1\,\text{m}$

$$A = 1\,\text{cm}^2$$

$$= (1 \times 10^{-2}\,\text{m})^2 = 1 \times 10^{-4}\,\text{m}^2$$

Using Equation 4:

$$\rho = \frac{RA}{l} = \frac{48\,\Omega \times 1.0 \times 10^{-4}\,\text{m}^2}{0.1\,\text{m}}$$

$$= 4.8 \times 10^{-2}\,\Omega\,\text{m}$$

Q 4   Combining Equations 4 and 5:

$$R = \frac{l}{\sigma A}$$

Q 5   The salty ditch was about 5 m from the gate (the resistance is lowest there) and the wall about 9 to 10 m from the gate (where the resistance is highest).

Q 6   On this scale, 1 cm represents $10^{-5}\,\Omega\,\text{m}$.

$1.0 \times 10^{12} = 1.0 \times 10^{17} \times 10^{-5}$, so the bar for glass would be 1.0×10^{17} cm long (1.0×10^{15} m).

$1.7 \times 10^{-8} = 1.7 \times 10^{-3} \times 10^{-5}$, so the bar for copper would be 1.7×10^{-3} cm long (1.7×10^{-5} m).

The shortest bar would be too small to see, while the longest would not fit on the Earth (in fact, it would extend beyond the limits of the Solar System).

Q 7   The change, q, on each mobile particle does not change. Heating a metal does not release a significant number of extra electrons, (n does not change significantly), but it increases the vibrations of the atomic lattice through which the free electrons move. This scatters the electrons, reducing their average drift speed. In terms of Equations 9, 13 and 14 it reduces the mobility k, thereby reducing the material's conductivity and increasing its resistivity.

Q 8   **(a)** Using Equation 8:

$$v = \frac{I}{nAq}$$

$$= \frac{0.70\,\text{A}}{8.48 \times 10^{28}\,\text{m}^{-3} \times \pi \times (0.20 \times 10^{-3}\,\text{m})^2 \times 1.60 \times 10^{-19}\,\text{C}}$$

$$= 0.000411\,\text{m s}^{-1} = 0.411\,\text{mm s}^{-1}$$

     (b) Equation 4:

$$R = \frac{\rho \ell}{A}$$

$$= \frac{1.7 \times 10^{-8}\,\Omega\,\text{m} \times 0.5\,\text{m}}{\pi \times (0.20 \times 10^{-3}\,\text{m})^2}$$

$$= 6.7 \times 10^{-2}\,\Omega$$

     (c) $V = IR = 0.70\,\text{A} \times 6.7 \times 10^{-2}\,\Omega$

$$= 4.7 \times 10^{-2}\,\text{V} = 47\,\text{mV}$$

Q 9   **(a) (i)** 4 V   **(ii)** 6 V   **(iii)** 4.8 V

     (b) (i) +8 V   **(ii)** +9 V   **(iii)** +7.2 V

Q 10   **(a)** The wire will get longer and thinner, and on both counts the resistance will increase.

     (b) If the length increases by 10% then the area must decrease by 10% to keep the volume constant.

If $R_{\text{original}} = \dfrac{\rho l}{A}$, then:

$$R_{\text{stretched}} = \frac{\rho(1.1l)}{(A \div 1.1)}$$

$$= R_{\text{original}} \times (1.1)^2$$

$$= 1.21\,R_{\text{original}}$$

i.e. the resistance increases by 21%.

     (c) Using Equation 4:

$R = \dfrac{\rho l}{A}$, then:

$$= \frac{2.6 \times 10^{-6}\,\Omega\,\text{m} \times 28 \times 10^{-2}\,\text{m}}{0.6 \times 10^{-3}\,\text{m} \times 0.002 \times 10^{-3}\,\text{m}}$$

$$= 606\,\Omega$$

     (d) See Figure 5.59. The pd across the fixed resistor is four times that across the gauge, so its resistance must be $4 \times 606\,\Omega = 2424\,\Omega$.

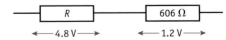

Figure 5.59   Diagram for the answer to Question 10 (d)

Q 11   **(a)** Aluminium: $R_{\text{Al}} = \dfrac{\rho \ell}{A} = \dfrac{2.9 \times 10^{-8}\,\Omega\,\text{m} \times 1.1 \times 10^3\,\text{m}}{\pi \times (1.5 \times 10^{-3}\,\text{m})^2}$

$$= 4.513\,\Omega$$

(b) Steel: $R_{St} = \dfrac{4.1 \times 10^{-7}\,\Omega\,m \times 1.1 \times 10^{3}\,m}{\pi \times (2.5 \times 10^{-3}\,m)^{2}} = 22.97\,\Omega$

(c) $\dfrac{1}{R_{Al\ total}} = \left(\dfrac{1}{R_{Al}} + \dfrac{1}{R_{Al}} + \dfrac{1}{R_{Al}} + \ldots\right) = 88 \times \dfrac{1}{R_{Al}}$

$\dfrac{1}{R_{St\ total}} = \left(\dfrac{1}{R_{St}} + \dfrac{1}{R_{St}} + \dfrac{1}{R_{St}} + \ldots\right) = 7 \times \dfrac{1}{R_{St}}$

so: $\dfrac{1}{R_{total}} = 88 \times \dfrac{1}{R_{Al}} + 7 \times \dfrac{1}{R_{St}}$

$= \dfrac{88}{4.513\,\Omega} + \dfrac{7}{22.97\,\Omega}$

$= 19.8\,\Omega^{-1}$

$R_{total} = \dfrac{1}{19.8\,\Omega^{-1}} = 0.050\,\Omega$

(d) The polymer would have much higher resistivity than steel, but that would make virtually no difference to the overall resistance. If resistivity is *very* large, then:

$\dfrac{1}{R_{polymer}} \approx 0$

$R_{total} \approx R_{Al\ total} = \dfrac{4.513\,\Omega}{88} = 0.051\,\Omega$

The polymer would have lower density than steel, but it is likely be much *less* stiff than steel, so there would be more sagging.

Q 12 See Figure 5.60.

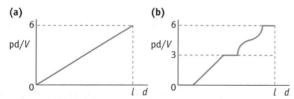

Figure 5.60 The answers to Question 12

Q 13 The term 'shadow radiograph' is appropriate because the photographic film has a shadow cast upon it of the more dense parts of the object being X-rayed. The X-rays pass through the less dense materials and the more dense materials, such as metals or bones, absorb them. In this way the film is blackened except where the X-rays were prevented from getting to it. These shadow areas remain white on the film.

Q 14 X-ray tomography is a technique whereby you acquire an image of a 'slice' of the body by blurring out the unwanted shadows below and above the plane of interest. A conventional X-ray image is a single 'shadow' produced by the transmission of X-rays through the thickness of the body and this may result in certain elements being 'hidden' by those in front.

Q 15 There was concern that the CAT (Computer Aided Tomography) scanner might not give satisfactory images because the machine was calibrated for objects of the density of the human body. The helmet, being made of metal, had a density beyond the scope of the scanner. (The effect was to produce images with less definition than might be required.)

Q 16 The use of horizontal and vertical radiographs allowed the position of items within the helmet to be pinpointed, as this provided two crossed slices by which the position of the item was defined – in much the same way as two coordinates define the position of a point on a graph (see Figure 5.61).

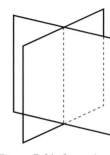

Figure 5.61 Crossed 'slices' pinpoint location

Q 17 The high-performance industrial radiography of the helmet gave conservators information on the technology involved in the helmet's construction, while microfocus radiography of the chain mail provided information on its construction.

Q 18 The wavefronts are circular (spherical in three dimensions). See Figure 5.62.

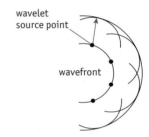

Figure 5.62 The answer to Question 18

Q 19 See Figure 5.63. Light travels more slowly in glass than in air, so the wavelength is shorter (wavefronts closer together) in glass. Tangents to the semicircular wavelets in the glass show the new plane wavefronts and the beam is refracted towards the normal.

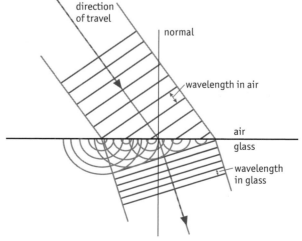

Figure 5.63 The answer to Question 19

Q 20 **(a)** $d = \dfrac{1\,\text{mm}}{300} = \dfrac{1 \times 10^{-3}\,\text{m}}{300} = 3.33 \times 10^{-6}\,\text{m}$

(b) Using Equation 16, $\sin\theta = \dfrac{589 \times 10^{-9}\,\text{m}}{3.33 \times 10^{-6}\,\text{m}} = 0.167$

$\theta = 10°$

(c) If $\sin\theta = 1$, $n = \dfrac{d}{\lambda} = \dfrac{3.33 \times 10^{-6}\,\text{m}}{589 \times 10^{-9}\,\text{m}} = 5.6$

The largest whole number that satisfies the diffraction grating equation is $n = 5$, so five orders of diffraction are possible.

Q 21 The straight-through beam is white, as all wavelengths satisfy the grating equation with $n = 0$. Each diffraction order, $n = 1, 2$, etc., contains all the colours of the spectrum spread over a range of angles, with the violet light at the smallest angle and red at the largest. A series of 'rainbows' would be projected onto the screen, each side of the straight-through white spot in the centre. However, because visible light ranges in wavelength from about 400–700 nm, the diffraction orders overlap; the red end of one order overlaps with the blue end of the next one, so the colours seen on the screen are not simply a series of 'rainbows'.

Q 22 The path difference is the distance AB + BC in Figure 5.38. AB = $d\sin\theta$, so AB + BC = $2d\sin\theta$. The reflected beam has maximum intensity when $2d\sin\theta = n\lambda$.

Q 23 The typical width of a doorway is 1 m, which is comparable with the wavelength of sound in air, so the sound wave can be diffracted and spread out into the room. The wavelength of light is much smaller so the beam of light is not noticeably diffracted.

Q 24 Using Equation 16, $\lambda = \dfrac{d\sin\theta}{2}$

$d = \dfrac{1\,\text{mm}}{500} = 2.00 \times 10^{-6}\,\text{m}$

$\lambda = \dfrac{2.00 \times 10^{-6}\,\text{m} \times \sin 35°}{2}$

$= 5.73 \times 10^{-7}\,\text{m} = 573\,\text{nm}$

Q 25 Fe_3O_4

Q 26 **(a)** Maximum kinetic energy:

$E_k = 100\,\text{eV}$

$= 100 \times 1.60 \times 10^{-19}\,\text{J}\,\text{eV}^{-1}$

$= 1.60 \times 10^{-17}\,\text{J}$

(b) Assuming the electrons reach their maximum possible kinetic energy:

$\dfrac{1}{2}mv^2 = eV$

$v^2 = \dfrac{2eV}{m}$

> **MATHS REFERENCE**
> See Maths Note 2.3
> Derived Units

$= \dfrac{2 \times 1.60 \times 10^{-19}\,\text{C} \times 100\,\text{J}\,\text{C}^{-1}}{9.11 \times 10^{-31}\,\text{kg}}$

$= 3.52 \times 10^{13}\,\text{m}^2\,\text{s}^{-2}$

Units of v^2 are $\text{J}\,\text{kg}^{-1}$, which is equivalent to $\text{m}^2\,\text{s}^{-2}$.

$v = 5.93 \times 10^6\,\text{m}\,\text{s}^{-1}$

(c) Using Equation 17:

$\lambda = \dfrac{h}{mv}$

$= \dfrac{6.63 \times 10^{-34}\,\text{J}\,\text{s}}{2\ 9.1 \times 10^{-31}\,\text{kg} \times 5.93 \times 10^6\,\text{m}\,\text{s}^{-1}}$

$= 1.2 \times 10^{-10}\,\text{m}$

Again, notice the units of λ: $\text{J}\,\text{s}\,\text{kg}^{-1}\,\text{m}^{-1}\,\text{s}$, which is equivalent to m.

(d) The Planck constant, h, has units J s (energy x time).

units of energy = units of $\dfrac{1}{2}mv^2 = \text{kg} \times (\text{m}\,\text{s}^{-1})^2$

$= \text{kg}\,\text{m}^2\,\text{s}^{-2}$

units of p = units of momentum = units of mv

$= \text{kg} \times \text{m}\,\text{s}^{-1}$

So units of $\dfrac{h}{p} = \text{kg}\,\text{m}^2\,\text{s}^{-2} \times \text{s} \div \text{kg} \times \text{m}\,\text{s}^{-1} = \text{m}$

Q 27 **(a)** Wavelength $\lambda = 100\,\text{nm}$. Rearranging Equation 17 to find the electron speed v:

$v = \dfrac{h}{m\lambda}$

Accelerating voltage V is related to the electron kinetic energy:

$eV = E_k = \dfrac{1}{2}mv^2$

so $V = \dfrac{E_k}{e} = \dfrac{\frac{1}{2}m\left(\dfrac{h}{m\lambda}\right)^2}{e} = \dfrac{h^2}{2me\lambda^2}$

(b) $V = \dfrac{(6.6 \times 10^{-34}\,\text{J}\,\text{s})}{2 \times 9.11 \times 10^{-31}\,\text{kg} \times 1.60 \times 10^{-19}\,\text{C} \times (100 \times 10^{-9}\,\text{m})^2}$

$= 6.03 \times 10^4\,\text{V}$

(c) Doubling the accelerating voltage doubles the electrons' kinetic energy. This multiplies their speed by $\sqrt{2}$ (= 1.414). This reduces their wavelength to $\dfrac{100\,\text{nm}}{\sqrt{2}}$ and the smallest objects that can be observed now have a size of $\dfrac{50\,\text{nm}}{\sqrt{2}} = 35\,\text{nm}$.

CHAPTER 6

SPARE PART SURGERY

Why a chapter called *Spare Part Surgery*?

You probably know someone who has had spare part surgery – perhaps an older relative or friend has had a hip replacement such as that shown in Figure 6.1(a), or a new heart valve or a pacemaker fitted. You might know someone who has had an operation for cataracts, in which the eye lens is replaced by an artificial implant. Figure 6.1(b) shows surgery in progress while Figure 6.1(c) shows how modern prosthetic limbs enable people to carry out extreme activities.

All of these spare parts help people to lead more pleasant and active lives, though there can be problems when a spare part wears out or is simply not as good as the original. Sometimes failures are dramatic and make the headline news. There have been cases involving heart valves that stick and replacement hips that fail within months – failures that are unpleasant and possibly dangerous for the users, and expensive for the makers. Physics plays a key role in the development of good spare parts. To design a replacement joint, you need to know about forces and the behaviour of materials in order to match the joint with natural bone.

Lens implants and contact lenses involve optics and materials science. Physics is also used to diagnose a problem and to decide what sort of spare part is needed. The example that probably springs to mind is X-ray imaging, but for some purposes ultrasound imaging is more useful and provides a quick and easy way to examine a heartbeat.

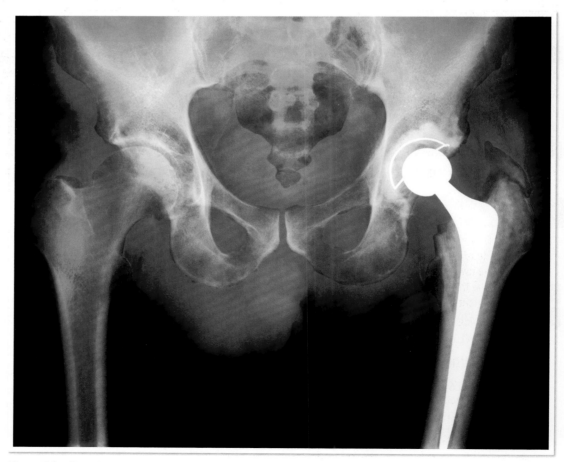

Figure 6.1a X-ray showing a replacement hip

Figure 6.1b Spare part surgery in progress

Figure 6.1c Modern prosthetic limbs allow athletic movement

OVERVIEW OF PHYSICS PRINCIPLES AND TECHNIQUES

In this chapter you will study the physics of materials, waves and light. Some of this work will build on and extend ideas that you have already met earlier, but you will also meet some new ideas – for example, you will learn how large-scale material properties can be related to small-scale structures. There are many opportunities in this chapter for practical work and to develop your skills in communication – both of which are very important in medical uses of physics.

In this chapter you will extend your knowledge of:

- behaviour of waves and light (from *The Sound of Music* and *Good Enough to Eat*)
- microscopic properties of materials (from *Technology in Space* and *Digging Up the Past*)
- bulk properties of materials (from *Higher, Faster, Stronger* and *Good Enough to Eat*).

In other chapters you will do more work on:

- bulk properties of materials (in *Build or Bust?*)
- microscopic properties of materials (in *The Medium is the Message*)
- waves (in *Build or Bust?* and *Reach for the Stars*).

1 Spare parts

1.1 Smart limbs

One of the most significant developments in medicine in recent years has been the ability to replace parts of the body, including whole limbs, with an artificial equivalent. This has been made possible through technological innovations based on full understanding of the science behind how a body works. The inspirational story of one individual's experience and relationship with prosthetic limbs (Figure 6.2) is given below.

Hugh Herr: bionic man

Hugh Herr (Figure 6.2) is a biophysicist who directs the biomechatronics group at the MIT Media Lab in Cambridge, Massachussetts USA. He is also a double amputee who uses the prosthetic legs developed and marketed by his own company iWalk. Mechatronics brings together mechanical and electrical engineering, electronics, computing and communication. Biomechatronics applies these disciplines to the design of devices that resemble and even extend the human body's natural systems.

As a teenager, Hugh Herr's ambition was to be a mountaineer. But in 1982, when Hugh was just 17 years old, it seemed his dreams had come to an end. He and a friend were caught in a storm while climbing Mount Washington – at 1917 m, the highest peak in the north-eastern USA. In the four days before they were rescued they succumbed to hypothermia and frostbite. Hugh's legs were so severely damaged that both had to be amputated below the knee.

After the surgery, Hugh was fitted with prosthetic legs. He was so keen to resume his active life that the rehabilitation staff were worried that he would damage his natural legs and the artificial ones so, unlike other patients, he was not at first allowed home at weekends.

Hugh was frustrated that his new legs were made of plaster, fine for standing still and walking slowly but fragile and no good for climbing. Rather than adapting his lifestyle to his new legs, he set about adapting the legs to his lifestyle. Drawing on his experience of making things from wood and metal, he spent hours designing and making limbs, trying out different structures.

At first, Hugh's aim was simply to make the best possible legs for climbing. But he soon realised that he was no longer limited by his natural body. He made himself legs of different length, so that he could go to school very tall one day and very short the next – just to amuse his classmates and show that being an amputee could be fun.

Figure 6.2 Rock-climber Hugh Herr

Hugh's early experiences with his own prosthetic legs led him to his career as a biophysicist. He became fascinated by the potential of artificial limbs, first to replicate the human body then to extend its functions. Now he and his colleagues use computer technology to make detailed models of limbs. They explore how muscles and tendons work, looking at their material properties, at the energy stored and transferred as a joint moves and at the way the movement is controlled by the nervous system. If these features can be incorporated into an artificial limb, then it becomes easy to use and the patient needs little or no training.

Hugh Herr has become an ambassador for users of prosthetic limbs. In April 2013 he was interviewed in the New York Times. In March 2014 he gave a TED talk which you can watch on YouTube. In this talk, Hugh demonstrated his own prosthetic limbs and was joined by Adrianne Haslet–Davis, a ballroom dancer who lost a leg in the 2013 Boston Marathon bombing; she performed again for the first time on the TED stage.

Looking to the future, Hugh has pointed out that prostheses could enhance the ways our bodies function. Robotic devices could reduce stress on weak or painful joints, or boost speed and acceleration when walking or running. He is already putting his vision into practice: he uses motorised prosthetic legs made from carbon, silicon, titanium and aluminium. Sensors and microprocessors enable them to adapt as he walks, boosting the power when he wants to move faster and decelerating as he walks downhill.

And – of course – he still climbs.

Thankfully, most people require less medical intervention than Hugh Herr, but in many families you will find someone who has required spare part surgery.

1.2 Informed consent

When deciding whether someone should have spare part surgery, several things need to be taken into account. These include the benefit to the patient and the cost of the operation.

The following activities provide a general introduction to this chapter.

ACTIVITY 1   THE PATIENT'S VIEW

Use a digital camera, tape recorder or smart phone to record an interview with someone who has had some type of spare part surgery. Ask them how it has affected their life. Ask them about the advantages and also ask if there have been any problems. Would they recommend the surgery to someone else? Is there any information they would like to pass on to other people having a similar operation?

ACTIVITY 2   SPARE PARTS

Look up information on the internet on the price of various spare parts. Suggest reasons why some of the parts (e.g. an electric heart pump) are so much more expensive than others (e.g. a knee ligament). The actual cost of spare part surgery is much more than the cost of the part; suggest reasons for this. Choose one of the parts and identify the aspects of physics that were probably involved in its development.

> **PRACTICAL SKILLS REFERENCE**
>
> Scientific questions and information research
>
> See Practical skills notes 1.1–1.4

ACTIVITY 3   THE DOCTOR'S VIEW

In the last decade there has been a large increase in the demand for prosthetic body parts, especially arm and leg parts. List any reasons you can think of for this increase.

As a doctor, you would have to assess the needs of each patient for prosthetics and prioritise them based upon your available resources.

Discuss with one or two other students how and why you might prioritise the treatment of the following patients:

- a soldier requiring two artificial legs
- a pensioner requiring a hip replacement
- an eight-year-old child needing a new electronic arm
- a professional athlete in need of a powered artificial knee joint and leg
- a 50-year-old businessman needing an artificial heart pump.

You might find it helpful to refer to the information below on ethical frameworks.

2 Boning up

As we age our joints begin to wear out, making movement difficult and painful. Joints can also be affected by diseases such as arthritis or may become injured. Nowadays, damaged or worn-out joints can be replaced relatively easily, and hip replacement is one of the commonest types of spare part surgery. This has become possible partly through the development of new materials and partly through improvements in surgical techniques.

In this chapter you will study the properties of bones and the materials used to replace them. In doing so, you will advance your knowledge of the mechanical properties of materials.

2.1 Bone and joint replacement

In order to understand what is involved in making a good replacement joint, it is important first to know something about bones and joints and their function in our bodies. The article below outlines some key features of bones and joints, discusses some of the issues involved in bone replacement and then describes a recent development in artificial bone technology.

> ⚙ **ACTIVITY 4 BONE AND JOINT REPLACEMENT**
> Read the following information about bones and joints and their replacement, and then answer Questions 1 to 6.

Bones and joints

Imagine what we would look like without a skeleton – we would certainly not be able to move! Our bony skeleton enables us to move against two important forces: weight (due to gravity) and the drag of the medium through which we are moving – this is usually air but may also be water. The cell is the basic building block of living material. Plant cells have rigid walls, so plants do not need skeletons, but animal cells are surrounded by a weak membrane that cannot be used for support. Our cells excrete materials to build up an internal skeleton (endoskeleton), while other animals have an external skeleton (exoskeleton). Recent technological innovation has led to the development of artificial exoskeletons that enable severely paralysed people to walk – and even to kick a football (Figure 6.3).

Human skeletons are made of bone that forms when proteins, such as collagen, are hardened by calcium and phosphorus salts excreted by cells. Bone is mainly crystalline calcium phosphate and calcium carbonate. About 20% of the bone is made up of living cells, which are fed with blood vessels through cavities in the bone.

The bones form levers in the body, ligaments hold the bones together, and tendons attach the muscles to the bones. A place where two bones meet is called a joint. Joints that allow free movement are called synovial joints (Figure 6.4).

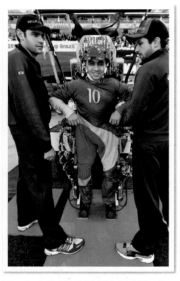

Figure 6.3 The 2014 football Word Cup was kicked off by someone in an artificial exoskeleton

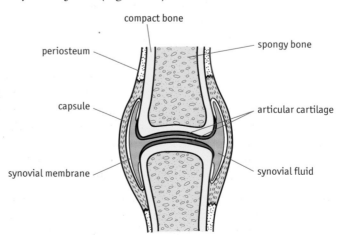

Figure 6.4 Schematic diagram of a synovial joint

The capsule holds the joint together and the synovial fluid acts as a lubricant. The cartilage on the bone ends provides a smooth surface to allow the bones to move over each other with the minimum of friction. There are two main types of joint: ball-and-socket joints (such as the hip) and hinge joints (such as the knee). (See Figure 6.5.)

(a) ball-and-socket joint (hip)　　　　**(b)** hinge joint (knee)

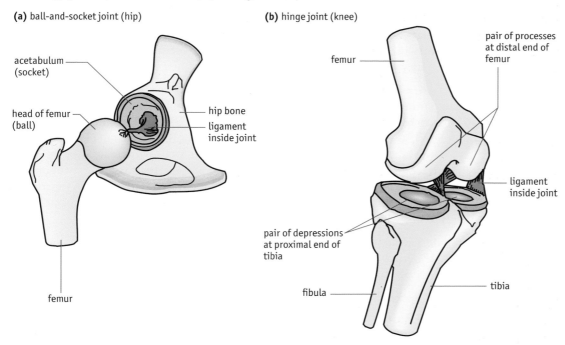

Figure 6.5 Exploded sketches of knee and hip joints

Replacement surgery

Like any mechanical device, joints undergo wear. Usually your body is able to repair any damage, but if the joint surfaces wear too quickly then osteoarthritis occurs. Disease can lead to a destruction of the surfaces; this is called rheumatoid arthritis. In severe cases, replacement of the joint is necessary. The commonest joint that requires replacing is the hip joint.

Bone cancer used to require amputation but now the bone and joint can usually be replaced.

Replacement is rarely as a result of fracture, since when this occurs blood vessels grow into the clot and a repair tissue develops, which holds the bones together. The repair tissue then hardens and calcium salts are deposited to form bone. The role of an orthopaedic surgeon is normally to make sure that the bones are aligned correctly. In the rare occasions that healing fails, bone grafts from another part of the body can be used. This exposes the patient to the stress of two operations and an increased risk of complications and pain. It also costs a lot to perform a double operation, and the long recovery time keeps the patient in an expensive hospital bed. Taking donor bone increases the risk of rejection or transmission of diseases such as hepatitis B or HIV.

Bone regrowth and replacement

When a bone breaks it normally heals within eight weeks. However, sometimes the two ends don't grow back together, and if you put in a metal plate it still doesn't heal. A stimulus is usually needed to get a new bone to grow. Bone regrows naturally when subjected to forces, but otherwise it wastes away. Astronauts who live for long periods in weightless conditions in the International Space Station suffered problems with their bones due to lack of exercise until a Resistive Exercise Device for orbital weightlifting was introduced in 2008 (Figure 6.6). Since then the bone density of astronauts has been maintained at pre-flight values.

Ideally, materials used for bone grafts and replacement joints should have properties that closely match natural bone. Materials that are too weak may break too easily, as happened with Hugh Herr's 'plaster legs'. If the replacement is much stiffer than the bone to which it is attached, then forces become concentrated in the replacement material and the bone does not regrow.

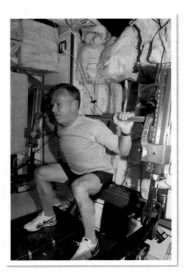

Figure 6.6 An astronaut using a resistive exercise device

The materials must also be sterile and must not cause the body's immune system to reject them. Polythene joint liners for hip replacements can now be infiltrated with vitamin E to reduce the likelihood of rejection.

New materials

Replacement hip joints used to be made of a metal ball in a polyethylene and titanium socket. They last for about 10 to 15 years, after which time small, abrasive particles from the metal ball begin to wear away the plastic parts and they need to be replaced. Hip replacements were not generally given to younger people since they would need several operations in the course of a lifetime.

In 2003 approval was given for the development of ceramic-on-ceramic replacement hip joints. Ceramic materials are far more durable than metal – they produce much less debris. One of the industry standard hip replacement joints used worldwide is the BHR – Birmingham Hip Replacement (Figure 6.7); as the name suggests, it was developed in Birmingham. The metal alloy hip joint has a special surface cast called Porocast™ that helps resist particulate wear by making the porous surface an integral part of the metal casting process. It also encourages bone in-growth, helping to fix the new joint better. The Porocast™ is covered with a hydroxyapatite $(Ca_{10}(PO_4)_6(OH)_2)$ ceramic coating. This prevents the body from rejecting the metal implant and allows bone minerals to grow into the hydroxyapatite.

Continuing research into ceramics promises further improvement. For example, ceramic calcium phosphate can stimulate bone regrowth (Figure 6.8) by attracting stem cells and 'growth factors'. The rate of bone repair rivals that of traditional grafts using a patient's own bone.

In the quest for the best materials for replacement bones, attention has turned to natural biological materials.

Figure 6.7 The Birmingham Hip Replacement

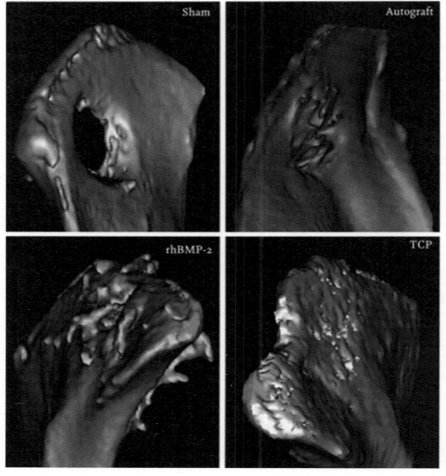

Figure 6.8 Bone formation around an implant

Coral is similar in many respects to bone and is used in some replacement joints. Tiny marine animals called corals feed off microscopic plankton and turn the consumed carbon into calcium carbonate. When they die their mineral skeletons become part of a reef (Figure 6.9). Some species of coral have the necessary porous inner structure to allow new blood vessels to develop into the graft, allowing the body to start the growth of new bone and tissue around the coral. As well as being tough and less likely to be rejected by the body's immune system, coral carries no risk of infection, unlike grafts of human bone. The only drawback is that coral has the potential to absorb toxic metals such as nickel, cadmium and mercury.

Italian scientists have developed a new procedure to turn blocks of wood into artificial bones. They chose wood because its physical structure is spongy like bone. To create the bone substitute, the scientists start with a block of wood such as red oak and heat it until all that remains is pure carbon, then spray calcium over the carbon, creating calcium carbide. Additional chemical and physical steps convert the calcium carbide into carbonated hydroxyapatite, which can then be implanted and serves as the artificial bone. The process takes about a week and costs about £600 for a single bone implant.

Another promising development (invented by British scientists) is artificial 'injectable bone' that flows like toothpaste and hardens in the body. This provides a scaffold for the formation of blood vessels and bone tissue, and can also deliver stem cells directly to the site of bone repair. It is hoped that injectable bone might one day reduce or eliminate the need for bone grafts to repair skeletal defects and fractures, which often require painful invasive surgery.

Figure 6.9 A coral reef

QUESTIONS

Q 1   Write down some of the key functions of a skeleton.

Q 2   Describe the main difference in the movement of a hinge joint compared with that of a ball and socket joint.

Q 3   List the main properties of bone that have to be met by any artificial substitute.

Q 4   How might bone behave if it was without living fibres?

Q 5   Summarise some of the advantages of using a bone substitute rather than using human bone in medical treatment.

2.2 The right stuff

To make a good bone substitute, a material must be strong enough to exert and withstand the forces involved in normal movement; if it is to be used in a hip replacement, it must support a person's weight. The substitute bone's **mechanical properties** (the way it behaves when subjected to forces) must be similar to those of real bone. In this section you will see how materials are tested, described and compared.

In the chapter *Good Enough to Eat*, you will have met several terms used to describe materials and their behaviour. Some of these are listed in Table 6.1, along with two extra terms (**smooth** and **durable**). In the course of this chapter, the meanings of some of these terms will be refined.

Elastic	Returns to its original shape when the load is removed
Plastic	Remains deformed when the load is removed
Brittle	Cracks and breaks without plastic deformation
Tough	Does not readily crack; can withstand dynamic loads such as shock or impact
Ductile	Can be deformed plastically under tension; can be pulled into a long thin shape
Malleable	Can be deformed plastically under compression; can be hammered into a sheet
Hard	Not readily scratched or indented
Stiff	Requires a large force to produce a small deformation
Smooth	Low friction surface
Durable	Properties do not worsen with repeated loading and unloading

Table 6.1 Terms used to describe the behaviour of materials

QUESTIONS

 Use terms from Table 6.1 to describe the ideal properties of the following spare parts: **(a)** blood vessel, **(b)** teeth and **(c)** thigh bone.

 Table 6.2 summarises some information about hip replacement options.

Metal on Plastic (polyethylene)	The longest tried and tested replacement Ball part of metal, socket liner of plastic Durable and least expensive Wear about 0.1 mm per year Polyethylene particles a source of infection within the body
Metal on Metal	Also long-standing regular use as a replacement Chromium, titanium, stainless steel alloys used of strength greater than original bone Wear about 0.01 mm per year Mid-range expense Wear products become soluble metal ions that can spread through the body
Ceramic on Ceramic or Ceramic on Plastic	A twenty-first century innovation Ceramic surfaces are hard and durable (harder than metal) and stretch resistant Wear about 0.01 mm per year for ceramic–plastic and less for ceramic–ceramic Least known toxic side effects on the body but occasional issues with joints squeaking Most expensive options, especially ceramic–ceramic

Table 6.2 Hip replacement options

What sort of factors might determine which hip replacement option is chosen? Consider possible preferred options for a young patient, an active patient, a very obese patient and patients in less developed countries.

Stitching up

In the chapter *Higher, Faster, Stronger*, you learned that for a material that obeys Hooke's law the extension x is proportional to the applied force, F:

$$F = kx \tag{1}$$

where k is a constant known as **stiffness**.

If a material does not obey Hooke's law, the force–extension graph is not a straight line and the stiffness changes as the sample is stretched. Defining stiffness as the increase in force, ΔF, that is needed to produce an additional extension, Δx, the stiffness at any given extension can be found from the gradient of the force–extension graph.

$$k = \frac{\Delta F}{\Delta x} \tag{1a}$$

The stiffness of the material used in sutures (stitches) in closing wounds and incisions of the skin is an important property. Some of the most commonly used suture materials are barbed by placing linear nicks along their length, which aids adhesion with the skin's surface. Once the skin is stitched the suture must be both strong and stiff enough to anchor the cut skin surfaces in place to ensure time for healing with minimum scarring. For example, consider stitching on the face: facial expressions such as smiling and laughing and motions such as chewing food can pit powerful muscles against the strength of the suture. Any stretching of the suture would potentially cause the wound to gape, with consequent facial scarring.

In a test comparing types of suture, forces were applied along the suture's length and its consequent extension measured. Six tests were done on each of three types of suture and the results were then averaged and plotted as force–extension graphs, as shown in Figure 6.10.

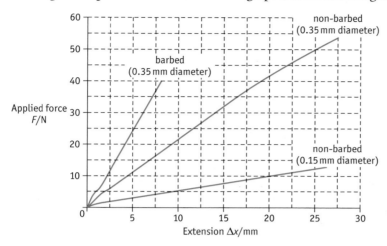

Figure 6.10 Force–extension plots for suture materials

QUESTION

Q 8 **(a)** Calculate the stiffness of the barbed and non-barbed 0.35 mm diameter threads. Comment on your results in terms of the best choice for facial stitching.

(b) The end of each graph line indicates the breaking point. Compare the average breaking forces for 0.35 mm diameter barbed and non-barbed threads. Suggest why the value for barbed is less than that for non-barbed.

(c) From the limited information in Figure 6.10, suggest a relationship between stiffness and thread diameter. What are the pros and cons of using thinner thread for facial stitching?

⚙ ACTIVITY 5 STITCHING UP

Produce force–extension graphs for a fishing line and a rubber band. Try to obtain material of a similar diameter to a medical suture (around 0.35 mm) so comparisons can be made. Do the materials obey Hooke's law? Can a measure of stiffness be obtained for each?

Stress and strain

In *Higher, Faster, Stronger*, you saw that the extension of a rope or cord under a given load depends on its length and thickness, as well as on the material from which it is made. One way to compare the behaviour of different materials is to use samples of a standard size. Another way is to define and measure properties in such a way that they depend only on the material and not on the size and shape of the sample; as bones do not come in standard sizes, it makes sense to compare their properties in this way.

Bones are normally subjected to compressive forces – that is, to forces that tend to squash them. Under a relatively small force, bone will deform slightly (though not much, because it is stiff), but if the force becomes large the bone may break. If two samples of different thickness are both subjected to compressive forces, the thinner one will break under a smaller force. If one sample has twice the cross-sectional area of the other then it will withstand twice the force, but for each sample the force divided by the area is the same. Applied force, F, divided by area of cross-section, A, is called the stress and is represented by σ (the Greek letter sigma):

$$\sigma = \frac{F}{A}$$ (2)

PRACTICAL SKILLS REFERENCE

Planning and experimental design

See Practical skills notes 2.1–2.2

Carrying out practical work

See Practical skills notes 3.1–3.2

Analysis and interpretation of data

See Practical skills notes 4.1–4.2

Conclusion and evaluation

See Practical skills notes 5.1–5.2

STUDY NOTE

In the chapter *Good Enough to Eat*, you will have seen that many tests used by the food industry require samples of standard size.

MATHS REFERENCE

SI prefixes

See Maths note 2.4

The same definition and symbols are used for **tensile stress** (when the sample is pulled) and for **compressive stress** (when the sample is squashed). The SI unit of stress is the pascal (Pa): $1\,Pa = 1\,N\,m^{-2}$. (You have probably met the unit before as it is also used for pressure.) 1 Pa is a very small stress; the SI prefixes kilo- and mega- are usually needed when measuring stresses in practical situations.

The stress needed to break a material is called its **ultimate compressive** (or tensile) **stress**, or simply the **breaking stress**, and is a measure of the **strength** of the material that does not depend on the size of the sample. The ultimate compressive stress of bone, or bone substitute, is clearly important to the user, as you will see in Questions 9 and 10 and Activity 6.

WORKED EXAMPLE

Q Spider silk is exceptionally strong and has a typical maximum breaking stress of $1.2 \times 10^9\,Pa$ for an average diameter of 0.15 mm. What mass could you hang from a single thread of spider silk before it breaks?

A Cross-sectional area $A = \pi r^2 = \pi\dfrac{d^2}{2}$

$$= \pi(0.075 \times 10^{-3}\,m)^2$$

$$= 1.77 \times 10^{-8}\,m^2$$

Breaking force = Breaking stress x cross-sectional area

$F = \sigma A = 1.2 \times 10^9\,Pa \times 1.77 \times 10^{-8}\,m^2$

$$= 21.2\,N$$

Breaking mass $m = \dfrac{F}{g}$

$$= \dfrac{21.2\,N}{9.81\,N\,kg^{-1}}$$

$$= 2.16\,kg$$

PRACTICAL SKILLS REFERENCE

Analysis and interpretation of data

See Practical skills notes 4.1–4.2

Conclusion and evaluation

See Practical skills notes 5.1–5.2

ACTIVITY 6   CRUNCHIE BONES?

The inside of a Crunchie bar is very similar to bone in structure and appearance. Measure the compressive breaking stress for a piece of Crunchie bar. Would it make an acceptable bone substitute?

QUESTIONS

Q 9 Estimate the compressive stress in your leg bones when you are standing still. Explain why their ultimate compressive stress needs to be much greater than this.

Q 10 A 70 kg man jumps from a wall 1.5 m high, lands on both feet together and takes 0.1 s to come to rest. The cross-sectional area of the bones in each of his lower legs is $30\,cm^2$.

(a) How fast is he moving just as he reaches the ground?

(b) What is his average deceleration?

(c) What is the average force exerted as he comes to rest?

(d) What is the stress in his lower legs as he comes to rest?

Use $g = 9.8\,m\,s^{-2} = 9.81\,N\,kg^{-1}$. You might need to look back at the work you did in *Higher, Faster, Stronger*. Note that you need to express the areas in m^2.

Q 11 Many footballers (notably David Beckham and Wayne Rooney) have suffered metatarsal injuries that have proved difficult to mend. Even a relatively small force, applied as shown in Figure 6.11, can cause damage because bone withstands tensile stress far less well that compressive stress.

Make an annotated sketch of a slightly bent metatarsal bone to explain how the bone fractures.

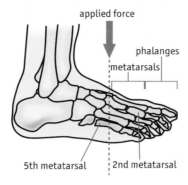

Figure 6.11 A long thin object, such as a metatarsal, can easily fracture if subjected to a small force as shown here.

The amount by which a sample deforms also depends on the stress. Figure 6.12 shows two samples that obey Hooke's law. They are both made of the same material and are the same length, but one has twice the cross-sectional area of the other. If the same force is applied to each, then the thicker sample is deformed by only half as much as the thinner one. However, if they are both subject to the same stress, then they both suffer the same deformation. So, for samples of the same length, compression (or extension) Δx is proportional to stress, and Hooke's law can be expressed as:

$$\Delta x \propto \sigma \qquad (3)$$

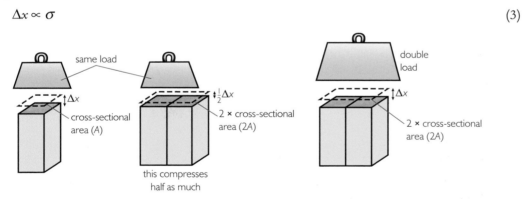

Figure 6.12 Samples of different thickness being subjected to compression

The extension or compression of a sample depends on its length as well as on its area of cross-section. As shown in Figure 6.13, doubling the length of the sample doubles the compression. For each sample, the ratio of compression or extension Δx to original length l is the same. This ratio is defined as the strain and is represented by the symbol ε (the Greek letter epsilon):

$$\varepsilon = \frac{\Delta x}{l} \qquad (4)$$

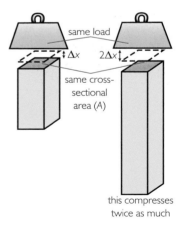

Figure 6.13 Samples of different length being subjected to compression

MATHS REFERENCE

Fractions, decimals and percentages
See Maths note 3.1

The same symbols are used for **compressive strain** and for **tensile strain**. Notice that strain is a ratio of two lengths and so it has *no units*. Strain is often expressed as a percentage – that is, the compression or extension as a percentage of the original length.

QUESTIONS

Q 12 In a test of a sample of a possible bone substitute, a sample of 40 cm long was compressed by 2.5 mm. What is the compressive strain expressed as a decimal and as a percentage?

Q 13 A metal wire is given a tensile strain of 0.15%. If the original length of the wire was 50 cm, by how much did it extend? Express your answer in mm. If a wire ten times as long is given the same strain, by how much will it extend?

Hooke's law and the Young modulus

In previous work, you have used force–extension graphs to show how a material sample deforms under a load. If, instead of force against extension, we plot stress against strain, then we get a graph that depends only on the nature of the material and not on the size and shape of the sample. Figure 6.14 shows such a **stress–strain graph** (b) plotted for a material sample alongside two force–extension graphs (a) for different samples of the same material. Notice all the graphs are the same shape, although they have different numbers on the axes.

The labels on the graphs in Figure 6.14 are related to the mechanical behaviour of the sample. In Figure 6.14(a), from O to H each graph is straight; H is the **limit of proportionality**. Force is proportional to extension, i.e. the sample obeys Hooke's law. In Figure 6.14(b), between O and H stress is proportional to strain, which is another way of expressing Hooke's law.

Elastic deformation occurs up to P, the **elastic limit**. This means that the material returns to its original length when released. Beyond P the material gains permanent extension and is therefore said to behave plastically. P is also known as the **yield point**. It is worth noting that if released at A (i.e. beyond P) the material recovers along AO′, which is parallel to HO, giving it a permanent extension of OO′. If stress is reapplied then the curve O′AB is followed. At B the sample breaks. In Figure 6.14(b), the stress at B is the breaking stress or ultimate tensile stress.

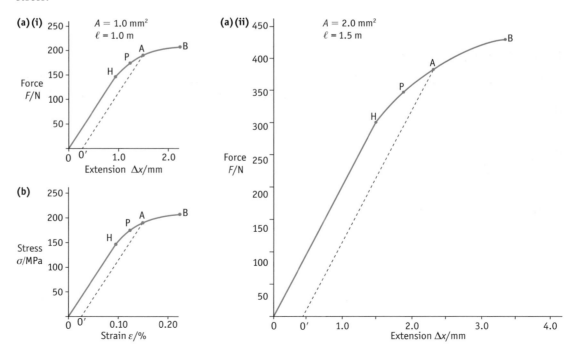

Figure 6.14 The results of testing a material sample displayed (a) (i) and (ii) as force against extension and (b) as stress against strain

Earlier we defined the stiffness, k, of a sample such that:

$$k = \frac{\Delta F}{\Delta x}$$ (Equation 1a)

Similarly, we can measure the gradient of the stress–strain graph. Now, though, we get a value that depends only on the material and not on the size or shape of the sample – it is a measure of the **stiffness of the material**. This value is known as the **Young modulus**, E, of the material:

$$E = \frac{\sigma}{\varepsilon}$$ (5)

Since strain has no unit, the SI unit of the Young modulus is that of stress, i.e. pascals, Pa.

The Young modulus is important when designing materials for replacement joints. Figure 6.15 shows a typical hip replacement. Bone typically has a Young modulus of about 1×10^{10} Pa. If the replacement has a smaller Young modulus than the natural bone into which it is inserted, then most if the load will be supported by the natural bone, which might then be under too much stress and become damaged. (You can model this using two springs side by side, as in Figure 6.16. If one spring is stiffer than the other, then as you squash both springs you feel the stiffer spring exerting a greater force.)

STUDY NOTE

The Young modulus is given the symbol E because it is a so-called 'elastic modulus'. There are other elastic moduli that you will meet in the chapter *Build or Bust?*

STUDY NOTE

The Young modulus of a metal can be related to the forces acting between its atoms. (See *Spare Part Surgery* Additional Sheet 1.)

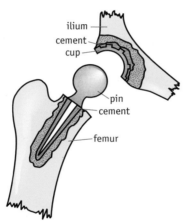

Figure 6.15 A typical hip joint replacement

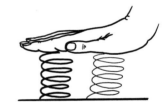

Figure 6.16 Squashing two springs of different stiffness

However, if the Young modulus of the replacement bone is too high, then it supports most of the load. Far from protecting the natural bone, this causes it to waste away because it is deprived of the stress that stimulates regrowth.

WORKED EXAMPLE

Q The bones of a healthy person have Young modulus $E = 1.0 \times 10^{10}$ Pa and maximum stress before fracture of 4.0 MPa. What will the compressive strain be around the fracture point, and what would be the compression in a bone 25 cm long?

A $E = \frac{\sigma}{\varepsilon}$

strain $\varepsilon = \frac{\sigma}{E}$

$= \frac{4.0 \times 10^6 \, \text{Pa}}{1.0 \times 10^{10} \, \text{Pa}}$

$= 4.0 \times 10^{-4} = 4.0 \times 10^{-2}\%$

$\varepsilon = \frac{\Delta x}{\Delta l}$

Compression $\Delta x = \varepsilon \Delta l$

$= 4.0 \times 10^{-4} \times 0.25 \, \text{m} = 1.0 \times 10^{-4} \, \text{m} = 0.10 \, \text{mm}$

Trabecular bone material is situated at the end of long bones such as the femur and in the spinal column. It transfers loads from joint faces into the midshaft of the bone and so is a bone most affected by osteoporosis and ageing. Figure 6.17 shows stress–strain tests on two bone samples carried out by the Paul Hansma Research group in Santa Barbara, USA. One sample is from a healthy 21-year-old male and the other is from a 65-year-old female suffering from osteoarthritis.

Questions 14–16 all refer to Figure 6.17.

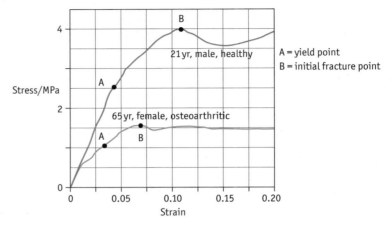

Figure 6.17 Stress–strain tests on bone samples

QUESTIONS

Q 14 Explain whether the bone in each sample obeys Hooke's law.

Q 15 The 21-year-old male bone had a cross-sectional area of $2.5 \times 10^{-3}\,\text{m}^2$. Using the graph for this bone:

(a) Explain what is happening to the bone at A (the yield point) and B (the initial fracture point).

(b) Estimate the stress at the yield point.

(c) Calculate the force that would produce the yield stress.

(d) Estimate the strain at the initial fracture point.

(e) If the femur bone was about 0.40 m long and constructed entirely of this same material, what would be the compression at the point of fracture?

(f) Calculate the Young modulus for the bone material and express it in standard form to two significant figures.

Q 16 Using technical terms and numerical values where possible, describe five significant differences between the stress–strain graphs for the bones of the 65-year-old osteoarthritic female and the healthy 21-year-old male.

2.3 By design

Modern prosthetics

Modern prosthetics can now do much more than just replace a limb. Advances in miniaturising microprocessors have led to the development of the C-leg by Otto Bock Healthcare (Figure 6.18). The advanced knee joint samples data 50 times a second and processes it to give the user a more stable limb for better balance and a more controlled gait. Two strain gauges measure pressures on the leg and note how often the heel strikes the ground. Magnetic sensors can detect changes in knee angle. It can recognise different actions (for example, walking up stairs, running, hopping) and adjust itself accordingly so the wearer doesn't need to think about it. As Hugh Herr's experience shows, these new prosthetics can give the users a better quality of life and allow them greater mobility to take part in a variety of sporting and leisure activities.

Figure 6.18 The C-leg

A person's likelihood of getting prosthetic limbs, however great their need, depends on where they live. In North America and most of Western Europe it is estimated that 90% of patients get their required prosthesis, whereas in Africa the figure is nearer 10%. In many parts of the developing world, when people are born with deformities or lose their limbs, many also lose their livelihoods, homes or families – and the most vulnerable even die.

Olivia Giles (Figure 6.19) was working as a lawyer when she caught meningococcal septicaemia and had to have her hands and feet amputated to save her life. She went on to found the charity 500 Miles, which supplies prosthetic limbs to developing countries. (The charity's name comes from The Proclaimers' famous lyrics, *I would walk 500 miles*.) Further details can be found on the charity's website.

Figure 6.19 Olivia Giles, founder of the 500 Miles charity

Developing a new material

You have read about several possible substitute bone materials and how the development of completely artificial, bone-like materials is the subject of much current thinking. This involves producing a sample from an initial idea, development and testing in research laboratories, further checks to ensure its safety, possible patenting, externally monitored clinical trials, and finally commercial usage in mainstream medicine if all goes well. Some materials turn out to have a specific application. For example, a material called hydroxyapatite ceramic has been used to replace the tiny bones in the middle ear that conduct sound (Figure 6.20).

Like hydroxyapatite ceramic, many of the most promising new materials are **polymers**, since these can be designed to have properties very similar to real bone and they are also very strong. They can also combine in composite materials, for example using a polymer (polyethylene) and a ceramic (hydroxyapatite), to create something similar to natural bone in structure and chemical composition.

Figure 6.20 A sample of hydroxyapatite used in bone reconstruction

Polymers

Polymers consist of molecules that are long chains made up of fairly simple arrangements of carbon and other atoms repeated many times over. Polyethylene is a polymer whose molecules are long chains of C_2H_2 units joined together (Figure 6.21). Its official chemical name is poly(ethene) (C_2H_2 is ethene) and it is known colloquially as polythene. The length of the chains depends on how the polymer is made. UHMWPE has very long chains – 'ultra-high-molecular-weight' means that the (average) mass of each molecule is large.

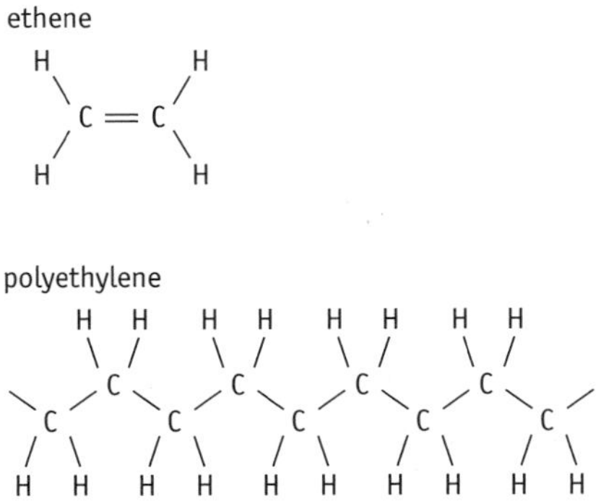

ethene

$$\begin{array}{c}
H \quad\quad\quad H \\
\diagdown \quad\quad\quad \diagup \\
C = C \\
\diagup \quad\quad\quad \diagdown \\
H \quad\quad\quad H
\end{array}$$

polyethylene

Figure 6.21 Ethene and poly(ethene)

UHMWPE has a very smooth surface and is also very tough, so it is used for many other purposes as well as for replacement joints. These include:

- coating of hoppers in the steel industry to allow coke to flow easily
- rear of boring heads for tunnel building to allow earth and clay to fall off easily
- sliders in railway points so that ice will not stick to them
- harbour fenders
- rail guides for conveyor belts.

Orthoplastics Ltd in Lancashire specialise in the production of UHMWPE. They can produce rods, sheets and machined components using computer-aided design machining equipment and presses. Their machines work in an environment controlled by electrostatic filtration to submicrometre size to ensure that airborne contaminants are kept to an absolute minimum. Any material introduced into the body must be free of microbes. This medical-grade material is used in hip joints (Figure 6.22(a)) and is supplied to users with a certificate that allows total traceability and provides test results of its important mechanical properties (Figure 6.22(b)).

(a)

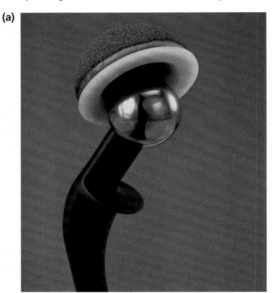

(b) **TEST CERTIFICATE**

Figure 6.22 (a) A hip joint made with UHMWPE; (b) a test certificate for medical-grade UHMWPE

PRACTICAL SKILLS REFERENCE

Planning and experimental design

See Practical skills notes 2.1–2.2

Carrying out practical work

See Practical skills notes 3.1–3.2

Analysis and interpretation of data

See Practical skills notes 4.1–4.2

Conclusion and evaluation

See Practical skills notes 5.1–5.2

Materials used in spare part surgery must meet strict standards, for example UHMWPE must satisfy the requirements in Figure 6.22(b). Surgical materials are tested to make sure they are fit for purpose. One such test involves determining the Young modulus of a material, and this is what you are asked to do in Activity 7.

> ⚙ **ACTIVITY 7 IS IT GOOD ENOUGH?**
> Carry out a stress–strain test on a material sample and use your results to determine its Young modulus.

Stress–strain graphs and the Young modulus are widely used in all areas of materials science, not just those concerned with medical applications, as Questions 17 to 19 illustrate.

QUESTIONS

Q 17 A steel wire of cross-sectional area 0.5 mm^2 and length 8.0 m is found to stretch 6.0 mm when the tension on it increases by 75 N. The steel wire returns to its original length when the extra tension is released.

(a) What is the wire's cross-sectional area in square metres?

(b) What stress was applied?

(c) What was the resultant strain?

(d) What is the Young modulus for steel?

(e) Bone typically has a Young modulus of about 1×10^{10} Pa. What problems would there be in using steel as a replacement bone material?

(f) A lift cable consists of 100 strands of this wire. The lift is limited to ten people of maximum mass 85 kg each. When the lift is full, by how much will the 90 m cable stretch? ($g = 9.81$ N kg^{-1})

Tension/ 10^3 N	Extension/ 10^{-3} m
0.0	0.0
35.0	0.1
38.0	0.2
36.5	0.4
36.0	0.7
37.0	1.0
40.0	1.4
45.0	2.1
50.0	3.1
55.0	5.1
57.5	7.2
60.0	9.1
60.0	13.1
57.5	14.7
55.0	15.2
52.5	15.8 (broke)

Table 6.2 Data for Question 18

Q 18 A steel rod was tested to destruction. It had a cross-sectional area of 1.3×10^{-4} m^2 and a length of 65×10^{-3} m. The results are listed in Table 6.2 in the order in which they were obtained.

(a) Use Table 6.2 to draw up a table of stress and strain and plot a stress–strain graph. Join the plotted points with a smooth curve, being careful to join them in the order in which they are listed. (You might need two graphs, one for small strains and one for large strains.)

(b) From your graph:
   (i) What was the yield stress of the steel?
   (ii) What was the ultimate tensile stress of the steel?
   (iii) What was the percentage strain when it broke?

Q 19 A nylon guitar string has a diameter of 0.4 mm. The length of the string from its fixed point to the tension key is 840 mm. Turning the tension key once extends the string by 4.0 mm. Calculate the tension in the string when the key has been turned eight times. (Young modulus for nylon = 3.0×10^9 Pa)

2.4 Take the strain

Elastic energy

Look back at Figure 6.1 and think again about the different types of materials used to make spare parts such as bones, ligaments and blood vessels. Bone substitutes need to be strong and stiff, but other replacement parts need to be more elastic. In some cases this is because they need to store and return energy. In the chapter *Higher, Faster, Stronger* you measured some of the energy transfers in sporting activities, and energies of a few hundred joules were common (for example, in jumping and weightlifting). UHMWPE's ability to store energy is not relevant to its use in hip joints, but it is important in some of its other uses (such as harbour fenders).

In *Higher, Faster, Stronger* you saw how to find elastic energy, ΔE_{el}, from a force–extension graph: it is equal to the area under the curve. If the sample obeys Hooke's law, then:

$$\Delta E_{el} = \frac{F\Delta x}{2} = \frac{1}{2}k(\Delta x)^2 \qquad (6)$$

where F is the magnitude of the force needed to produce an extension Δx (see Figure 6.23(a)). If the sample does not obey Hooke's law, then the area can be found by counting squares (Figure 6.23(b)).

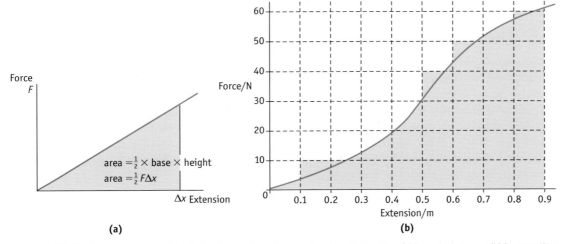

Figure 6.23 Elastic energy is found from the area under a force–extension graph either (a) by calculation or (b) by counting squares

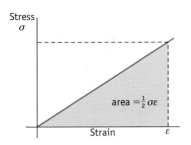

Figure 6.24 The area under a stress–strain curve for a material that obeys Hooke's law

What about stress–strain graphs? We have seen that the gradient of such a graph has a meaning (it is the Young modulus), but what about the area under the curve? Think of a material that obeys Hooke's law. At a given strain ε, the area under the stress–strain curve is $\dfrac{\sigma\varepsilon}{2}$ (Figure 6.24).

Since:

$$F = \sigma A \qquad\qquad \text{(Equation 1)}$$

and:

$$\Delta x = \varepsilon l \qquad\qquad \text{(Equation 3)}$$

we can write Equation 6 as:

$$\Delta E_{el} = \frac{\sigma A \times \varepsilon l}{2} = A l \times \left(\frac{\sigma\varepsilon}{2}\right)$$

Yet Al is just the volume, V, of the sample, and so:

$$\text{area under stress–strain curve} = \left(\frac{\sigma\varepsilon}{2}\right) = \frac{\Delta E_{el}}{V} \qquad\qquad (7)$$

In other words, the area under the curve is equal to the energy stored per unit volume, or the **energy density**, U.

For a material that obeys Hooke's law, we can rewrite Equation 7 using the Young modulus, E:

$$\sigma = \varepsilon E \qquad\qquad \text{(Equation 5)}$$

and so:

$$U = \frac{\Delta E_{el}}{V} = \frac{E\varepsilon^2}{2} \qquad\qquad (8)$$

For a material that does not obey Hooke's law, Equation 8 does not apply, but the area under a stress–strain curve is still equal to the stored energy density.

QUESTIONS

Q 20   Suppose you want a material that is capable of storing a large amount of elastic energy per unit volume (for example, to make an artificial tendon). What particular mechanical properties would you look for?

Q 21   **(a)** Look back at your answer to Question 18 and use your graph to find the energy density in steel when it breaks.

      (b) Given that the density of steel is about $8 \times 10^3\,\text{kg m}^{-3}$, estimate the speed of a steel wire when it breaks.

2.5 The inside story

As you saw in Section 2.3, polymer materials are being developed to make substitute bones and replacement ball-and-socket joints. These materials have mechanical properties (Young modulus, strength, smoothness) that enable them to match natural materials. Another recent development is artificial skin, which is particularly useful when treating people who have become badly burned or whose skin has become ulcerated. Artificial skin is much more elastic than artificial bone, to match natural skin. (You can demonstrate this elasticity by pinching a fold of skin on the back of your hand and noticing that it springs back. The elasticity of skin declines with age; ask an older person to repeat the 'pinch test' and compare observations.)

A skin substitute called Dermagraft, made by Advanced Tissue Sciences Inc. in the USA, combines a bioengineered human dermal (skin) layer with a synthetic polymer covering. On being transplanted, the polymer covering dissolves and the patient's own cells start to grow.

Why do polymers play such a key role in spare part materials? The clue lies in their small-scale structure.

Polymer structures

Figure 6.25 shows polymer molecules in a stretched and an unstretched polymer sample. Unstretched polymers have no regular structure and are said to be amorphous: the long-chain polymer molecules are intertwined and jumbled up (Figure 6.25(a)). A stretching force tends to uncoil the chains and straighten them into orderly lines (Figure 6.25(b)), and in this way they produce regular diffraction patterns. When released, the molecules coil up again. When fully extended the chains are stiff because their interatomic bonds are then stretched directly. This explains why polymers have a Young modulus 10 000 times less than that of a metal but can be extended to perhaps ten times their original length (1000% strain).

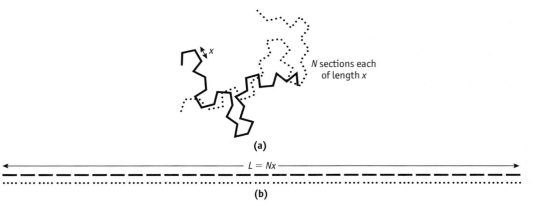

(a)

$L = Nx$

(b)

Figure 6.25 Schematic diagrams of polymer chains (a) in an unstretched polymer and (b) in a stretched polymer

Low-density low-molecular-weight polyethylene is similar to rubber, with lots of jumbled-up polymer chains. In fact the very long molecules fold up as shown in Figure 6.26 and stack up in what is referred to as a lamella formation (lamella means 'little plate'). As can be seen, the vertical strands are parallel and regular and so resemble a crystalline structure.

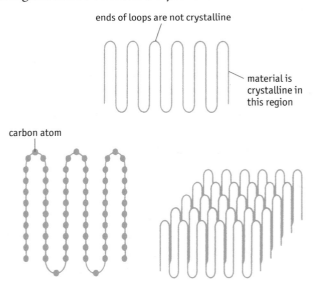

ends of loops are not crystalline

material is crystalline in this region

carbon atom

Figure 6.26 Lamella formation in high-molecular-weight polyethylene

When the material is unstretched, the lamellae are randomly orientated as shown in Figure 6.27; as the material is stretched, they start to align. This is a reversible effect, and so the material behaves elastically. It is quite stiff and therefore makes a good material for cups. Increased stress leads to a breakdown of the lamellae into fibrils (tiny fibres). The long polymer chains line up and then the material becomes strong as the carbon–carbon bonds are stretched.

Polyethylene and PVC are man-made polymers, but there are also many natural polymers found in living things. Plant fibres such as cotton are made up of polymers, as are animal fibres such as hair and wool.

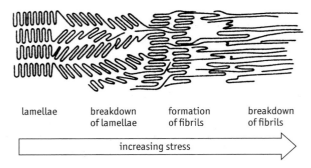

lamellae   breakdown   formation   breakdown
        of lamellae   of fibrils   of fibrils

increasing stress

Figure 6.27 Stretching UHMWPE

Hair is a natural polymer made from keratin, a type of protein. In hair, the keratin molecules are held together by hydrogen bonds to form helices (spirals). As hair is stretched, the hydrogen bonds between the helices break, causing the helices to unravel and form sheets. Figure 6.28 shows stress–strain curves obtained by increasing the force applied to human hair and to a horse hair.

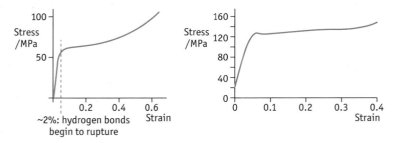

Figure 6.28 Stress-strain curves for (a) human hair (b) horse hair from a violin bow

When the stress is removed, the helices re-form gradually. However, the area under the 'unloading' curve is much smaller than that under the 'loading' curve: the work done *by* the hair as it returns to its original length is much less than the work done *on* the hair when it was stretched. The area between the two curves is known as a **hysteresis** loop and represents the energy dissipated due to heating during the process. Figure 6.29 shows hysteresis loops for human hair, dry horse hair (as used in violin bows) and 'replasticised' horse hair (the same type of horse hair but soaked in water).

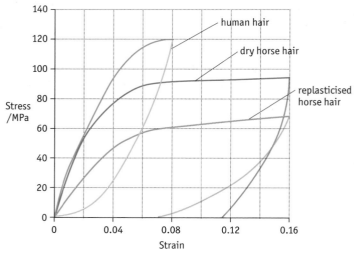

Figure 6.29 Hysteresis loops for human and horse hairs

QUESTION

Q 22   For each of the three graphs in Figure 6.29, estimate:

    (i)   the area under the loading graph

    (ii)   the area under the unloading graph

    (iii) the energy lost per unit volume in loading and unloading.

It is because they can imitate natural fibres that man-made polymers find a use in spare part surgery. As you have seen, the mechanical properties of a polymer depend on the way its chain molecules arrange themselves, and this in turn depends on the length of the molecules and their chemical make-up. The disciplines of physics and chemistry come together in polymer science, enabling a vast range of polymers to be developed that have a very wide variety of properties.

2.6   Summing up Part 2

In this part of the chapter you have extended your knowledge of the physics of materials and seen how knowledge of the small-scale structure of a material can help explain its large-scale behaviour. This understanding can help materials scientists to develop materials with properties to suit a particular purpose.

⚙ ACTIVITY 8   SUMMING UP PART 2

Look back through your work and make sure you know the meanings of all the key terms printed in bold. Then write each term on a slip of paper (e.g. a sticky note) and arrange them on a large sheet of paper to make a concept map for this part of the chapter. Link the slips of paper by writing a few words or an equation or by sketching a diagram.

When completed, your concept map should provide you with a summary of what you have learned about large-scale and small-scale properties (particularly polymers) and how they are interrelated.

QUESTION

    Figure 6.30 shows a schematic stress–strain graph for a polymer material.

Q 23   **(a)** How would a stress–strain graph for a metal differ from Figure 6.30?

    (b) Suggest a physical interpretation for the area enclosed between the 'loading' and 'unloading' curves in Figure 6.30.

    (c) Sketch the arrangement of molecules you would expect to see when the sample was at point A and at point C.

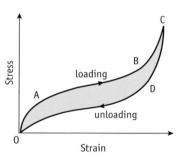

Figure 6.30 Stress–strain graph for a polymer

FURTHER INVESTIGATION

Explore the behaviour of various materials that appear 'bone-like', such as cuttlefish bone (available from pet shops), seaside rock and 'oasis' (used in flower arranging). Try to measure the Young modulus and ultimate compressive strength. Observe the way they fracture. Comment on their resemblance (or otherwise) to real bone.

3 A sight better

3.1 One in the eye

Lens implants

Our eyes are our most important sense organs (Figure 6.31). They account for about 80% of our brains' sensory input, which tells us what's going on around us. So if something goes wrong with our eyes, we're in trouble.

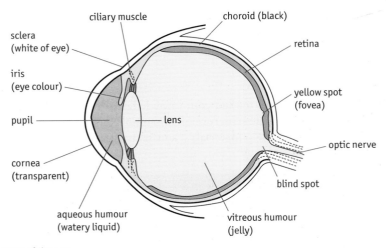

Figure 6.31 Structure of the eye

For most people, the worst problem we are ever likely to have with our eyesight is cataracts. A cataract is a cloudy region within the lens of the eye, and seeing through a cataract-affected eye can be like looking through a steamed-up window.

Cataracts are common among elderly people. They may result from injuries, from disease or even from some medications. However, they can also occur simply as a result of the deterioration of the material of the lens as it ages. Some children are born with congenital cataracts. A small speck of cataract in the lens may have little effect on your vision, but a larger cataract in the centre of the lens can be very serious.

As a cataract develops, the sufferer is likely to notice two effects: their vision gets dimmer and it gets more hazy — it's harder to see a clearly focused image. At first, spectacles can be prescribed to improve focusing, but eventually an operation may be necessary. In the past it was common simply to remove the lens and provide the patient with spectacles with very strong lenses. This was a good solution at the time, but strong lenses tend to give you a clear view straight ahead but not to the sides, and what you see is enlarged. Nowadays patients are given lens implants.

Cataract surgery: a step-by-step guide

The lens of the eye is rather like a grape. The lens capsule is the grape's skin. Here's how to replace a faulty lens with an intra-ocular lens (an IOL). It only takes 20 to 30 minutes and can be done in the Outpatients' department of a hospital. Don't try this at home!

- Make a tiny incision in the white of the eye, next to the cornea.
- Insert a fine tool and peel off the front of the lens capsule.
- Emulsify the material of the inside of the lens capsule.
- Suck out this fluid using a tiny vacuum tube.
- Slide a substitute plastic lens into the lens capsule.
- Seal the incision.

Surgery is not appropriate for all patients with cataracts. There can be complications. Patients may be suffering from other complaints such as glaucoma or diabetic retinopathy (extra blood vessels in the retina resulting from diabetes), and cataract surgery may make these conditions worse. For the right patients, however, this operation can be very successful, greatly improving the brightness and clarity of their eyesight.

Figure 6.32 Visual impairment caused by cataracts

Contact lenses

A piece of grit in the eye is most uncomfortable. You eye waters uncontrollably, and you have to stop what you are doing until you have got rid of the problem.

Our eyes are very sensitive to small particles of dirt, and no-one wants to be poked in the eye with a sharp stick; even thinking about it can make you blink. So, at first, the idea of wearing contact lenses can seem pretty nasty. Who wants to have to put a piece of plastic in each eye, every day? Most people quickly learn to manage with modern contact lenses, and their smoothness means you often don't even notice that you're wearing them.

The first contact lenses – over a century ago – were made of glass. They fitted right over the front of the eye (the cornea) and under both eyelids. They were awkward to put in place, and so only a few people for whom spectacles were completely unsuitable used them. These early lenses were followed by much smaller lenses made of hard plastic that covered the central part of the cornea and were precisely shaped to fit. The next development was 'soft' plastic lenses that were more comfortable to wear. (See Figure 6.33.)

(a)

(b)

Figure 6.33 (a) An early contact lens; (b) a modern 'silicone hydrogel' contact lens

The cornea of the eye is an unusual part of the body. It consists of living tissue but it has no blood supply. To get the oxygen supply needed for its cells to metabolise, it uses oxygen from the air that has dissolved in the tears and can then be absorbed by the cornea. Today, contact lenses are made from plastics that are permeable. Oxygen can diffuse through the moisture to reach the cornea – some lenses are more permeable to oxygen than others (see Table 6.3). Carbon dioxide must be able to diffuse away in the opposite direction.

Rigid gas-permeable (hard)	Made of hard plastic Cover central part of cornea Allow oxygen through Do not have to be replaced as often as soft lenses.
Hydrophilic or hydrogel (soft)	Most common Usually cover the whole iris Depending on material, may be replaced daily (disposable) or up to 3 monthly May be worn daily and removed at night, or for extended wear up to 30 days Allow oxygen through
Silicone hydrogel (soft)	Allow much more oxygen through Originally developed for extended wear, now used for all types

Table 6.3 Modern contact lens types

ACTIVITY 9 VISION ON

Who do you know who wears spectacles or contact lenses? When do they wear them? Do you know anyone with lens implants or who has had any other kind of eye surgery?

Compare notes with other members of the class. Estimate the proportion in your age group who need to wear spectacles or contact lenses. How does the proportion change as people get older?

3.2 Seeing eye to eye

Our eyes are complex organs, similar to the eyes of most other vertebrates. They have evolved to collect light from a wide angle in front of us and to focus it into an image on the retina. Figure 6.34 shows how rays of light are bent (refracted) as they travel to the retina.

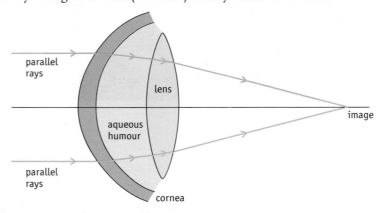

Figure 6.34 Parallel rays of light from a distant object are made to converge on the retina

You have already studied the **refraction** of light, in the chapter *Good Enough to Eat*. You should recall that light changes speed and direction when it crosses a boundary between materials. Here's where a ray is bent as it passes into the eye:

- entering the cornea: this is where most bending occurs; there is a big change in density on passing from air to corneal cells

- cornea/aqueous humour: there is small change in density, resulting in just a small amount of bending

- the lens: the ray bends as it enter the lens, and again as it leaves.

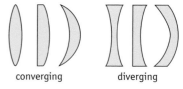

Figure 6.35 Lens shapes

Lenses

Lenses come in two varieties, **converging** and **diverging**. They get their names from what they do to parallel rays of light, which depends on their shape (Figure 6.35).

- A **converging lens** makes parallel rays converge (come together).

- A **diverging lens** makes parallel rays diverge (spread out).

- A converging lens is thicker in the middle than at its edges.

- A diverging lens is thinner in the middle than at its edges.

(Note that it is not very helpful to categorise lenses as convex or concave because this doesn't tell you what they do to light. Also, a lens may be convex on one side and concave on the other – indeed, most spectacle lenses are like this.)

⚙ ACTIVITY 10 LOOKING THROUGH LENSES

Find some converging and diverging lenses. Check which is which by examining their shapes. Look through the lenses as follows, and try to summarise how they differ.

View a distant scene through each lens. Can you see an image? If so, is the image enlarged or reduced? Is it upside down (inverted) or the right way up (erect)?

Look through each lens at a nearby object – perhaps this page of text. What do you observe? Which type of lens can be used as a magnifying glass?

Which lenses can you use to make an image on a screen?

What effect does the curvature of the lens have on what you see?

Converging lenses

Figure 6.36 shows what a converging lens does to a beam of light. In Figures 6.36 (a), (b) and (c) the beam converges through a point and in Figure 6.36(d) the lens reduces the divergence of the beam.

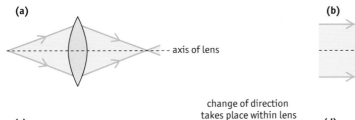

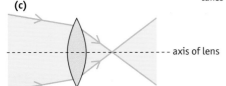

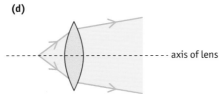

Figure 6.36 Converging a beam of light

Figure 6.36(b) shows a parallel beam converging through a point F, known as the **principal focus** of the lens. (There is one on either side of the lens.) The distance from the lens to this point is called the **focal length**, f, of the lens. Opticians prefer to use a measure, called the **power of the lens**, P, which is the reciprocal of the focal length in metres:

$$P = \frac{1}{f} \tag{9}$$

The unit for the power of a lens is the **dioptre**, D. Note that the stronger the lens the shorter its focal length. It is often useful to rearrange Equation 9 by taking the reciprocal of each side:

$$\frac{1}{P} = f \tag{9a}$$

MATHS REFERENCE

Reciprocals

See Maths note 3.3

QUESTIONS

 (a) If a lens has a focal length of 20 cm, what is its power?

(b) What is the focal length of a 4 D lens?

 A parallel beam of light enters a 2 D lens. If the lens has a diameter of 4 cm, what would you see on the other side of the lens:

(a) less than 50 cm from the lens?

(b) at 50 cm from the lens?

(c) more than 50 cm from the lens?

 Figure 6.37 shows two rays about to enter a magnified section of a lens. Copy the diagram and continue the paths to show how Snell's law of refraction predicts convergence.

Q 27 A parallel beam of light enters an eye and is focused on the retina (see Figure 6.34). If all the refracting surfaces, including the cornea and lens, act as a combined lens with a centre 17 mm from the retina, what must be (a) the focal length and (b) the power of this combined lens?

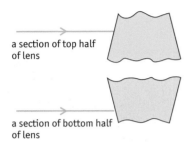

a section of top half of lens

a section of bottom half of lens

Figure 6.37 Light rays approaching a lens

Lens equation

In the eye, the cornea, the lens and its distance from the retina have to be such that the beam is focused on the retina. How is this done? To explore the behaviour of a lens, it is useful to make measurements of the position of the object and image.

When a lens converges light, it carries with it an image of the source object correct in every detail — the sort you can see in a cinema. This type of image that can be projected on to a screen is called a **real image**. To project a clear image on to a fixed screen it is necessary to place the object an exact distance from the lens (see Figure 6.38). The **thin lens** equation that connects the distance of an object from the lens and the distance for its image is:

$$\frac{1}{u} + \frac{1}{v} = \frac{1}{f} \tag{10}$$

where u is the object-to-lens distance, v is the image-to-lens distance and f is the focal length.

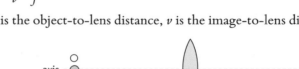

O = object u = object-to-lens distance
I = image v = image to lens distance

Figure 6.38 Producing a focused image with a converging lens

WORKED EXAMPLE

Q An object is placed 40 cm from a lens with focal length 25 cm (power +4 D). Where will a focused image be found?

A Rearranging the lens equation:

$$\frac{1}{v} = \frac{1}{f} - \frac{1}{u}$$

Substituting f = 25 cm, u = 40 cm, we get:

$$\frac{1}{v} = \frac{1}{25\,cm} - \frac{1}{40\,cm} = 0.040\,cm^{-1} - 0.025\,cm^{-1}$$

$$v = \frac{1}{0.015\,cm^{-1}} = 67\,cm$$

Note that if you include units at each step then you automatically get correct units in the final answer — we could have converted the units of u and f to metres, in which case we would get the answer v = 0.67 m.

Real is positive

The lens equation applies to both converging and diverging lenses, and can predict the sort of image (called a **virtual image**) that does not project on to a screen but can only be seen by looking through the lens – as with a magnifying glass. To fit all possible situations, the lens equation comes with a sign convention (referred to as the **real is positive** convention):

- the focal lengths of converging lenses are positive
- the focal lengths of diverging lenses are negative
- real objects and images have positive distances
- virtual distances are negative.

If your experiments or calculations give you a negative image distance then this means that you will not be able to project the image on to a screen.

> **⚙ ACTIVITY 11 CONVERGING LENS**
>
> Use a convex lens and two small coloured light sources (Figure 6.39) to find the focal length of a converging lens and explore some other properties of the image that it produces.

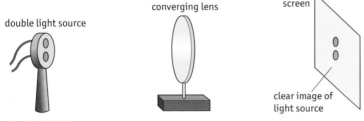

double light source   converging lens   screen

clear image of light source

Figure 6.39 Diagram for Activity 11

There are two common ways of predicting the position of an image. Putting the data into the lens formula is very precise, but there is an alternative. It is possible to predict an image position by construction: plotting the paths of individual rays of light. An advantage of this method is that it gives a clearer picture of what is happening.

Drawing a ray diagram

Rays leave a light source, like the one in Activity 11, in all directions. At the image all the rays from the original source converge together. To locate the exact site of this image we only need to follow the paths of two rays (or three to be extra certain). Which rays are the easiest to plot? Consider the following:

1 Any ray that goes through the centre of a lens will continue travelling in the same direction.

2 Any ray that travels parallel to the axis will be deflected to pass through the principal focus.

3 Any ray passing through a principal focus before it gets to the lens will emerge parallel to the axis.

Figure 6.39 shows how to draw a ray diagram to locate the image of a lamp, 2 cm high, placed 30 cm from a 5 D lens.

Look carefully at Figure 6.40. The object must be drawn a little off the axis. All you can say about points along the axis is that they have their images on the axis too. Notice that the vertical and horizontal scale factors do not have to be the same. Note, too, that so far we have drawn a fat lens out of all proportion to reality, but when we draw a ray diagram we assume that all the refraction takes place in the middle, and so we show the lens simply as a straight line.

The light, X, is to the left of the diagram with its top point, O, on the diagram 2 cm above the axis. The rays are numbered 1, 2, 3, as in the list above. Look carefully to see how the construction is completed according to the guidelines. Follow each ray from its start on the top of the object (point O) to the right of the diagram. The rays do not stop at I. Note that the position of the top of the image, point I on the diagram, is used to predict where the bottom of it will be seen, Y.

PRACTICAL SKILLS REFERENCE

Carrying out practical work
See Practical skills notes 3.1–3.2

Analysis and interpretation of data
See Practical skills notes 4.1–4.2

Conclusion and evaluation
See Practical skills notes 5.1–5.2

STUDY NOTE

For some object positions it is not possible to focus an image on the screen with a converging lens. This occurs when the object distance is smaller than or equal to the focal length. When $u > f$ the image is virtual. (We will look at this in Section 3.3.)

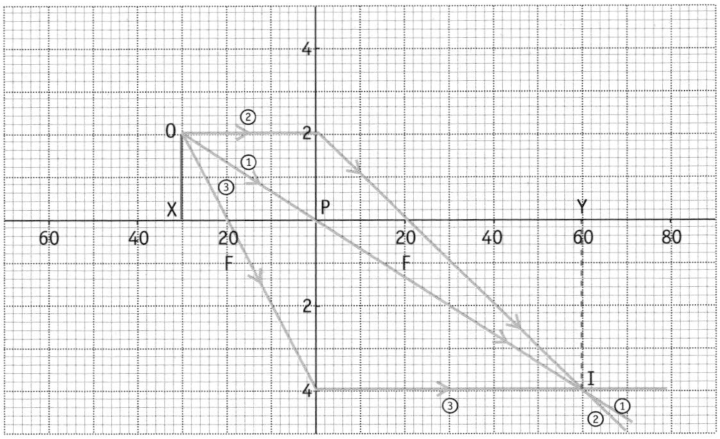

Figure 6.40 Drawing a ray diagram

Several facts can be established from Figure 6.40:

- The value of v, i.e. the position of the image.

- The fact that the image is inverted. Look again to see how this is obvious.

- The size of the image and its **magnification**, m, which is defined as:

$$m = \text{height (size) of image} \div \text{height of object} \qquad (11)$$

- Magnification is a ratio and has no units.

QUESTIONS

Q 28 Study Figure 6.40.

    (a) Give the scale used (i) for u, v and f and (ii) for the object height.

    (b) Determine the magnification of the image of X from the diagram.

Q 29 Use the values of u and f from Figure 6.40. Substitute into the lens equation (Equation 10) and find the image distance, v. Does it give the same value as the construction method?

Q 30 Construct accurate ray diagrams to determine the position of the images for the situations listed in Table 6.4. Draw a table like Table 6.4 but with extra columns for image distance, image height, magnification, v/u and description (whether the image is real or virtual, inverted or erect, and magnified, diminished or the same size.) For each example, check your answer by calculation.

Note: Drawing accurately to scale is a skill to be learned. You need a sharp pencil to draw lines accurately. It is best to use a transparent ruler so that, while you are positioning it, you can see the whole diagram. Choose your scales for each example carefully and be prepared to start again if your first choice doesn't work very well.

Situation	Focal length f/cm	Object distance u/cm	Object height /cm
a	15	30 (=2f)	6
b	30	45 (>f and <2f)	2
c	40	40 (=f)	5
d	50	60 (>f and <2f)	10
e	50	300 (>>2f)	10

Table 6.4 Data for Question 30

Q 31 **(a)** From your answers to Question 30, identify the situation where the magnification is 1. What do you notice about the values of u, v and f in this case?

(b) What do you notice about the magnification and the value of u/v?

Q 32 A digital camera uses a converging lens to focus an image of the Moon on to its CCD sensor. The lens is 50 mm from the sensor surface.

(a) What is the focal length of the lens?

To focus an image of a rock that is 1.0 m from the lens, the distance between the lens and the sensor must be changed.

(b) What is the new distance between the lens and the sensor?

STUDY NOTE

For more about the images produced by a converging lens, see *Spare Part Surgery* Additional Sheet 3.

Magnification

As you have seen in Questions 30 and 31:

$$\frac{\text{image height}}{\text{object height}} = \frac{\text{image distance}}{\text{object distance}}$$

so we have another equation for magnification:

$$m = \frac{v}{u} \tag{12}$$

You can see this from the ray diagram in Figure 6.39. The triangle formed by the object OXP and the triangle formed by the image IYP are similar triangles, so the ratio IY/OX is the same as the ratio YP/XP.

3.3 Seeing near and far

Because parallel rays of light are made to converge, we can regard the eye as a converging lens system. Its focal length is about 2.5 cm – roughly the distance from the front of the eye to the retina.

Look out of a window into the distance. Then hold a finger up in front of your eyes. You can't focus on both a distant object and a near object at the same time. You will probably feel your eyes adjusting as you focus first on one and then on the other. This adjustment is known as **accommodation**. What's going on during this process?

To focus on objects at different distances, your eye must change its focal length. It does this by adjusting the lens in two ways:

- The ring of ciliary muscles can relax, making the ring larger. This pulls the ligaments radially outwards and stretches the lens, making it thinner. When the muscles contract, the ring gets smaller and the lens regains its fatter shape.

- The ciliary muscles can also pull the lens forward slightly, increasing the lens–retina distance.

At the same time, when you focus on a near object, your eyes rotate inwards slightly so that they are turned towards the object. If the object is too close, you may become cross-eyed.

STUDY NOTE

Compare this with the focusing of a camera: the camera lens's focal length is fixed, and you focus simply by moving the lens back and forth, altering the lens–CCD distance.

QUESTIONS

Q 33 At how many points does a ray of light bend between entering the eye and reaching the retina?

Q 34 If you are suffering from eye strain, your ciliary muscles may be tired. Explain whether it is better to rest them by watching television or by looking at distant view.

Q 35 Does the focal length of the lens increase or decrease as it is stretched?

Q 36 Assuming that, for a person with perfect vision, the eye is a converging lens system and that the retina is 1.7 cm from the centre of this lens system, what would the focal length and power of the lens need to be to focus on a book 25 cm from the front of the eye? How does this compare with the focal length and power when viewing objects in the far distance?

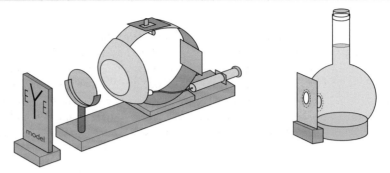

Figure 6.41 Two types of model eye

Young people are lucky – they generally have better eyesight than older people. In fact, our eyes are able to accommodate less and less as they age – that is, it gets harder and harder to focus on objects, particularly those close to us. The range over which we can focus is limited by the **near point**, usually about 20 cm for a teenager but even closer for young children, and the **far point**, which is ideally at an infinite distance.

The decrease in the range of focusing with age is known as **presbyopia** and happens for a variety of reasons: the ciliary muscles become weaker; the lens becomes stiffer, so the muscles have to pull on the ligaments, making it harder to change its shape. Figure 6.42 shows how the average position of the near point changes with age. The solution is usually to wear spectacles. Bifocal lenses combine a lens for distance vision at the top with a lens for close-up vision at the bottom, so that the wearer looks through the top part at distant objects and looks down for reading and other close-up tasks. Varifocals have a smooth transition from a lens for distance viewing to one for close up, and these are now very commonly used by people with presbyopia.

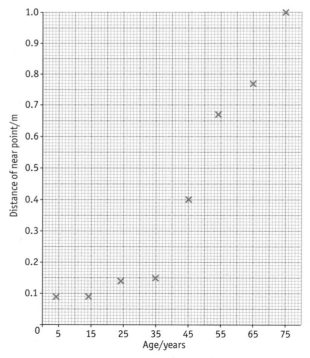

Figure 6.42 The near point changes with age

If you cannot see distant objects clearly, you are short-sighted and you are said to be suffering from **myopia**. Myopia is caused by having a slightly elongated eyeball. As shown in Figure 6.43(a), parallel rays of light from a distant object are focused at a point in front of the retina. The ciliary muscles cannot adjust the shape or position of the lens sufficiently to bring the focus on to the retina.

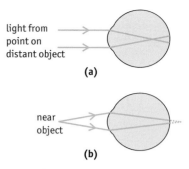

Long-sighted people find it impossible to focus on objects close to their eyes, and are said to suffer from **hypermetropia** or **hyperopia.** This is a problem particularly if you want to read. The focused image would only be produced behind the retina (Figure 6.43b) because, even with the ciliary muscles completely relaxed, the lens cannot become fat enough to focus correctly. If you are long-sighted, your eyes can focus clearly on the horizon by contracting the muscles slightly. Using your muscles all the time like this can lead to eye strain and headaches. You will still be able to focus on distant objects, even when wearing spectacles that are intended to help you to read.

Figure 6.43 (a) A short-sighted eye and (b) a long-sighted eye

For all of these problems, an optician can prescribe spectacles or contact lenses. Figure 6.44 shows a typical prescription.

OPTICAL PRESCRIPTION

Surname .... Smith .... Mr/Mrs/Ms

Other names .... David H

Address .... 44 Acacia Ave

Newtown

Postcode ....

Date of birth (if under 16) ...../...../......

I have tested this patient's eyesight today in accordance with the regulations.

[X] A prescription was issued as below
[ ] No prescription was required
[ ] The patient was referred to their G.P.

RIGHT EYE					LEFT EYE				
Sph	Cyl	Axis	Prism	Base	Sph	Cyl	Axis	Prism	Base
-0.25	-0.50	15			-0.50	-0.50	100		

Corrective lenses are required for:

[X] Myopia   [ ] Hyperopia   [ ] Presbyopia   [X] Astigmatism

Signature

.... BT Johnson .... Date .10./.12./.14.

Figure 6.44 A typical optician's prescription might look like this

In the course of an eye test, the optician is also looking for evidence of **astigmatism**. If the eyeball is irregularly curved, the result can be blurred vision. Figure 6.44 shows an astigmatism chart. The lines in all directions on this chart should look equally dark. If not, you may be one of the many people whose eyes are astigmatic. (The person whose prescription is shown in Figure 6.45 suffers from mild astigmatism. When the number 11 bus was approaching, the number looked like 1111!) Astigmatism can also be corrected using spectacles or contact lenses.

Figure 6.45 Astigmatism chart

Like converging lenses, diverging lenses also have a **principal focus** or **focal point** F, and the **focal length** of the lens is the distance from its centre to F.

ACTIVITY 13 DIVERGING LENSES

Use a ray box to explore the effect of a diverging lens on parallel rays. Draw diagrams to show the incident and refracted rays. You should now recognise the ray diagram for a diverging lens, and be able to decide which diagram in Figure 6.46 is correct. Find the focal length of each lens you used.

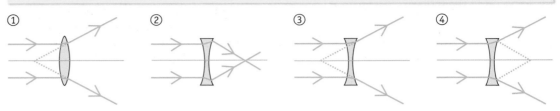

Figure 6.46 Which diagram is correct?

The correct diagram in Figure 6.45 shows how rays parallel to the axis of the lens are made to diverge. The dashed lines are known as construction lines; they show how the rays appear to diverge from the focal point F.

Ray diagrams

Now that you know how a diverging lens affects parallel rays of light, you can go on to draw ray diagrams that show how a lens forms such an image. The approach is the same as that used for converging lenses.

For a converging lens, the ray diagram that results depends on the position of the object relative to the lens's principal focus F. Here we will consider an object closer to the lens than F. (This is the situation when a converging lens is used as a magnifying glass.) The situation is simpler for a diverging lens. Think back to Activity 10; no matter where you held the diverging lens relative to the object, the lens always made it look smaller.

In Figure 6.47, the lens is represented by a vertical line with a tiny sketch of the shape of the lens at the top. (Alternatively, you can draw a large lens in the centre, but this can be a distraction.) For the purposes of drawing ray diagrams, we show all the refraction taking place at the line.

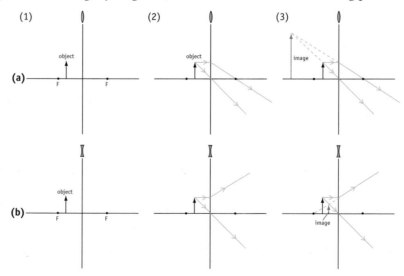

Figure 6.47 Steps in drawing ray diagrams that give virtual images: (a) converging lens and (b) diverging lens

1 Draw the lens, its axis, the principal focus on each side, and the object.

2 Draw two rays from the top of the object: one parallel to the axis, the other straight through the centre of the lens. For the converging lens, the horizontal ray is deflected down through F. For the diverging lens, the horizontal ray is deflected so that it appears to come from F.

3 Extend the rays back to find the point from which they appear to diverge. Draw in the virtual image.

As you saw in Activity 10, you cannot use a diverging lens on its own to make a real image. With a diverging lens, you produce a virtual image – the rays of light only *appear* to come from the image. As you can see from Figure 6.46(a), a converging lens also produces a virtual image of an object if it is closer to the lens than F.

What else do the ray diagrams show us? For the converging lens, the image is beyond the object, magnified and the right way up (erect). This is how a converging lens is used as a magnifying glass. For the diverging lens, the image is closer to the lens than the object, reduced in size (diminished) and erect. This should tie in with your observations from Activity 10.

QUESTION

Q 37　Draw a ray diagram for a diverging lens where the object is beyond F.

The thin lens equation again

You have used the thin lens formula (Equation 10) with the 'real is positive' sign convention for converging lenses. To see how to use the formula with a diverging lens, study the following worked example. Then test yourself with Questions 38 to 40.

WORKED EXAMPLE

Q　An object is placed at a distance of 20 cm from a diverging lens of focal length 10 cm. How far from the lens will the image be formed?

(Start by thinking: What answer would you expect? From the ray diagram in Figure 6.47, we would expect the image to be closer to the lens than the object, so the image distance, v, should be less than 20 cm.)

A　We know two quantities, u (the object distance) and f, and we want to find v.

$u = 20$ cm

$f = -10$ cm

Note that, in the 'real is positive' sign convention, a diverging lens has a negative focal length. Rearranging the thin lens formula gives:

$$\frac{1}{v} = \frac{1}{f} - \frac{1}{u}$$

$$= \frac{1}{(-10\,\text{cm})} - \frac{1}{20\,\text{cm}} = -\frac{1}{20\,\text{cm}}$$

$$v = \frac{-20\,\text{cm}}{3} = -6.67\,\text{cm}$$

So the image is formed at 6.67 cm from the lens. This is, as we predicted, less than 20 cm. The minus sign tells us that the image is virtual.

MATHS REFERENCE

Adding and subtracting fractions

See Maths note 3.5

QUESTIONS

Q 38　An object is placed at the principal focus of a diverging lens. The lens's focal length is 10 cm. Where will the image be formed?

Q 39　An object is placed at a distance of 6 cm from a lens. The image is found to be formed at a distance of 2 cm from the lens. What is the lens's focal length?

Q 40　A ray diagram drawn accurately to scale should give the same answer to a problem as the lens formula.

An object 3 cm high is placed at a distance of 12 cm from a diverging lens. The lens's focal length is 6 cm.

(a) Draw an accurate ray diagram on a sheet of graph paper to deduce where the virtual image will be formed.

(b) Deduce the size of the image.

(c) Check your answers by calculation.

Prescribing lenses

The flask model of the eye that you used in Activity 12 can be used to show how lenses can correct long and short sight.

> **ACTIVITY 14 CORRECTING LONG AND SHORT SIGHT**
>
> Use the flask model eye to demonstrate short and long sight. In each case, place various additional lenses in front of the eye, so that the image is focused on the retina.

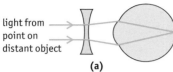

light from point on distant object

(a)

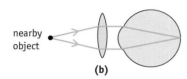

nearby object

(b)

Figure 6.48 Using lenses to correct (a) short sight and (b) long sight

STUDY NOTE

Note that in reality, refraction takes place at several surfaces in the eye, not just at the front as shown in Figure 6.48.

In Activity 14 you will have seen that the solution to short sight is to use a diverging spectacle or contact lens, as this deflects the rays outwards slightly, so that they focus further back in the eye (Figure 6.48a). Long sight can be corrected using a converging lens (Figure 6.48b).

If you look at an optician's prescription you will see a series of numbers that describe the lenses that have been prescribed as a result of an eye test. The patient whose prescription is shown in Figure 6.44 suffers from mild short sight (myopia) and needs to wear spectacles with diverging lenses in them.

The prescription gives several figures to specify each lens. The first figure for each lens (under the heading 'sphere' or 'sph') shows the power P of the lens (the reciprocal of its focal length f; see Equation 9). For a converging lens, P and f are both positive, while for a diverging lens both are negative. A converging lens is sometimes known as a positive lens, and a diverging lens as a negative lens.

The right eye in the prescription of Figure 6.43 requires a lens of power −0.25 D. The focal length of this lens will therefore be:

$$f = \frac{1}{-0.25\,\text{D}} = -4.0\,\text{m}$$

The left eye requires a lens of power −0.50 D; this is twice the power of the right lens, and so its focal length is half of that of the right lens: −2.0 m. Both lenses have negative values of P and f, so we know that they are both diverging lenses.

The problem of astigmatism is overcome by using lenses with a slight cylindrical curvature, as shown by the figures in the cylinder (or 'cyl') and 'axis' columns in Figure 6.43.

When opticians test your eyes, they place lenses in front of your eyes until you see the clearest possible image. Rather than having a large number of lenses of all possible powers, they have a few that they can combine to give many different values. The optician determines which two or three lenses together give the clearest image. How do they then calculate the required lens to prescribe?

PRACTICAL SKILLS REFERENCE

Planning and experimental design
See Practical skills notes 2.1–2.2

Carrying out practical work
See Practical skills notes 3.1–3.2

Analysis and interpretation of data
See Practical skills notes 4.1–4.2

Conclusion and evaluation
See Practical skills notes 5.1–5.2

> **ACTIVITY 15 POWER PUZZLE**
>
> Devise your own experiment to find out how powers combine. Use a ray box. Take two converging lenses and determine the power of each. Then find the power of the two together. What rule relates the combined power to the individual powers?
>
> Test your answer using a different combination of lenses. Does the rule also work if one or more of the lenses is a diverging lens? For the rule to work, do the lenses need to be in contact?

Use your result from Activity 15 to answer Questions 41 to 44. You should have found that:

$$P = P_1 + P_2 + \dots \qquad \text{(Equation 13)}$$

Using your result from Activity 15, you can adapt the method of using the focal length of a converging lens (by producing a real image and measuring the object and image distances) in order to find the focal length of a diverging lens. Questions 41 to 44 provide some hints on how to do this.

QUESTIONS

 Q 41 A patient has the clearest vision when looking through a combination of three lenses of powers 1.0 D, 0.5 D and 0.25 D.

    (a) What power of lens should be prescribed?

    (b) What is the focal length of the prescribed lens?

 Q 42 Calculate the power of the following combinations of lenses:

    (a) two identical converging lenses of power 2.0 D, in contact

    (b) a 0.5 D converging lens in contact with a 1.5 D diverging lens

    (c) two converging lenses of focal lengths 10 cm and 25 cm, in contact.

 Q 43 Calculate the focal length of the following lenses in contact:

    (a) two identical converging lenses of power 8.0 D

    (b) two diverging lenses of power −5 D and −15 D

    (c) two diverging lenses of focal lengths 10 cm and 5 cm.

 Q 44 This question describes an investigation carried out by a student. She wanted to see the effect of placing a diverging spectacle lens of power −1.0 D next to a converging lens.

First, she focused a sharp image of a distant object onto a screen using a converging lens on its own. She measured the distance from the lens to the screen and found it to be 20.0 cm. Then she placed the diverging lens in contact with the converging lens. She predicted that she would have to move the screen further away to get a focused image. In fact, she had to move the screen a further 5.0 cm away from the lenses.

    (a) What was the focal length of the converging lens? What was its power?

    (b) Calculate the focal length of the combination of the two lenses. Does your answer agree with the student's experimental findings?

The student then repeated her experiment using a converging lens of focal length 10.0 cm.

    (c) What results would you predict for this part of her investigation?

    (d) In which case did the image distance change the most when the diverging lens was added?

ACTIVITY 16 FINDING THE FOCAL LENGTH

Devise and carry out a method to find the focal length of a diverging contact lens or spectacle lens. In addition to this lens, you may use a selection of other lenses (converging or diverging, as you choose) and a point source of light.

An easy life

When you go for an eye test, the optician will want to know about the lenses in your existing spectacles. They can take them away and measure the powers of the lenses in a matter of seconds. How do they do this? No setting up light sources and screens for opticians! They use the idea that the focal length of a lens depends on its curvature. A fat lens has a short focal length. Opticians have a machine that measures the curvature of the two sides of each lens. Then, knowing the refractive index of the glass or plastic used, they can deduce the prescription that was used to make them.

PRACTICAL SKILLS REFERENCE

Planning and experimental design

See Practical skills notes 2.1–2.2

Carrying out practical work

See Practical skills notes 3.1–3.2

Analysis and interpretation of data

See Practical skills notes 4.1–4.2

Conclusion and evaluation

See Practical skills notes 5.1–5.2

3.4 Lenses for all occasions

Optical properties

Of course, it's essential that the materials that are chosen for lens manufacture are transparent. So, just how transparent is glass?

Glass is very good at transmitting light; it absorbs very little. The problem, however, is that glass reflects a proportion of the light that falls on it. (You will have noticed that windows often reflect light, so that you can see yourself reflected in a shop window.) The proportion of light reflected depends on the refractive index of the glass, and is typically about 10%. Adding an anti-reflection coating to the lens will reduce the proportion of reflected light (Figure 6.49). Such a coating often gives a coloured tint to the lens, which may then reflect 1% of less of the light that falls on it. Coatings are often used on the lenses of cameras and binoculars to maximise transmission and so to give the brightest possible view.

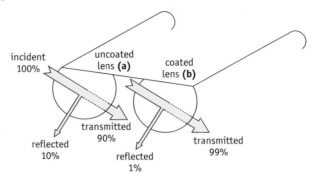

Figure 6.49 Transmission and reflection of light by (a) uncoated and (b) coated lenses

You can understand how an anti-reflection coating works if you think back to the ideas of the superposition and interference of waves, which you studied in *The Sound of Music*. The coating is a thin layer; its thickness is about one-quarter of the wavelength of light. A fraction of the light falling on the lens is reflected by the top surface of the coating, and more is reflected by the surface of the lens after it has passed through the coating. Now we have two reflected waves, one of which has travelled half a wavelength further than the other. Their path difference is half a wavelength, and this is the condition needed for destructive interference. The two reflected waves cancel out, more or less.

QUESTION

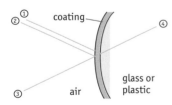

Figure 6.50 Light is reflected at both surfaces of the anti-reflection coating layer

Q 45 Figure 6.50 shows an anti-reflection coating on a lens.

(a) Which is the incident ray, and which are the two reflected rays?

(b) If the two reflected rays are to cancel out completely (interfere destructively), what can you say about their amplitudes?

(c) What can you say about the phase difference between them?

(d) If the thickness of the coating is 100 nm and its refractive index is 1.4, what wavelength of light will interfere most strongly? At what angle must it strike the lens if this is to happen? (You will need to think about how the refractive index of a material affects the wavelength of light passing through it. Hint: the frequency is unchanged, so the wavelength must decrease if speed decreases.)

(e) Visible light has wavelengths in the range 400 nm to 700 nm. Light strikes the lens at a range of angles. Use these ideas to help you explain why it is impossible to make a perfect anti-reflection coating for a lens, one that would prevent all reflection of light from the lens. Include diagrams in your answer and suggest a suitable thickness for an effective coating.

The refractive index is important for another reason: the higher the refractive index, the thinner the lenses can be made. This is because a strong lens must have highly curved surfaces, and so it must be thick. A high refractive index material bends the light more, and so the surfaces can be less curved. Thick 'pebble' lenses are heavy and unattractive. Nowadays, high refractive index plastics have been devised, and so thin, high-power plastic lenses are possible.

Underwater eye

Penguins, crocodiles and whales – they can all do something you can't: they can see clearly underwater (Figure 6.51). If you open your eyes underwater, everything looks blurred. The reason is that light passes in to your eye from the water, and your eye is designed to work in air. As shown in Figure 6.52, a ray of light deflects more when there is a bigger change in the refractive index of the material it passes through. When light passes from water in to your cornea, there is little change in refractive index and so the rays are bent very little. Therefore your lens cannot bend them enough to focus a clear image.

Figure 6.51 This penguin needs to see underwater in order to find its food

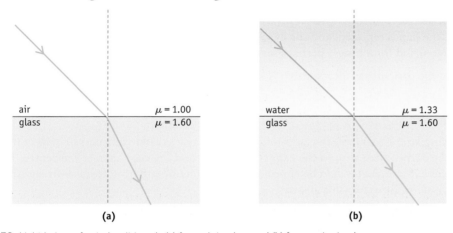

| air | $\mu = 1.00$ |
| glass | $\mu = 1.60$ |

(a)

| water | $\mu = 1.33$ |
| glass | $\mu = 1.60$ |

(b)

Figure 6.52 Light being refracted as it travels (a) from air to glass and (b) from water to glass

To see underwater, many waterbirds have a lens that is able to deform much more than the human lens, or can move back and forth in the eye to a greater extent. Fish have a more spherical lens, which has a refractive index of about 1.65, higher than any other vertebrates.

QUESTION

Q 46   The refractive index of water is 1.33; the value for the cornea is 1.34. What can you say about the bending of a light ray as it passes from water into the cornea?

3.5 Eyes right – Summing up Part 3

The following short passage uses ideas that you have studied in this part of the chapter. Use it, and the questions and activities that follow, as a reminder of what you have done and to help you look back over your work.

Getting in shape with laser treatment

Many people are unhappy with their spectacles or contact lenses. This may be because they find them uncomfortable, or simply because they think they are unattractive. More seriously, some people have eye defects such as a deformed cornea, which can cause very poor vision and cannot be cured simply with a lens. For these people, the solution to their problem may lie in laser treatment.

Lasers provide a very fine beam or pulse of light that can be directed accurately at a point. The light delivers a highly controlled amount of energy to the desired spot. This is made use of in delicate operations to improve eyesight. Usually, the front of the cornea is permanently reshaped to the required curvature for focusing light on the retina (Figure 6.53).

STUDY NOTE
Refraction at a boundary between two materials is described in the chapter *Good Enough to Eat*.

Today, there are four main types of laser eye surgery, and the most common in the UK is LASIK (laser in situ keratomileusis). A cut is made across the cornea and a flap of tissue is raised. The exposed surface is then re-shaped with the laser and the flap is replaced. It is not suitable for some people who are very short-sighted. For people with natural irregularities that result in the eye focusing incorrectly, there is a technique called wavefront-guided LASIK.

In LASEK (laser epithelial keratomileusis), the outer layer of corneal cells is weakened with an alcoholic solution and folded back, so that the cornea can be reshaped and then the flap replaced. If the flap cannot be replaced, it is discarded as this thin outer layer of cells regrows.

The first type of laser eye surgery was PRK (photorefractive keratectomy), in which a laser reshapes the cornea without a flap of tissue being cut. Usually today, it is used only for moderately short-sighted eyes. Before treatment, the patient's eyes are accurately tested to determine the amount of reshaping needed. Local anaesthetic drops are applied. The surface layer of cells is removed (PRK) or weakened (LASEK) or a flap is cut (LASIK). The laser is programmed to scan the cornea, delivering the correct amount of energy as pulses of light to the appropriate parts of the cornea. The average treatment time is 30 seconds. Depending on the technique, the flap is replaced, and the eye is covered with a plastic shield. The patient's vision is likely to be blurred for a time – perhaps several weeks – after the operation.

So what do the patients say afterwards?: 'I didn't realise how bad my eyesight was!'; 'It changed my life!'

QUESTION

Q 47 During laser treatment, the laser might burn away a greater thickness of cells at the centre of the cornea than around the edge, or more around the edge than at the centre. Which of these treatments would be appropriate for someone suffering from short sight? Draw a diagram to illustrate your answer.

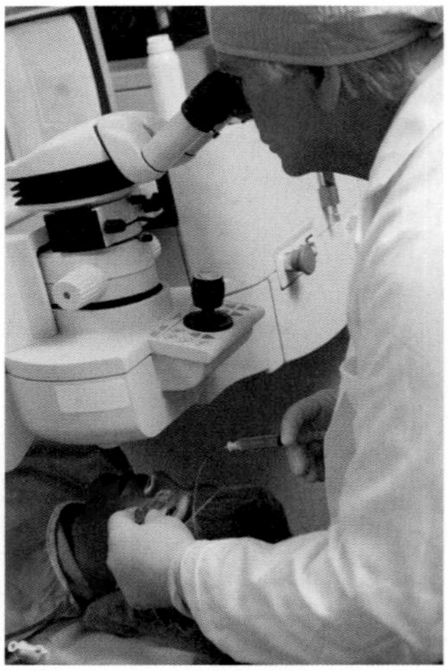

⚙ ACTIVITY 17 LASER TREATMENT

Laser treatment is increasing in popularity. Discuss the following points:

- What makes this treatment an attractive alternative for patients? What negative aspects can you identify?
- Why might it be attractive to surgeons?
- Are the benefits to the patient likely to be permanent? Might they need a further course of treatment later?
- Would you have this treatment if it was offered to you?

⚙ ACTIVITY 18 OPTICAL EXPLANATIONS

Find a cooperative individual who wears spectacles or contact lenses – it might be a fellow student (but not one who is following this course), an adult in your family or some other adult.

Prepare a report on your interviewee's eyesight. Use as many of the ideas from this unit as you can, including at least five of the terms printed in bold, to explain what you have found out. Present your report to the rest of the class.

Ask your interviewee about some or all of the following points:

- Do they wear glasses or contact lenses? When do they have to wear them?
- What changes have they noticed in their eyesight over the years?
- Examine their lenses. Try to estimate their powers – perhaps by comparing them with some standard lenses. Are they converging or diverging lenses?
- What are their lenses made of? Do they have coatings? Are they tinted? Why did they choose this type of lens?
- Do they have an optician's prescription that you can look at? What features of the prescription can you explain?
- What difference do the correct lenses make to their life? What would they be unable to do without their lenses?

Figure 6.53 Laser treatment in progress

QUESTIONS

Q 48 Explain why you may sometimes see an older person holding a book at arm's length in order to read it.

Q 49 Why do older people sometimes use two or more pairs of different spectacles? Might they be better off with a single pair of contact lenses?

Q 50 If you suffer from long sight, is your eyeball too long or too short?

Q 51 People who suffer from cataracts often have their lenses replaced with intraocular lenses (IOLs). These can be set for distance vision, or one for distance vision and one for close-up, or there are multifocal lenses that have different focal rings and are designed to move when the eye muscles contract and relax. Explain the advantages and disadvantages of each type.

Q 52 Figure 6.54 shows graph paper observed through three lenses. Describe how the three lenses differ and explain how you can tell this from the images.

Q 53 Someone's closest distance of focusing (their near point) is at 50 cm. The image distance is then 1.7 cm.

(a) What is the effective focal length of the person's eye?

(b) What power of lens is required to enable the person to focus on a book at a distance of 20 cm? Is a converging or diverging lens needed?

Q 54 Someone's farthest distance of focusing (their far point) is at 3.00 m. The image distance is then 1.7 cm.

(a) What is the effective power of the person's eye?

(b) What power of lens is required to enable the person to focus on the stars (at a distance of infinity)? Is a converging or diverging lens needed?

Q 55 A patient sees a clear image of objects if they are between 80 cm and 400 cm from his eyes. The optometrist prescribes varifocal lenses so that distant objects are clear when seen through the top half of the lens, and print is clear when held at a distance of 25 cm. What are the powers at the top and the bottom of the lenses?

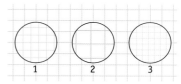

Figure 6.54 Graph paper observed through three lenses

4 Heartbeat

4.1 Ultrasound imaging of the heart

Rest a finger lightly against the inside of your wrist and feel your pulse. Hold your hand against your chest and feel your heart beat. A healthy human heart is made of muscle and beats about 70 times per minute, circulating blood to the lungs to pick up oxygen and then to the other organs of the body (Figure 6.55). Blood enters the heart and is drawn into the lower chambers (the ventricles) when the upper chambers (the atria) contract, the bicuspid and tricuspid valves are open and the pocket valves closed. Then, with the bicuspid and tricuspid valves closed and the pocket valves open, deoxygenated blood is pumped to the lungs and oxygenated blood to the rest of the body. The rhythm of the heartbeat is controlled by a set of muscles known as the pacemaker, which are located in the atrium wall near the vena cava blood vessel.

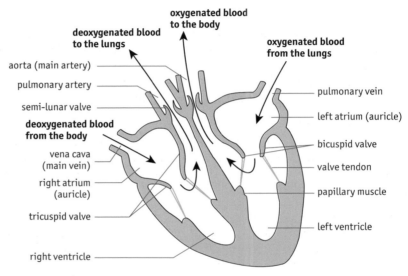

Figure 6.55 Diagram of the human heart showing the direction of blood flow

Any interruption to the heart's action can have serious, even fatal, results. In this part of the chapter, you will see how ultrasound can be used to help diagnose heart problems. The most common problem is coronary heart disease, which affects the blood supply to the heart muscle itself. Other problems can occur with the pacemaker, upsetting its rhythm, or with the valves, allowing blood to leak back into the atria when the ventricles contract. Complete replacement heart pumps are very expensive and still at the developmental stage, but they are now successfully used temporarily in patients who are waiting for a donated heart. Problems arising from an irregular heartbeat are routinely treated with battery-operated pacemakers (Figure 6.56) that deliver a regular electrical pulse to control the heartbeat. In addition, artificial valves made from metal or plastic (Figure 6.57) are used to replace defective natural valves.

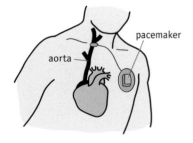

Figure 6.56 A heart pacemaker

Figure 6.57 Replacement heart valve

Consultant cardiologist

Consultant cardiologists use ultrasound imaging to produce an echocardiogram (Figure 6.58) to help diagnose heart problems.

An ultrasound probe is placed against the patient's chest, which has been smeared with ultrasound coupling gel. The best subjects are young and slim, so that there is not too much fat or air (due to lung problems, for example) to get in the way. For other patients, the probe can be lowered down the throat to examine the heart 'from behind'.

Immediately, a fuzzy grey moving image of the heart appears of the monitor screen. You can see the muscles contract and the valves open and close. The technique called 4D echocardiography gives a real-time three-dimensional moving image. The information can be displayed in various ways; for example, a small area of the image can be selected with an on-screen cursor and displayed as a colour-coded image to show blood flow. Changes in heart volume can be measured, and measurements of blood flow can indicate leaks and constrictions. There is also a small single probe that can be used to produce an audio signal related to blood flow (it sounds rather like a stethoscope). The advantage of the ultrasound system is that it is very quick and simple to use – non-invasive and so non-threatening for the patient, allowing the doctor to make a diagnosis in a matter of minutes.

Hospital physicist

Hospital physicists are concerned with all aspects of medical imaging, including ultrasound, as this interview shows.

What is ultrasound used for in medicine?

The most common use of ultrasound in medicine is to examine the internal structure of the body and to study the movement of organs and blood.

X-rays are used for the same thing aren't they, so why is ultrasound used too?

Yes, X-rays are also used to obtain images of our bodies non-invasively, but they have limitations. If you look at X-ray plates you will notice that it is very difficult to see the structure of soft tissues. Bones are very clearly shown, but different soft tissues are hardly distinguishable at all from each other (see Figure 6.59). Patients mustn't be given high doses of X-rays, so they cannot be used to look at the movement of organs.

So ultrasound is safe for the patient?

Ultrasound is a pressure wave, much like audible sound. At the power levels used in medicine there are no harmful effects. The patient can be examined for quite long periods of time so that moving images can be built up. Even a foetus can be safely examined, which would be virtually out of the questions with X-rays normally.

You said that the movement of blood can be studied too. How is that done?

Yes, we can use ultrasound to discover how quickly blood is moving through blood vessels. When the ultrasound beam is reflected off the blood cells the frequency of the ultrasound – remember it is like sound – changes due to the Doppler effect. This information reveals how well the heart is functioning and the state of the blood vessels themselves.

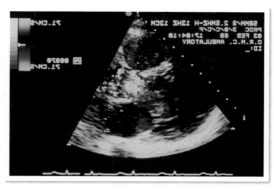

Figure 6.58 An echocardiogram

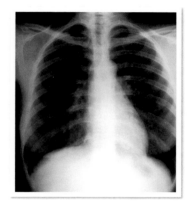

Figure 6.59 An X-ray image shows bones clearly but not the soft tissues

> **STUDY NOTE**
>
> The Doppler effect is introduced in Section 4.3.

4.2 Ultrasound echoes

What is ultrasound?

In the chapter *The Sound of Music*, you learned about sound. Sound is a longitudinal pressure wave that moves through material (it cannot travel through a vacuum) by making the particles oscillate parallel to the direction in which the wave travels. Generally, we think of sound as something that we can hear. In fact, we can only hear sounds in the frequency range of approximately 20 Hz to 20 kHz, which changes from individual to individual, with age and, of course, is different for other animals. Sound with a frequency above the upper limit of the human audible range, i.e. above 20 kHz, is known as **ultrasound.**

Figures 6.59 and 6.60 show various ways to depict sound, or ultrasound, waves. Figure 6.60 shows the particles of a material 'caught' during their oscillation. Where the particles are moving

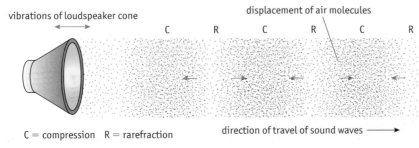

Figure 6.60 A snapshot of a sound wave

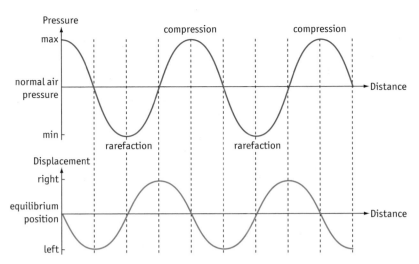

Figure 6.61 Pressure–distance and displacement–distance graphs for a longitudinal wave

towards each other, the pressure is higher than the normal pressure; and where they are moving away from each other, the pressure is lower. The **frequency** of the wave determines the number of oscillations of the particles per second, and the **wavelength** of the wave is the distance between two pressure (or displacement) maxima or between two pressure (or displacement) minima (see Figure 6.61).

Like audible sounds, ultrasound is produced by vibrations. However, ultrasound frequencies are so high that devices such as loudspeakers are not able to produce the vibrations. Instead, ultrasound transducers (generators) make use of piezoelectric crystals. A piezoelectric crystal is one that expands and contracts when an alternating potential difference is applied across it. A particular crystal will have a resonant frequency, at which the amplitude of oscillation is a maximum. This resonant frequency can be very high. As the crystal surface vibrates, it sets the surrounding air in motion and a wave of ultrasound travels outwards from the generator.

Figure 6.62 shows a piezoelectric crystal sandwiched between backing material, which damps the oscillation of the crystal so that it does not reverberate (continue to oscillate when the applied pd is switched off), and an **acoustic lens**, which protects the crystal and focuses the ultrasound beam. The piezoelectric crystal is also used to detect the ultrasound waves. When the reflected waves return to the crystal, the pressure variations cause a series of compressions that produce an alternating pd across the crystal. To produce a 3D image, a matrix array of piezoelectric crystals is used.

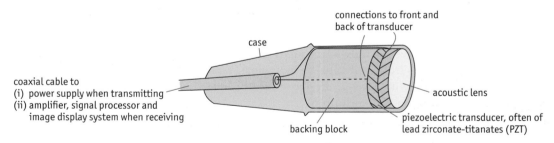

Figure 6.62 Diagram of an ultrasound transducer

The wavelength, λ, of the ultrasound depends on its frequency, f, and on the wave speed, v, in the material through which it is travelling. As with all waves, these quantities are related via the **wave equation**:

$$v = f\lambda \qquad (13)$$

The frequency is the same as the frequency of the crystal oscillations, which is the same as that of the applied alternating pd. The speed can be measured using similar methods to those used to measure the speed of audible sound waves. In *The Sound of Music*, you measured the speed of sound in air using a microphone and speaker, and a recorder. The first of those two methods relates to ultrasound imaging.

⚙ ACTIVITY 19 SPEED OF SOUND

Figure 6.63 shows apparatus used for determining the speed of sound. Look back at your work for *The Sound of Music* where you carried out this experiment. Remind yourself of the procedure and revise your knowledge and understanding of the wave equation.

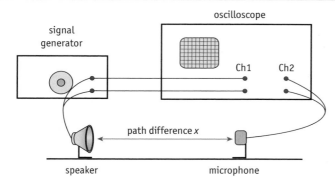

Figure 6.63 Apparatus for determining the speed of sound

QUESTION

Q 56 Ultrasound has a speed of $1500\,\text{m s}^{-1}$ in a sample of soft tissue. If its frequency is $10\,\text{MHz}$, what is the wavelength of the ultrasound wave in the soft tissue?

Pulse–echo techniques for measuring distance

How can we measure how far away something is if we can't get to it? One way is to use a **pulse–echo technique**. A signal pulse is sent towards the object, and the time the pulse takes to travel to the object and return is measured. If we know the speed of the wave we can calculate the object's distance. It is important to remember that the distance travelled by the wave is twice the actual distance; the wave has travelled 'there and back'.

This technique is widely used with different types of waves for different applications: radar (radio detection and ranging) uses microwaves, Lidar (light detection and ranging) uses lasers, and sonar (sound navigation and ranging) uses sound or ultrasound waves.

⚙ ACTIVITY 20 ULTRASOUND TAPE MEASURE

Use a commercial ultrasound or 'laser' tape measure to measure the dimensions of a room. In fact the laser is just to help you to aim the device accurately. The signal is ultrasound. Why is this? (Hint: compare the time taken by a light beam and a sound beam to cross the room and return.)

⚙ ACTIVITY 21 PULSE–ECHO

Demonstrate distance measurement using a pulse–echo technique,. Discuss why the signal should be pulsed rather than continuous.

This pulse–echo technique is a safe, non-invasive way to measure distances inside the body and is applied to many medical investigations including those of eyes and foetuses.

QUESTIONS

Q 57 An ultrasound probe is placed on a patient's skin and a reflection from a bone is received $16\,\mu\text{s}$ after transmission. How far below the skin is the bone? (Speed of the ultrasound in soft tissue = $1500\,\text{m s}^{-1}$)

Q 58 A fishing boat uses sonar to detect the depth of the seafloor. The sound waves have a frequency of $12\,\text{kHz}$ and travel at $1500\,\text{m s}^{-1}$ in water. The time between pulse transmission and echo detection is $0.22\,\text{s}$.

(a) What is the wavelength of the sound waves?

(b) How deep is the water?

Q 59 The mean Earth–Moon distance is approximately 378 000 km, and the speed of light is $3.00 \times 10^8\,m\,s^{-1}$. How long does it take for a pulse of light to travel from the Earth to the Moon and back?

Why ultrasound?

Images are produced when waves reflect from an object and are detected. In Part 3, you saw how light waves can reflect from objects to form images on the retina of the eye. The wavelength of light is very small, so it is only when we try to look at very small objects that the diffraction of the waves is a problem.

You will have seen in Activity 19 that, in air, the wavelengths of fairly high-pitched audible sounds are typically a few tens of centimetres. To avoid diffraction effects and produce images of structures in the body (which are typically less than a few centimetres), the wavelength of any radiation must be smaller than a few centimetres – which, for sound waves, means frequencies above the audible range.

Reflection and refraction at a boundary

Sound, including ultrasound, travels at different speeds in different materials. This has several consequences:

- The time for an echo to return depends on the nature of the material as well as on the distance travelled.

- The wavelength of the ultrasound depends on the material as well as on the frequency.

- A beam of ultrasound is reflected and refracted at a boundary, rather than going straight on.

In Part 3 of this unit you used optical lenses to direct and control beams of light. You saw that a lens makes use of the fact that light is refracted when it meets a boundary between materials. Exactly the same principle can be used with sound to make an acoustic lens such as the one on the front of an ultrasound transmitter–receiver. Activity 22 uses audible sound to make a simple large-scale acoustic lens.

⚙ ACTIVITY 22 ACOUSTIC LENS

Use the apparatus shown in Figure 6.64 to show that a balloon filled with carbon dioxide can act as a simple acoustic lens and focus a beam of sound. Make a rough measurement of the focal length of this lens. What can you deduce about the speed of sound in carbon dioxide compared with its speed in air?

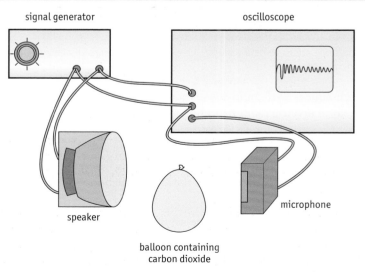

Figure 6.64 A carbon dioxide acoustic lens

In *Good Enough to Eat* and Part 3 of this chapter you saw that light is partially (or totally) reflected at a boundary (it is this that enables you to see your reflection in shop windows). The same thing happens to sound waves – and indeed to all types of waves, as you can demonstrate by fastening two different types of rope together and observing what happens when you send a wave pulse along the composite rope (Figure 6.65). The more similar the materials, the smaller the amplitude of the reflected wave compared to that of the transmitted wave.

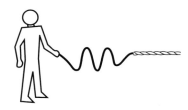

Figure 6.65 Sending a wave pulse along a composite rope

Table 6.5 lists the speed of ultrasound in various materials found inside the body. It also lists the density of the materials, because the amount of reflection at a boundary depends on the density of the two materials.

Material	Speed of sound/m s^{-1}	Density/kg m^{-3}
Air	330	1.3
Water	1500	1000
Blood	1570	1060
Fat	1450	950
Soft tissue (including skin)	1500	1050
Muscle	1600	1080
Bone	4000	1500

Table 6.5 Typical sound speed and density for various materials

At each boundary, some of the wave is reflected and some transmitted, so the intensity of the pulses that return are reduced. In Section 4.1 you read that 'coupling gel' is smeared on the skin of a patient who is to have an ultrasound examination. This gel is a water-based jelly, with a density and sound speed very similar to those of water and soft tissue. This reduces reflections when the ultrasound beam enters and exits the body.

Medical investigations using ultrasound

Now consider a pulse of ultrasound that is directed through a patient's body so that it reaches the heart, as in Figure 6.66.

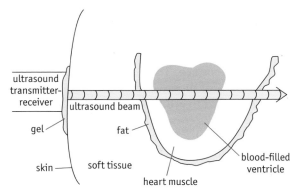

Figure 6.66 Sketch showing ultrasound travelling from the transducer into a patient and through the heart

Only small proportions of the ultrasound are reflected by interfaces met on the way to the heart, provided there is no bone or air in the way. Some of the ultrasound will then be reflected by the interfaces associated with the heart – soft tissue/fat outside the heart, fat/heart muscle, heart muscle/blood and so on.

Once the ultrasound transducer has produced the pulse of ultrasound, its function is reversed from transmitter to receiver. The signal from the transducer as it receives the reflected ultrasound can be amplified and displayed on an oscilloscope, as shown in Figure 6.67. The horizontal axis is time. The delays between the various peaks can be used to calculate distances by an experienced ultrasound technician if the tissues between the peaks are identified.

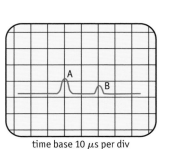

time base 10 μs per div

Figure 6.67 Oscilloscope display of reflected ultrasound detected by a transducer

The time between any two peaks is the time taken for the ultrasound pulse to travel back and forth between the interfaces they represent. The time t and the distance s are related to the speed v by the equation:

$$s = vt \qquad (14)$$

Questions 60 and 61 illustrate this pulse–echo technique and two important limitations. One is that a pulse cannot be sent until the previous pulse has returned, so this puts an upper limit on the number of pulses that can be sent per second. This **pulse frequency**, f_p is *not* the same as the frequency of the ultrasound wave, which must be much higher as each pulse is made up of many oscillations.

A second limitation is that the duration of the pulse limits the detail that can be obtained. If the pulse duration is longer than the time interval between signals reflected from two layers, then the two reflected pulses superpose and appear like a single reflection.

QUESTIONS

Use data from Table 6.5 to answer these questions.

Q 60   On leaving the transmitter–receiver, a pulse of ultrasound travels 5 cm through soft tissue and is then reflected back. How long is the time delay between sending and receiving the pulse? What is the greatest number of pulses that could be transmitted per second if each echo is to return before the next pulse is sent?

Q 61   **(a)** Calculate the thickness of the heart wall from the delay between the two peaks labelled A and B in Figure 6.66.

      (b) Suppose the test had been carried out with a pulse that lasted $30\,\mu s$. Sketch the reflected pulses A and B and the trace that would be seen on the screen when the two reflected pulses are superposed.

Moving images

Real-time moving images can be produced using ultrasound. These are particularly appropriate for images of the heart, which is always moving: a still image that took more than a fraction of a second to obtain would be blurred and useless anyway.

Figure 6.68 shows how an ultrasound scanner is used to obtain the moving images. Basically it is an array of a number of piezoelectric transducers. Each of the transducers sends out a pulse of ultrasound slightly after the previous one. To get a focusing and scanning effect, pulses to each transducer are arranged to arrive at slightly different times. A computer processes the signals received back by the transducers to produce the image. The array can cover an arc of 90 degrees, and the firing of the transducers in the array can be done as frequently as 150 times per second. Still images produced with this type of scanner appear quite fuzzy (see Figure 6.68), but the apparent quality is much higher when a full sequence is viewed, as each frame adds a little more detail. Even slowed down by a factor of three or more, a scan can be viewed as a flicker-free film.

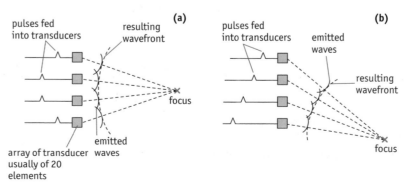

Figure 6.68 A phased array scanner

4.3 Doppler ultrasound

As you read in Section 4.1, ultrasound examinations can reveal the speed, as well as the location, of objects within the body. This aspect of the technique uses the **Doppler effect**. You have probably experienced the Doppler effect yourself. If an ambulance or police car has passed you with its siren sounding, you will have noticed that the pitch of the sound changed. It was higher as the siren approached you and lower when it was going away, and just as it passed you it was the same as it would have been if the siren had been stationary. The change in pitch is most noticeable if the source of the sound is moving at high speed directly towards or away from you.

> ⚙ **ACTIVITY 23 THE DOPPLER EFFECT**
>
> The Doppler effect can be demonstrated by whirling a small loudspeaker, or a whistle, in a large horizontal circle (Figure 6.69). Listen for the change in frequency as the source of sound moves towards/away from you.
>
> Use the *Audacity* software to record and display sounds that illustrate the Doppler effect.

STUDY NOTE

For guidance on using *Audacity*, refer to the work you did in *The Sound of Music*, Additional Sheets 2 and 4.

The Doppler effect is a difference in the frequency of the waves received by a detector to that emitted by a source due to relative motion between the source and the detector. It does not matter whether the source or the detector is moving, or both. The Doppler effect depends on the *relative* movement of the source and the observer. If the two are moving at exactly the same speed in the same direction there will be no Doppler shift. It is also important to realise that the effect does *not* depend on the distance between the source and the detector.

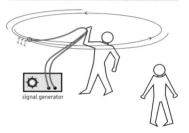

signal generator

Figure 6.69 Demonstrating the Doppler effect

SAFETY NOTE

This activity should be done outside, and make sure that the listeners stand well away from the whirling object.

The Doppler effect

When a moving object emits or reflects waves, the frequency of the waves received by a stationary detector differs from the frequency at which they were produced. Figure 6.70 shows how this comes about. When the source is at rest, as in Figure 6.70(a), the wavelength and therefore the detected frequency are the same for the detectors placed each side of the source. With the source moving towards one detector and away from the other with a speed, v, as in Figure 6.70(b), the waves are squashed up on one side (decreased wavelength, increased frequency). On the other side the waves are spread out (increased wavelength, decreased frequency). This is because the source has moved to a new position by the time it produces each subsequent wave, but the waves themselves always travel at the same speed, c.

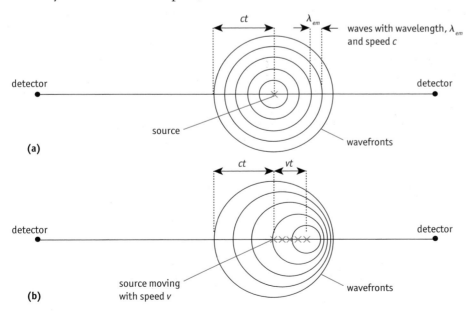

Figure 6.70 A source emitting waves (a) while at rest and (b) while in motion

The Doppler effect also occurs when a detector moves towards or away from a source of waves. Imagine one of the detectors in Figure 6.69(a) moving towards the source with speed v; it would encounter more waves per second than if it were at rest, so it would measure a higher frequency, f_{rec} (shorter apparent wavelength, λ_{rec}) than that emitted by the source, f_{em} (emitted wavelength, λ_{em}). Similarly, if a detector is moving away from the source it measures a lower frequency (longer wavelength).

The Doppler shift

The **Doppler shift** in frequency, Δf, is the difference between the frequency emitted by the source, f_{em}, and the frequency received by the detector, f_{rec}.

$$\Delta f = f_{em} - f_{rec} \qquad (15)$$

The Doppler shift can also be expressed as a shift in wavelength, where λ_{em} is the wavelength emitted by the source, λ_{rec} is the wavelength of waves received by the detector, and:

$$\Delta\lambda = \lambda_{em} - \lambda_{rec} \qquad (16)$$

Note that if the frequency increases, the wavelength decreases, and vice versa.

Provided the speed, v, of the source or detector is much less than the wave speed, c, then:

$$\frac{\Delta f}{f_{em}} \approx \frac{\Delta\lambda}{\lambda_{em}} \approx \frac{v}{c} \qquad (17)$$

STUDY NOTE

By convention, a positive value of Δf corresponds to an increase in wavelength and therefore to a decrease in frequency, which occurs when the source and receiver are moving apart, while a negative Δf corresponds to a decrease in wavelength and an increase in frequency.

STUDY NOTE

In the chapter *Reach for the Stars* you will see how the Doppler effect is used by astronomers.

The Doppler effect applies to all types of waves. With electromagnetic waves, we are generally not aware of the effect because the wave speed ($3.00 \times 10^8 \,\text{m s}^{-1}$) is so much greater than typical speeds of objects. However, even small changes in frequency can quite easily be detected using suitable equipment. For example, police radar speed traps measure the Doppler effect in radio waves reflected from moving vehicles, and astronomers use the change in frequency of the radiation received from galaxies and stars to calculate their speed relative to us.

The Doppler effect in medicine

In a medical examination, blood flow can be measured using the change in frequency due to the Doppler effect when ultrasound is reflected from red blood cells. The technique can be used to measure the flow of blood through, for instance, an artery, the walls of the heart or a valve within the heart. Blockages in blood vessels and thickening of their walls can be diagnosed very easily. Foetal heart monitoring is another common use of Doppler ultrasound. The Doppler shift from a single transducer can be converted into an audible signal and the technique amounts to a sensitive stethoscope. Using a phased ultrasound array, speed can be measured at many points simultaneously. These measurements are often displayed as colour-coded images in which the different colours represent different speeds, as in Figure 6.71.

QUESTIONS

Q 62 A beam of ultrasound reflected from blood cells has a lower frequency than the emitted beam. What does this tell you about the blood flow?

Q 63 Ultrasound waves are reflected from blood travelling towards the ultrasound probe. Explain what happens to the wavelength of the reflected ultrasound if the blood starts to travel faster.

Q 64 What change in reflected ultrasound frequency would be detected if a blood clot blocked an artery in which the blood was travelling towards the probe?

FURTHER INVESTIGATION

Use PC software *Audacity* to record and analyse sounds from moving objects. You could study the sounds produced by road vehicles such as cars and motorbikes, and relate your results to their speeds.

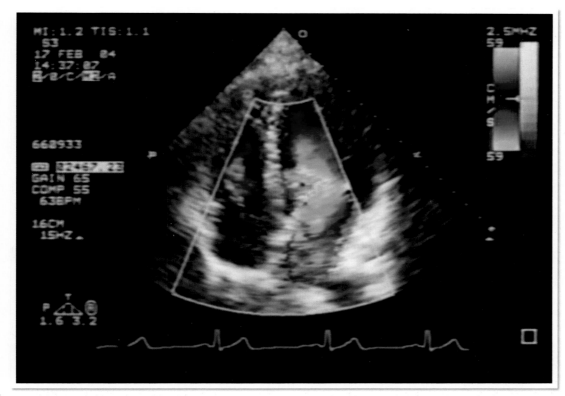

Figure 6.71 Doppler echocardiogram of the heart. Doppler ultrasound is used to display the speed and direction of blood through the heart.

4.4 Summing up Part 4

In this part of the chapter, you have extended your knowledge of waves – the way they behave at boundaries between materials and the Doppler effect.

⚙ ACTIVITY 24 SOUND ADVICE

Look back through your work on this part of the chapter and make sure you know the meaning of all the terms printed in bold.

Then look back at Activity 25 in *The Sound of Music*. Add two new rows to the bottom of your table: one on the Doppler effect, and one on reflection/transmission at a boundary.

LINK THE LEARNING

5 Recovery

5.1 Getting better

This chapter has touched on several areas of physics, and has built on much of the work that you have done in earlier chapters. Use the following activities to remind yourself of the work that you have done.

> ⚙ ACTIVITY 25 GETTING BETTER
>
> Look back through your work on other chapters in this course, and look for links with this chapter. Annotate your notes to show where similar ideas come up in different situations, and extend them where you think it is relevant (for example, you could add some notes on stress and strain in the relevant sections of *Higher, Faster, Stronger* and *Good Enough to Eat*).

> ⚙ ACTIVITY 26 BEDSIDE MANNERS
>
> Imagine that you are talking to someone who is to have spare part surgery, such as a knee or hip replacement, and they are a bit unsure about what is involved. Decide how you could help to inform and reassure them. Either talk to another student who is role-playing the patient or make a tape recording that the patient could play on their own. Think carefully about what information would be helpful, how you could explain it in an appropriate way — and what not to include.

5.2 Questions on the whole chapter

Q 65 When new materials are developed, their physical properties are recorded so that users can decide whether a material is suitable for a particular purpose. The graphs in Figure 6.72 show the performances of two materials, X and Y.

(a) Up to point A, the graph for material X is a straight line from the origin. Up to point B, the material returns to its original condition if the stress is removed. Beyond point C, the material continues to stretch while a constant stress is applied. What are the names of points A, B and C?

(b) Which of materials X and Y is the stiffer? Explain your answer.

Q 66 Figure 6.73 shows a cliff railway. It is designed using a multi-strand steel cable to pull a 3.5 tonne (3500 kg) carriage on rails up a slope of 34° when fully laden with 10 passengers (of average mass 70 kg). An additional frictional resistive force of 12500 N acts along the slope opposing the motion.

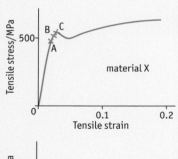

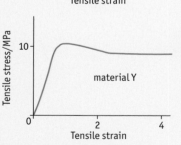

Figure 6.72 Graphs for Question 65

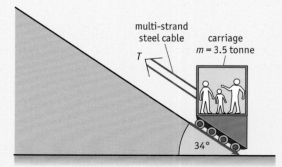

Figure 6.73 Diagram for Question 66

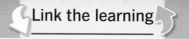

(a) Calculate the minimum tension, T, in the cable required to start the carriage moving up the slope.

In the safe design of this cliff railway, the cable needs to be able to withstand a tension of *three times* the value of T calculated in part (a) and must be made of steel with ultimate tensile stress of 400 MPa.

(b) By initially finding the total cross-sectional area of cable required to withstand the tension 3T, calculate how many strands of steel of diameter 2.0 mm will be needed to construct the multi-strand cable.

(c) Suggest a reason for using multi-strand cables rather than a single cable of the required cross-sectional area.

 Q 67 A student was attempting to measure the Young modulus for the sweet jelly used in an apple lace. He used a micrometer screw gauge to measure the diameter of the lace, and obtained five results, moving the gauge down the lace, and rotating it 1.02, 0.99, 1.04, 1.03 and 1.05 mm. He marked a length of 200 mm on the lace, and obtained the results in Table 6.6.

Load/g	Length/mm	Extension/mm	Strain	Load/N	Stress/Pa
0	200				
20	220				
40	240				
60	260				
80	280				
100	320				
120	380				
140	480				
160	snapped				

Table 6.6 Data for Question 67

You may find it simplest to use a spreadsheet programme to answer this question.

(a) Calculate the mean diameter of the lace, in m, and then the cross-sectional area in m^2.

(b) Copy and complete the table (use $g = 9.81 \, N\,kg^{-1}$).

(c) Plot a stress–strain graph.

(d) Measure the gradient of the linear part of the graph to obtain a value for the Young modulus of the apple jelly.

(e) (i) What was the uncertainty in the diameter of the lace?
　　(ii) What was the percentage uncertainty in the area?

(f) Assuming that lengths were measured to the nearest mm, what was the percentage uncertainty in the marked length?

(g) What was the percentage uncertainty on the extension for a load of 80 g?

(h) Assuming that the uncertainty in the masses used to stretch the lace was ±1%, estimate the uncertainty in the Young modulus.

Q 68 In 1986 the Polaroid company produced a camera that used ultrasound to measure the distance between the lens and the object and a motor to move the lens so that the image was in focus on the film. The time for the reflected pulse was measured and was used to adjust the focus. Today, many cameras have a similar system but use an infrared pulse.

(a) The lens system of an autofocus camera can be considered as a simple converging lens of power +18.2 D. At what distance from its optical centre would this lens produce a sharp image of a very distant object?

(b) The camera is now pointed at a much closer object. The delay between transmitting and receiving the infrared pulse is 5.2 ns. (Assume that the speed of infrared rays in air is the same as their speed in a vacuum.)
    (i) How far away from the camera is this object?
    (ii) How far must the lens be from the film in order to produce a sharp image of this object?

(c) The maximum distance possible between the lens and the CCD sensor is 6.3 cm. What is the closest that an object can be to the lens and still be in focus?

 Q 69 Table 6.7 shows the measurements a student made when determining the focal length of a lens. Figure 6.74 shows a graph of her results.

u/m	v/m	u^{-1}/m^{-1}	v^{-1}/m^{-1}
0.21	0.16	4.8	6.3
0.30	0.13	3.3	7.7
0.38	0.12	2.6	8.4
0.48	0.11	2.1	9.1

Table 6.7 Data for Question 69

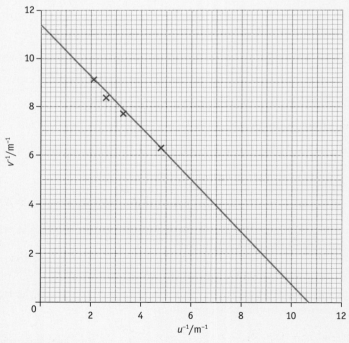

Figure 6.74 Graph for Question 69

(a) What was the focal length of the lens, together with any experimental uncertainty?

(b) Suggest three ways in which the student could have reduced the experimental uncertainty in her final result.

Q 70 Ultrasound of frequency 15 MHz is used to scan the heart. The speed of ultrasound in heart muscle is 1600 m s⁻¹.

(a) How big are the smallest features that can be resolved using this radiation?

(b) Figure 6.75 shows a display of the reflected ultrasound pulses from the two boundaries of the heart wall. Calculate the thickness of the wall.

(c) A Doppler ultrasound scan is taken to look at the blood flow through the heart. Explain what happens to the frequency of the ultrasound beam when it is reflected from blood travelling (i) towards and (ii) away from the ultrasound probe.

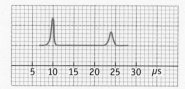

Figure 6.75 Ultrasound display for Question 70

Q 71 Ultrasound scans are used to examine the eye. Figure 6.76 shows an ultrasound trace produced from an eye examination. The frequency used is 10 MHz. The speed of ultrasound in the lens is 1640 m s⁻¹ and in the vitreous humour between the lens and the retina is 1530 m s⁻¹.

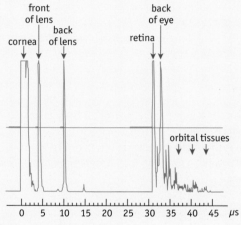

Figure 6.76 Ultrasound scan of an eye for Question 71

(a) Calculate the thickness of the lens.

(b) Calculate the distance between the lens and the retina.

(c) The probe and the cornea form one peak, indicating there is no reflection from the front surface of the cornea. Why is this?

When all the sections are measured and added together, the length of the eye can be used to calculate the power of replacement lens needed when a lens with a cataract is removed. This must be done accurately.

(d) What effect would there be on the vision if the measurement of the eyeball were too short?

(e) The total length of the eye is 23.5 mm. What power of lens is needed to form a sharp image of a distant object on the retina?

5.3 Achievements

Now you have studied this chapter you should be able to achieve the outcomes listed in Table 6.8.

TABLE 6.8 ACHIEVEMENTS FOR THE CHAPTER *SPARE PART SURGERY*

	Statement from Examination Specification	*Section(s) in this chapter*
1	know and understand the distinction between base and derived quantities and their SI units	2.2, 2.4
2	demonstrate their knowledge of practical skills and techniques for both familiar and unfamiliar experiments	2.2, 2.3, 3.2, 3.3
3	be able to estimate values for physical quantities and use their estimate to solve problems	2.2, 2.4, 4.2
4	understand the limitations of physical measurement and apply these limitations to practical situations	2.3
5	be able to communicate information and ideas in appropriate ways using appropriate terminology	2.2, 3.4, 5.1
6	understand applications and implications of science and evaluate their associated benefits and risks	1.2, 2.1, 3.4
8	understand the ways in which society uses science to inform decision making	1.2, 3.4
54	understand how to use the relationships • (tensile/compressive) *stress = force/cross sectional area* • (tensile/ compressive) *strain= change in length/original length* • *Young modulus = stress/strain*	2.2
55	be able to draw and interpret tensile/compressive stress–strain graphs, and understand the term *breaking stress*	2.2
57	CORE PRACTICAL 5: Determine the Young modulus of a material	2.3
58	be able to calculate the elastic strain energy E_{el} in a deformed material sample, using the equation $\Delta E_{el} = \frac{1}{2}F\Delta x$, and from the area under the force/extension graph the estimation of area and hence energy change for both linear and non-linear force/extension graphs is expected	2.4
74	understand the term *focal length* of converging and diverging lenses	3.2, 3.3
75	be able to use ray diagrams to trace the path of light through a lens and locate the position of an image	3.2, 3.3
76	be able to use the equation power of a lens $P = \dfrac{1}{f}$	3.2
77	understand that for thin lenses in combination $P = P_1 + P_2 + P_3 + \ldots$	3.3
78	know and understand the terms *real image* and *virtual image*	3.2
79	be able to use the equation $\dfrac{1}{u} + \dfrac{1}{v} = \dfrac{1}{f}$ for a thin converging or diverging lens with the real-is-positive convention	3.2, 3.3
80	know and understand that magnification $= \dfrac{\text{Image height}}{\text{Object height}}$ and $m = \dfrac{v}{u}$	3.2
88	understand that waves can be transmitted and reflected at an interface between media	3.4, 4.2
89	understand how a pulse–echo technique can provide information about the position of an object and how the amount of information obtained may be limited by the wavelength of the radiation or by the duration of pulses	4.2

Answers

Q 1 You might include: supports the body's weight; provides levers for movement; anchors the muscles; protects internal organs.

Q 2 A hinge joint can move in one plane only, whereas a ball and socket joint can rotate and move in any plane.

Q 3 Among the key properties are: durability, strength, toughness, generally stiff, but with some elasticity (especially under compression), hard, smooth surfaced, not brittle.

Q 4 It would be very brittle (the fibres help it to become tough).

Q 5 Taking bone from another part of the body exposes the patient to two operations, leading to increased risk (and increased cost). Taking bone from another person may lead to infection.

Q 6 (a) Elastic, tough and durable.

(b) Stiff, tough, hard and durable.

(c) Stiff, tough, smooth, hard and durable.

Q 7 For young and active patients the key aims are to provide a long-lasting, durable option that enables the patient to remain active. In a very obese patient the strength of the replacement is crucial to cope with the size of forces expected, although the patient would also be strongly encouraged to lose weight. In Third World countries, issues of cost are likely to be even more of an issue than in the previous cases and there may also be issues of how the surgery is carried out that limits choice.

Q 8 (a) Reading values from the graph and using Equation 1a:

$$k = \frac{\Delta F}{\Delta x}:$$

Barbed 0.35 mm diameter,

$$k = \frac{40\,\text{N}}{(8 \times 10^{-3}\,\text{m})} = 5 \times 10^3\,\text{N m}^{-1}$$

Non-barbed 0.35 mm diameter,

$$k = \frac{40\,\text{N}}{(20 \times 10^{-3}\,\text{m})} = 2 \times 10^3\,\text{N m}^{-1}$$

(linear region of graph)

The non-barbed thread is less stiff so might be more suitable for facial surgery where flexibility could be important.

(b) Barbed 40 N, non-barbed 55 N. Presumably the barbing process, in which the suture is nicked along its edge, introduces a 'crack', so a fracture starts more easily at these weaker places.

(c) The graph for the thinner suture has a lower gradient, indicating that it is less stiff. The 'pros' of using thicker suture are its strength and stiffness, keeping wounds sealed that are subject to large forces. Thinner sutures would be used in the smallest-scale microsurgery, where the feature being sewn up is so tiny that size is more important than strength.

Q 9 You need to estimate your weight and the area of your bones. If mass = 60 kg, then F = weight = $mg \approx 600$ N. If diameter of leg bone = 6 cm, then area of one bone $\approx \pi r^2 \approx 30\,\text{cm}^2 = 30 \times 10^{-4}\,\text{m}^2$. When standing on both feet, total area $A = 60 \times 10^{-4}\,\text{m}^2$.

$$\sigma = \frac{F}{A} \approx \frac{600\,\text{N}}{(60 \times 10^{-4}\,\text{m}^2)} = 10^5\,\text{Pa}$$

$$= 100\,\text{kPa}$$

Bones are commonly subject to much larger stresses, for example, when moving or simply when standing on one leg.

Q 10 (a) Using $v^2 = u^2 + 2as$, with $u = 0$, $a = 9.81\,\text{m s}^{-2}$, $s = 1.5$ m (taking downwards as positive):

$$v^2 = 29.4\,\text{m}^2\,\text{s}^{-2}, \ v = 5.42\,\text{m s}^{-1}$$

(b) Magnitude of deceleration:

$$a = \frac{\Delta v}{\Delta t} = 54.2\,\text{m s}^{-2}$$

(c) Magnitude of force $F = ma = 70\,\text{kg} \times 54.2\,\text{m s}^{-2}$

$$= 3.80 \times 10^3\,\text{N}$$

(d) Total cross-sectional area = 60 cm² = $60 \times 10^{-4}\,\text{m}^2$

$$\text{Stress} = \frac{380 \times 10^{-3}\,\text{N}}{60 \times 10^{-4}\,\text{m}^2}$$

$$= 6.3 \times 10^5\,\text{Pa}$$

$$= 0.63\,\text{MPa}$$

Q 11 See Figure 6.77. In this middle section, the forces along the bone's length are compressive at the top surface and tensile at the bottom surface. Toe bones accept compression well (think about a ballet dancer's foot position supported on their toes). However, bones cannot support tensile stress, so in this case the metatarsal is likely to crack on the lower surface.

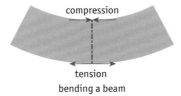

compression

tension
bending a beam

Figure 6.77 Answer to Question 11

Q 12 Strain = 2.5 mm/400 mm = 6.3×10^{-3} = 0.63% (Notice that you get the same answer if you express both lengths in cm or both in mm — it does not matter which units you use, provided you use the same for both lengths.)

Q 13   Expressed as a decimal:

$$\text{strain} = \frac{0.15}{100} = 1.5 \times 10^{-3}$$

From Equation 3:

$$x = \varepsilon l = 0.15 \times 10^{-3} \times 50\,\text{cm}$$

$$= 7.5 \times 10^{-2}\,\text{cm}$$

$$= 0.75\,\text{mm}$$

If the original length were ten times longer, then the extension, too, would be ten times as great, i.e. 7.5 mm, to achieve the same strain.

 Q 14   The graph for the 21 year male is a good approximation to straight lines through the origin up to the yield point (A), so Hooke's law applies. The graph for the 65 year female is only straight for strains less than about 0.02, so Hooke's law only applies in this region.

Q 15   (a)   After the yield point (A), the bone has suffered some permanent compression, such that if the load were removed the bone's molecular bonds would show some displacement. At point (B), the initial fracture point, some of this molecular bonding would have broken leaving severe damage that further loading could only make worse.

(b)   From the graph, $\sigma = 2.5\,\text{MPa}$

(c) $F = \sigma A = 2.5 \times 10^6\,\text{Pa} \times 2.5 \times 10^{-3}\,\text{m}^2 = 6.25 \times 10^3\,\text{N}$

(d)   From the graph, $\varepsilon = 0.011$

(e)   Compression $\Delta l = \varepsilon l = 0.11 \times 0.40\,\text{m} = 0.044\,\text{m}$
$$= 44\,\text{mm}$$

(f)   Using the linear portion of the graph up to point A:

$$\varepsilon = 0.045$$

$$\text{Young modulus E} = \frac{\sigma}{\varepsilon} = \frac{2.5 \times 10^6\,\text{Pa}}{0.045} = 5.6 \times 10^7\,\text{Pa}$$

 Q 16   For the 65-year-old osteoarthritic female:

Stress at yield point = 1.0 MPa

Strain at yield point = 0.03

Stress at initial fracture = 1.5 MPa

Strain at initial fracture point = 0.07

Using linear part of graph:

$$\text{Young Modulus } E = \frac{\sigma}{\varepsilon} = \frac{1.0 \times 10^6\,\text{Pa}}{0.03} = 3.3 \times 10^7\,\text{Pa}$$

Based on all five comparisons, the bone of the 65-year-old osteoarthritic woman is both less strong and less stiff than the bone of the 21-year-old male.

 Q 17   (a) $A = 0.5 \times 10^{-6}\,\text{m}^2$

(b) $\sigma = \dfrac{F}{A} = \dfrac{75\,\text{N}}{0.5 \times 10^{-6}\,\text{m}^2} = 1.5 \times 10^8\,\text{Pa}$

(c) $\varepsilon = \dfrac{6.0 \times 10^{-3}\,\text{m}}{8.0\,\text{m}} = 7.5 \times 10^{-4}$

(d) $E = \dfrac{\sigma}{\varepsilon} = \dfrac{1.5 \times 10^8\,\text{Pa}}{7.5 \times 10^{-4}} = 2.0 \times 10^{11}\,\text{Pa}$

(e)   Steel has a much greater Young modulus than bone, so it would take most of the stress in a replacement joint and the natural bone would waste away.

(f)   Total area of cross-section of 100 strands:

$$A = 100 \times 0.5 \times 10^{-6}\,\text{m}^{-2}$$

$$= 5 \times 10^{-5}\,\text{m}^2$$

Weight of ten people:

$$F = mg = 850\,\text{kg} \times 9.81\,\text{N kg}^{-1}$$

$$= 8.33 \times 10^3\,\text{N}$$

Stress due to weight of people:

$$\sigma = \frac{8.33 \times 10^3\,\text{N}}{5 \times 10^{-5}\,\text{m}^2} = 1.67 \times 10^8\,\text{Pa}$$

Strain $\varepsilon = \dfrac{\sigma}{\varepsilon} = \dfrac{1.67 \times 10^8\,\text{Pa}}{2.0 \times 10^{11}\,\text{Pa}} = 8.33 \times 10^{-4}$

Extension $= \varepsilon l = 8.33 \times 10^{-4} \times 90\,\text{m} = 7.5 \times 10^{-2}\,\text{m}$

Q 18   (a)   See Table 6.9 and Figure 6.78.

Tension/ 10^3 N	Extension/ 10^{-3} m	Stress/ 10^8 Pa	Strain
0.0	0.00	0.00	0.00
35.0	0.10	2.69	1.53
38.0	0.20	2.92	3.08
36.5	0.40	2.81	6.15
36.0	0.70	2.77	10.8
37.0	1.00	2.85	15.4
40.0	1.40	3.08	21.5
45.0	2.10	3.46	32.3
50.0	3.10	3.85	47.7
55.0	5.10	4.23	78.5
57.5	7.20	4.42	111
60.0	9.10	4.62	154
60.0	13.1	4.62	202
57.5	14.7	4.42	226
55.0	15.2	4.23	234
52.5	15.8 (broke)	4.04	243

Table 6.9 The answer to Question 18(a)

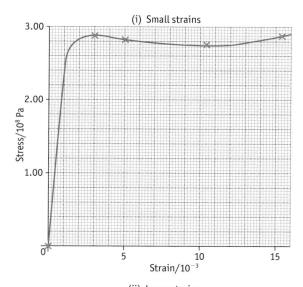

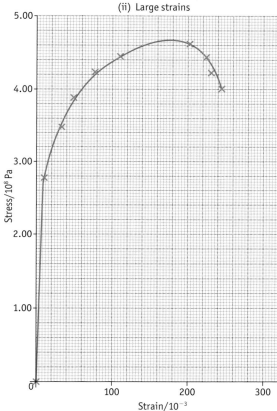

Figure 6.78 The answer to Question 18(a)

(b) (i) Yield stress: about 2.6×10^8 Pa (where the graph in Figure 6.77 (i) starts to curve and the sample extends with no additional stress).

(ii) Ultimate tensile stress: about 4.7×10^8 Pa (from Figure 6.77 (ii)).

(iii) Breaking strain = $243 \times 10^{-3} = 0.243 \approx 24\%$

Q 19 Area of string, $A = \pi(0.2 \times 10^{-3}\,\text{m})^2$

$$= 1.26 \times 10^{-7}\,\text{m}^2$$

Strain produced by eight turns:

$$\varepsilon = \frac{8 \times 4.0\,\text{mm}}{840\,\text{mm}}$$

$$= 3.8 \times 10^{-2}$$

Stress, $\sigma = \varepsilon E = 3.8 \times 10^{-2} \times 3.0 \times 10^9\,\text{Pa}$

$$= 1.14 \times 10^8\,\text{Pa}$$

Tension $= \sigma A = 1.14 \times 10^8\,\text{Pa} \times 1.26 \times 10^{-7}\,\text{m}^2$

$$= 14.4\,\text{N}$$

The Young modulus of the material must be high, and it must be able to achieve quite large strains without breaking (which means that its breaking stress must be high).

Q 20 The material would need to have a large Young modulus (large E) and be capable of undergoing large strains (large ε) without failing.

Q 21 **(a)** See Figure 6.79: each large square represents an energy density of $1 \times 10^7\,\text{J}\,\text{m}^{-3}$, and each small square represents $4 \times 10^5\,\text{J}\,\text{m}^{-3}$. From counting the squares, the area under the curve therefore represents about $10.5 \times 10^7\,\text{J}\,\text{m}^{-3}$.

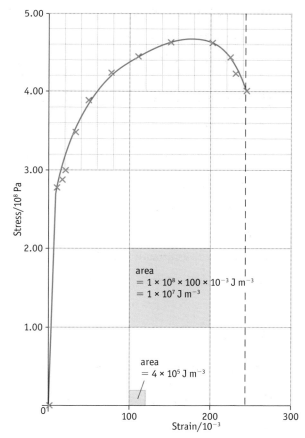

Figure 6.79 The answer to Question 21(a)

(b) If we assume that all the stored elastic energy becomes kinetic energy when the wire breaks, that all parts of the wire move at the same speed and deal with a volume V of the wire, then we can write:

mass $m = \rho V$ (ρ is the density)

$E_{el} = UV$

kinetic energy $E_k = \frac{1}{2}(\rho V)v^2 = UV$

and so: $\frac{1}{2}\rho v^2 = U$

$$v^2 = \frac{2U}{\rho}$$

$$= \frac{2 \times 10.5 \times 10^7\,\mathrm{J\,m^{-3}}}{8 \times 10^3\,\mathrm{kg\,m^{-3}}}$$

(Note that the units of v^2 are $\mathrm{J\,kg^{-1}}$ and that $1\,\mathrm{J\,kg^{-1}} = 1\,\mathrm{m^2\,s^{-2}}$.)

MATHS REFERENCE
See Maths note 2.3
Derived units

So: $v = 1.6 \times 10^2\,\mathrm{m\,s^{-1}}$

This answer shows that the wire will move very fast when it breaks. As the kinetic energy will not, in practice, be evenly distributed, the moving end of the wire will in fact move at several hundred metres per second.

Q 22 Each square on the graph represents

$20\,\mathrm{MPa} \times 0.02 = 4.0 \times 10^5\,\mathrm{Pa} = 4.0 \times 10^5\,\mathrm{J\,m^{-3}}$

Human hair:

(i) Area under loading graph ≈ 16.5 squares, so:

energy density $U_{load} = 16.5 \times 4.0 \times 10^5\,\mathrm{J\,m^{-3}}$

$= 6.6 \times 10^6\,\mathrm{J\,m^{-3}}$

(ii) Area under unloading ≈ 7 squares, so:

$U_{unload} = 7 \times 4.0 \times 10^5\,\mathrm{J\,m^{-3}}$

$= 2.8 \times 10^6\,\mathrm{J\,m^{-3}}$

(iii) Energy lost per unit volume

$U_{load} - U_{unload} \approx (6.6 - 2.8) \times 10^6\,\mathrm{J\,m^{-3}}$

$= 3.8 \times 10^6\,\mathrm{J\,m^{-3}} \approx 4 \times 10^6\,\mathrm{J\,m^{-3}}$

Dry horse hair:

(i) $U_{load} = 30 \times 4.0 \times 10^5\,\mathrm{J\,m^{-3}} = 1.2 \times 10^7\,\mathrm{J\,m^{-3}}$

(ii) $U_{unload} = 5.5 \times 4.0 \times 10^5\,\mathrm{J\,m^{-3}} = 2.2 \times 10^6\,\mathrm{J\,m^{-3}}$

(iii) $U_{load} - U_{unload} \approx (12.0 - 2.2) \times 10^6\,\mathrm{J\,m^{-3}} = 9.8 \times 10^6\,\mathrm{J\,m^{-3}}$
$\approx 1 \times 10^7\,\mathrm{J\,m^{-3}}$

Replasticised horse hair:

(i) $U_{load} = 20 \times 4.0 \times 10^5\,\mathrm{J\,m^{-3}} = 8.0 \times 10^6\,\mathrm{J\,m^{-3}}$

(ii) $U_{unload} = 5 \times 4.0 \times 10^5\,\mathrm{J\,m^{-3}} = 2.0 \times 10^6\,\mathrm{J\,m^{-3}}$

(iii) $U_{load} - U_{unload} \approx (8.0 - 2.0) \times 10^6\,\mathrm{J\,m^{-3}} = 6 \times 10^6\,\mathrm{J\,m^{-3}}$

Q 23 **(a)** The graph for a metal would be much steeper (as its Young modulus would typically be a thousand times greater) and it would not reach such a large strain (polymers can be strained by several hundred per cent, while metal breaks at strains of a few per cent.) The graph for the metal might curve over as it yielded (as in Figure 6.77 (ii)).

(b) The area represents the difference between energy transferred to the sample on stretching and the energy recovered as it is unloaded: it represents the energy dissipated due to heating.

(c) For point A your sketch should resemble Figure 6.25(a), and for point C it should resemble Figure 6.25(b).

Q 24 **(a)** Equation 9: $P = \frac{1}{f} = \frac{1}{0.2\,\mathrm{m}} = 5\,\mathrm{D}$

(b) $f = \frac{1}{P} = \frac{1}{4\,\mathrm{D}} = 0.25\,\mathrm{m} = 25\,\mathrm{cm}$

Q 25 **(a)** A circle of light with a diameter less than 4 cm.

(b) A point of intense light – this is the principal focus.

(c) A circle of light.

Q 26 See Figure 6.80.

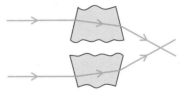

Figure 6.80 The answer to Question 26

Q 27 **(a)** The focal length $f = 17\,\mathrm{mm} = 17 \times 10^{-3}\,\mathrm{m}$

(b) $P = \frac{1}{f} = \frac{1}{(17 \times 10^{-3}\,\mathrm{m})} = 59\,\mathrm{D}$

Q 28 **(a)** **(i)** 1 cm represents 10 cm for f, u and v.
(ii) Object and image heights are shown actual size (1 cm to 1 cm).

(b) Magnification $= \dfrac{4\,\mathrm{cm}}{2\,\mathrm{cm}} = 2$

Q 29 $u = 30\,\text{cm}$, $f = 20\,\text{cm}$

Rearranging equation (10):

$$\frac{1}{v} = \frac{1}{f} - \frac{1}{u}$$

$$\frac{1}{v} = \frac{1}{20\,\text{cm}} - \frac{1}{30\,\text{cm}}$$

$$= \frac{3}{60\,\text{cm}} - \frac{2}{60\,\text{cm}}$$

$$= \frac{1}{60\,\text{cm}}$$

$v = 60\,\text{cm}$ – which is the same as the value found using the construction method.

Q 30 See Table 6.10.

Q 31 (a) When the magnification is 1, $u = v = 2f$. (This is always true, and in such a situation the object and image are at their closest together.)

(b) The value of $\dfrac{u}{v}$ is the same as the ratio of image height to object height.

Q 32 (a) The Moon is a very distant object so u can be treated as infinite (rays entering the lens are parallel)

so $\dfrac{1}{u} = 0$ and, $v = f = 50\,\text{mm}$

(b) $u = 1.0\,\text{m}$

$$\frac{1}{v} = \frac{1}{(50 \times 10^{-3}\,\text{m})} - \frac{1}{1.0\,\text{m}} = 0.053\,\text{m} = 53\,\text{mm}$$

Q 33 Four (on entering and leaving the cornea; and on entering and leaving the lens)

Q 34 You want the ciliary muscles to be relaxed. This corresponds to a stretched lens, which is the condition for looking into the distance.

Q 35 It increases. (If you are not sure, compare some fat and thin lenses: thin lenses have a long focal length.)

Q 36 When looking at the book (object):

$u = 25\,\text{cm}$ and $v = 1.7\,\text{cm}$ (distance to the retina).

$$\frac{1}{f} = \frac{1}{(25 \times 10^{-2}\,\text{m})} + \frac{1}{(1.7 \times 10^{-2}\,\text{m})}$$

$$= \frac{(25 + 1.7) \times 10^{-2}\,\text{m}}{((25 \times 10^{-2}\,\text{m}) \times (1.7 \times 10^{-4}\,\text{m}))}$$

$$= 62\,\text{D}$$

$$f = \frac{1}{62\,\text{D}} = 0.016\,\text{m}$$

When the eye is relaxed, objects at infinity are in focus, so the distance from lens to retina is the focal length.

$f = 1.7\,\text{cm} = 0.017\,\text{m}$

$$P = \frac{1}{0.017\,\text{m}} = 59\,\text{D}$$

In adjusting to look at the book, the lens's focal length decreases by 0.1 cm and its power increases by 3 D.

Fractional change in focal length is: $\dfrac{0.1\,\text{cm}}{1.7\,\text{cm}} = 0.06 = 6\%$

Q 37 Your diagram should resemble Figure 6.81, i.e. the image is diminished, erect and between F and the lens.

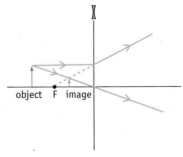

object   F   image

Figure 6.81 The answer to Question 37

Situation	Focal length f/cm	Object distance u/cm	Object height/cm	Image distance v/cm	Image height/cm	Magnification	v/u	Description
a	15	30 (= 2f)	6	30	6	1	1	Real, inverted, same size
b	30	45 (>f and <2f)	2	90	4	2	2	Real, inverted, magnified
c	40	40 (= f)	5	infinite	–	–	–	No image
d	50	60 (>f and <2f)	10	300	50	5	5	Real, inverted, magnified
e	50	300 (>>2f)	10	60	2	0.2	0.2	Real, inverted, diminished

Table 6.10 The answers to Question 30

Q 38 $u = 10\,\text{cm}\ f = -10\,\text{cm}$

Rearranging the lens formula gives $\dfrac{1}{v} = \dfrac{1}{f} - \dfrac{1}{u}$

$$\frac{1}{v} = \frac{1}{10\,\text{cm}} - \frac{1}{10\,\text{cm}}$$

$$= \frac{-2}{10\,\text{cm}} = \frac{-1}{5\,\text{cm}}$$

$$v = -5\,\text{cm}$$

So the image is 5 cm away from the lens – and it is virtual.

Q 39 $u = 6\,\text{cm}$, $v = -2\,\text{cm}$. Substituting in the thin lens formula gives:

$$\frac{1}{f} = \frac{1}{6\,\text{cm}} - \frac{1}{2\,\text{cm}} = -\frac{1}{3\,\text{cm}}$$

So the lens's focal length is 3 cm – and it is a diverging lens.

Q 40 (a) See Figure 6.82.

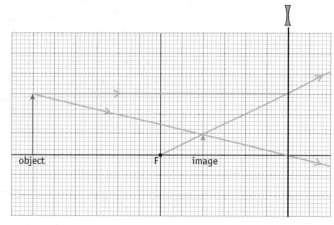

Figure 6.82 The answer to Question 40(a)

(b) Image height = 1 cm

(c) $u = 12\,\text{cm}$, $f = -6\,\text{cm}$

$$\frac{1}{v} = \frac{1}{6\,\text{cm}} - \frac{1}{12\,\text{cm}} = -\frac{1}{4\,\text{cm}}$$

$$v = -4\,\text{cm}$$

Image height = object size $\times \dfrac{v}{u} = 3\,\text{cm} \times \dfrac{4\,\text{cm}}{12\,\text{cm}} = 1\,\text{cm}$

So the image is 4 cm from the lens – and it is virtual.

Q 41 (a) From Activity 15 the combined power P of three lenses in contact is given by Equation 13.

Required power $P = 1.0\,\text{D} + 0.5\,\text{D} + 0.25\,\text{D} = 1.75\,\text{D}$

(b) $f = \dfrac{1}{P} = \dfrac{1}{1.75\,\text{D}} = 0.57\,\text{m}$

Q 42 (a) Adding the powers gives 4.0 D.

(b) Combined power = $+0.5\,\text{D} + (-1.5\,\text{D}) = -1.0\,\text{D}$

(c) Powers are $+10\,\text{D}$ and $+4\,\text{D}$, so combined power = $+14\,\text{D}$

Q 43 (a) Combined power = $+16\,\text{D}$,

so focal length = $\dfrac{1}{16\,\text{m}^{-1}} = 0.0625\,\text{m} = 6.25\,\text{cm}$

(b) Combined power = $-20\,\text{D}$,

so focal length = $\dfrac{1}{20\,\text{m}^{-1}} = -0.05\,\text{m} = -5\,\text{cm}$

(c) $\dfrac{1}{f} = \dfrac{1}{10\,\text{cm}} + \dfrac{1}{5\,\text{cm}} = \dfrac{3}{10\,\text{cm}}$

so $f = \dfrac{10\,\text{cm}}{3} = 3.3\,\text{cm}$

(Note that it is easier to combine the powers first and then work out the focal length.)

Q 44 (a) Focal length = 20.0 cm (because rays are parallel from a distant object and the parallel rays focused at 20.0 cm).

Power $P = \dfrac{1}{0.20\,\text{m}} = +5.0\,\text{D}$

(b) Combined power = $+5.0\,\text{D} + (-1.0\,\text{D}) = +4.0\,\text{D}$

Combined focal length = $1\,\text{m}/4.0 = 25\,\text{cm}$.

So the image should be formed at 25 cm from the lenses, which is what the student found.

(c) Image distance without diverging lens = 10 cm

Combined power of lenses = $+10\,\text{D} + (-1.0\,\text{D}) = 9.0\,\text{D}$

So the image will be formed at $\dfrac{1}{9.0\,\text{m}} = 11.1\,\text{cm}$ from the lenses.

(d) The image moved further in the first case, i.e. when the diverging lens was added to the longer focal length (weaker) converging lens.

Q 45   **(a)** Ray 3 is the incident ray; rays 1 and 2 are the reflected rays.

(b) Their amplitudes must be equal.

(c) The two waves must be exactly out of phase (there must be a phase difference of 180° between them).

(d) The thickness is one-quarter of the wavelength of light inside the coating material. So this gives the wavelength as 100 nm × 4 = 400 nm. However, the wavelength in air will be longer than this, by a factor equal to the refractive index: Wavelength = 400 nm × 1.4 = 560 nm. The light must strike the surface at right angles, otherwise the distance it travels through the material will be more than 200 nm.

(e) From part **(d)** above, you can see that a coating of thickness 100 nm will only result in perfect cancelling for light with wavelength 560 nm. Light with wavelength greater or less than this will not experience perfect cancelling when it falls normally (at right angles) on the coating. At different angles, the rays of light travel different distances through the coating. At any particular angle, only one wavelength will be perfectly cancelled. A suitable thickness for an effective coating will correspond to a wavelength near the middle of the visible range, for example, 550 nm.

Q 46   As a ray of light passes from water into a cornea, it is entering a material with a slightly higher refractive index, so it will bend slightly away from the normal. We rely on our corneas to bend rays *towards* the normal, so helping to focus them on the retina. (Recall that the lens plays only a small part in the focusing of the image.) This explains why we cannot see clearly under water.

Q 47   If someone is short-sighted, parallel rays from a distant object are focused in front of the retina. To focus them further back, the front of the eye must be less curved. To achieve this, more cells must be removed from the centre of the cornea (Figure 6.83).

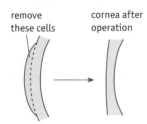

remove these cells   cornea after operation

Figure 6.83 Diagram for the answer to Question 47

Q 48   By the age of 45, the near point has moved to about 40 cm (see Figure 6.41). To achieve this, a book must be held at arm's length.

Q 49   The range over which older people can focus gets more and more limited, so they need one pair of spectacles for close-up and one for distance viewing. The problem would not be solved by a single pair of ordinary contact lenses; however, older people could:

wear contact lenses for distance viewing and have spectacles for close-up, to wear in addition to the contact lenses

use bifocal or multifocal contact lenses that have areas of the lens with different powers

have one eye for distance vision and one eye corrected for close-up vision.

Q 50   Your eyeball is too short because the rays focus beyond the retina.

Q 51   If the intraocular lens (IOL) has one power then it is suitable for one distance and cannot be adjusted for viewing at different distances. Depending on the usual activities of the person, he or she may choose to have IOLs for distance vision and use spectacles for close up, or vice versa. Multifocal lenses take more time to get used to and may not be suitable for some people. If you are using one eye or part of each eye, there is less information being received and it may be more difficult to judge distances, for example.

Q 52   Lens 2 is a converging lens – it gives a magnified view of the grid.

Lens 3 has the greater power – it reduces the apparent size of the grid more than lens 1.

Since Lens 1 has a lower power than Lens 3: its focal length must be greater.

Q 53   **(a)** Using the lens formula (Equation 10) gives:

$$\frac{1}{f} = \frac{1}{0.017\,\text{m}} + \frac{1}{0.5\,\text{m}} = 61\,\text{m}^{-1}$$

$f = 0.016\,\text{m} = 1.6\,\text{cm}$

(b) From part **(a)**, the power of the patient's unaided eye is +61 D. Now we can follow the same procedure to calculate the power required when they have a lens to help them focus on an object at 20 cm:

$$\frac{1}{f} = \frac{1}{0.017\,\text{m}} + \frac{1}{0.20\,\text{m}} = 64\,\text{m}^{-1}$$

So the new power is +64 D and the lens must have a power of +3 D to achieve this. It must be a converging lens.

Q 54 (a) Using the lens formula (Equation 10) gives:

$$P = \frac{1}{f} = \frac{1}{0.017\,\text{m}} + \frac{1}{3.00\,\text{m}} = 59\,\text{D}$$

(b) From part (a), the power of the patient's unaided eye is +59 D. We can follow the same procedure to calculate the power required when they have a lens to help them focus on an object at infinity:

$$\frac{1}{f} = \frac{1}{0.017\,\text{m}} + \frac{1}{\infty} = 58\,\text{m}^{-1}$$

So the new power is 58 D, and the lens must have a power of −1 D to achieve this. It must be a diverging lens.

Q 55 We have not been told the image distance, but as this is the same whether the patient is wearing spectacles or not, it will cancel out in the calculations.

For the converging lens at the bottom:

Required u = 0.25 m, actual u = 0.80 m

v = lens to retina distance (constant value)

Required power $P_r = \frac{1}{u} + \frac{1}{v} = \frac{1}{0.25\,\text{m}} + \frac{1}{v}$

Actual eye power $P_a = \frac{1}{0.80\,\text{m}} + \frac{1}{v}$

Lens power = $P_r - P_a$

$$= \left(\frac{1}{0.25\,\text{m}} + \frac{1}{v}\right) - \left(\frac{1}{0.80\,\text{m}} + \frac{1}{v}\right)$$

$$= \frac{1}{0.25\,\text{m}} - \frac{1}{0.80\,\text{m}} = 2.75\,\text{D}$$

For the diverging lens at the top:

Required u = ∞, actual u = 4.00 m

v = lens to retina distance

Required power $P_r = \frac{1}{u} + \frac{1}{v} = \frac{1}{\infty} + \frac{1}{v}$

Actual eye power $P_a = \frac{1}{4.00\,\text{m}} + \frac{1}{v}$

Lens power = $P_r - P_a$

$$= \left(\frac{1}{\infty} + \frac{1}{v}\right) - \left(\frac{1}{4.00\,\text{m}} + \frac{1}{v}\right)$$

$$= \frac{1}{\infty} - \frac{1}{4.00\,\text{m}} = -0.25\,\text{D}$$

Q 56 Using the wave equation:

$$\lambda = \frac{v}{f} = \frac{1500\,\text{m s}^{-1}}{10 \times 10^6\,\text{Hz}}$$

$$= 1.5 \times 10^{-4}\,\text{m} = 0.15\,\text{mm}$$

Q 57 $v = \dfrac{2s}{ts} = \dfrac{vt}{2s} = \dfrac{1500\,\text{m s}^{-1} \times 16 \times 10^{-6}\,\text{s}}{2} = 0.012\,\text{m} = 12\,\text{mm}$

Q 58 (a) $\lambda = \dfrac{v}{f} = \dfrac{1500\,\text{m s}^{-1}}{12 \times 10^3\,\text{Hz}} = 0.125\,\text{m}$

(b) $s = \dfrac{vt}{2} = \dfrac{1500\,\text{m s}^{-1} \times 0.22\,\text{s}}{2} = 165\,\text{m}$

Q 59 $t = \dfrac{2s}{v} = \dfrac{2 \times 37\,000 \times 10^3\,\text{m}}{3.00 \times 10^8\,\text{m s}^{-1}} = 2.52\,\text{s}$

Q 60 Speed in soft tissue is 1500 m s⁻¹. Distance s = 10 cm (there and back), $s = vt$, so:

$$t = \frac{s}{v} = \frac{0.1\,\text{m}}{1500\,\text{m s}^{-1}} = 6.7 \times 10^{-5}\,\text{s} = 0.067\,\text{ms}$$

The interval between pulses must be less than 0.067 ms, so the frequency of pulses must be given by:

$$f_p > \frac{1}{6.7 \times 10^5\,\text{s}} \quad \text{i.e.} f_p > 1.5 \times 10^4\,\text{kHz} \,(= 15\,\text{k Hz})$$

Q 61 (a) For muscle, speed v = 1600 m s⁻¹

The time delay between A and B t = 20 μs

This is the time to travel twice the thickness of the heart wall, s, as it is the difference in the times for each pulse to travel there and back, so:

$$s = \frac{vt}{2} = \frac{1600\,\text{m s}^{-1} \times 20 \times 10^{-6}\,\text{s}}{2} = 0.016\,\text{m}$$

At the point where it is measured, the wall is 1.6 cm thick.

(b) See Figure 6.84. If the time interval between reflections is shorter than the duration of each pulse, then the two reflected pulses overlap and appear like a single reflection, giving little useful information about the thickness of the heart muscle.

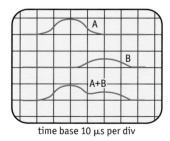

time base 10 μs per div

Figure 6.84 Diagram for the answer to Question 61(b)

Q 62   The beam has a different frequency, which indicates that the blood is moving relative to the source of the ultrasound and, as the frequency is lower, the blood is moving away from the source.

Q 63   The blood is travelling towards the source of the waves, so wavelength received by the blood and reflected towards the probe will be reduced due to the Doppler effect. As the blood is travelling towards the detector, the wavelength received by the detector will be reduced again. (A signal reflected from a moving target undergoes a double Doppler shift.) As the blood starts to travel faster, the shift in wavelength will increase and the wavelength will get shorter.

Q 64   When the blood is travelling towards the probe, the frequency will be increased. If a clot blocks an artery so that the blood stops moving, the frequency will decrease to the same value as the emitted ultrasound. There will be no Doppler shift.

PRACTICAL SKILLS

Developing practical skills in SHAP

Throughout the SHAP course there are opportunities to develop your practical skills. A structured framework for developing practical skills through an investigative approach is outlined below. The SHAP Teacher and Technician Resource Pack provides a practical skills self-evaluation sheet which you can use to record and reflect on the skills you develop within practical activities. You will not necessarily address all the skills in every practical activity; rather, an activity might focus on one or more specific aspects of practical work. You will need draw on these practical skills when completing the written assessment at the end of your AS or A level course. Evidence of the development of practical skills will also enable you to obtain a practical endorsement alongside your A level grade.

1 Scientific questions and information research

1.1 State the scientific problem to be investigated

Before you start any practical task, you should have a clear idea of what you are setting out to do. Any report of your work should begin by saying what this is. It is helpful to express the task as an **hypothesis** (an 'educated guess') to be tested, for example as a question or as a design brief:

- Is the refractive index of glass independent of the angle of incidence?
- How does the frequency of a vibrating string vary with tension?
- Design and carry out an experiment to find the Young modulus of copper.
- Calibrate a thermistor and potential divider circuit for use as a thermostat.

Sometimes you might start with only a general idea of a topic for investigation (for instance, you might be interested in absorption of radiation). You will need to research some information and discuss your ideas with your teacher before stating your research question or design brief (using this example, you might investigate how the intensity of gamma radiation varies with thickness of absorber).

1.2 Research relevant information

When preparing to carry out your task, you might need to research some or all of the following aspects:

- applications and implications: try to relate your task to a 'real life' problem or situation and find some information about it;
- background science, including relevant equations;
- methods that other people have used to tackle a similar task (What problems did they encounter? How were they overcome? What were the advantages and disadvantages of their approach?);
- outcomes of other people's investigations into similar questions.

For your research, you should consult *at least three* information sources (online or offline).

Wikipedia might seem an obvious starting point, but it is not always reliable so don't treat it as the only information source; consult some of the other references given in the articles.

If using an internet search engine, don't just consult the first 'hit'. Scroll down and have a look at some of the others.

Write a summary of what you find out *in your own words*; don't just copy and paste.

1.3 Give details of your sources

A written report should include details of your sources. Wherever you refer to a printed source, give the surname(s) of the author(s) in brackets followed by the year of publication e.g. (Smith, 2013). When you refer to a website, give the name of the person or organisation, the url and the date you accessed it, e.g. (Institute of Physics, www.iop.org, 17/06/14)

List details of all your sources in alphabetical order in a **bibliography** at the end of the report. To help other people locate the same sources, there are conventions for presenting this information:

Books

- Surname(s), initials (Year of publication in brackets), *Title of book in italic*, Publisher, Place of publication, Chapter number, Page number(s).

Journals and magazines

- Surname(s), initials (Date of publication in brackets), *Title of journal/magazine in italic*, **Volume number (and issue number if relevant) in bold**, Page number(s).

Websites

- Organisation/author/editor, (Year) *Title in italic*, (Date of last update if known), URL, Date when you visited the site.

Comment on your sources

You should comment critically on the reliability of each of your information sources. Questions to ask yourself include:

- Who produced this source? What authority do they have?
- Why was it produced? Is there a vested interest or likely bias?
- How recent is the information?

In a word-processed research summary, you could insert a footnote on the first occasion that you mention each source and use it to record your comments on the source.

2 Planning and experimental design

2.1 Identify the variables to be measured and controlled

At an early stage in your planning and design, decide what you are going to measure in order to answer your research question or fulfil your design brief.

Identify the relevant independent and dependent variables. Think about the range of values that you will use for the independent variable(s) and the range that you might expect to find for the dependent variable(s).

Consider variables that need to be controlled or otherwise accounted for. For example, if you are investigating how the length of a vibrating string affects its frequency, how can you ensure that you change *only* the length and that other factors that might be important (such as tension) are kept constant? If you think that external factors you can't control (such as room temperature) might affect your results, how will you account for them?

2.2 Describe the experimental apparatus and methodology

The report of your work should include a clear, labelled diagram of the apparatus that you intend to use. If you have been given a basic arrangement to start with, explain how you will adapt and improve it. Add notes and labels to your diagram to show what you will be measuring.

Sometimes you need to carry out a trial experiment to get a rough idea of what will be involved and what measurements to make. Include a brief report of any such experiment and say how it has helped you to plan your main investigation.

Explain why you will be using specific items of apparatus in order to carry out the task. For example, if you have chosen to use a micrometer, say why you are using that rather than callipers or a ruler.

Describe and explain the method that you will be using. Include a summary of standard procedures (e.g. for handling radioactive sources) and any techniques that you have used in order to address a particular problem (e.g. avoiding parallax when reading a scale). It can be helpful to write yourself a set of instructions that lists what needs to be done. This is particularly useful if there will be several steps that must be carried out in a certain order.

In some tasks, you might be given instructions to follow for all or part of the practical work. If so, make sure you know and understand what will be involved before you start setting up apparatus or making measurements.

2.3 Identify sources of systematic and random error

As part of your planning, you need to think about sources of error, and how errors could be minimised through appropriate apparatus and methodology.

Systematic errors affect each reading in the same way (e.g. zero errors on a micrometer).

Random errors arise because there is always some uncertainty in reading an instrument (due to the size of scale divisions) and sometimes repeated attempts to make the same measurement give different results.

MATHS REFERENCE
Experimental measurements
See Maths note 7.1

For each measurement, consider what might contribute to its uncertainty and estimate a ± range within which you are confident the measurement will lie. Table 1 shows a way to record this.

Measurement	Source of error/ uncertainty	Systematic or random?	Estimate of size of error	Comment

Table 1 Table for recording sources of error

A particular measurement might have both a systematic and random error, so could appear twice. Consider how you might modify your experimental design to reduce sources of error, paying most attention to factors that are likely to have the greatest effect.

2.4 Identify safety issues, discuss how to reduce risk and complete a risk assessment

When carrying out any practical work your own safety is important, and so is the safety of other people. You should also consider how to avoid damage to apparatus.

Think about the design of the apparatus and how everyone can be safe in its vicinity. List any safety issues in your experiment and note how you will deal with each one. Table 2 shows a way to record this.

Safety issue	How it will be minimised

Table 2 Table for recording safety issues

Consider how you might modify your experimental design to address safety issues.

3 Carrying out practical work safely and ethically

3.1 Carry out the experiment following correct procedures and with appropriate safety precautions

Having planned your work carefully and considered safety issues, you should be in a good position to carry out your practical work in a safe, ethical and well-organised manner, following your own plan and any instructions that you might have been given. 'Ethical' in this context means that you should behave considerately towards people and other living things and the environment. This is important if, for example, you are working outdoors, or if you involve other people in your investigation (e.g. if you ask people to carry out a sporting activity so that you can make measurements).

If unexpected ethical or safety issues arise, deal with them sensibly, taking advice where needed, and make a note of them to include in the final report.

3.2 Make measurements and record data in an appropriate format using suitable precision

Record all measurements, including repeated ones, as soon as they are taken and with appropriate precision (i.e. a suitable number of significant figures) and units.

Make a blank table for recording your measurements, and include columns for quantities that you will calculate. For example, if you are investigating how a sample extends under a load, you could start with the headings in Table 3.

Added mass m/kg	Load $F = mg$/N	Length x/m	Extension $\Delta x = (x - x_0)$/m

Table 3 Partial results table for investigating extension produced by a load

Set up your results table in such a way that you can use it to record *all* your measurements as soon as you make them. Include repeated measurements, and use the units of the measuring instrument even though you might later need to convert to some other unit. Table 4 shows how you might do this if measuring the diameter of a wire in mm in order to work out its cross-sectional area in m^2.

Diameter measurements d/mm	Average diameter d/mm	Average diameter d/m	Cross sectional area $A = \pi(d/2)^2$/m^2

Table 4 Table for recording diameter measurements and calculations

As you make your measurements, note possible systematic and random errors, especially where they differ from original estimates.

4 Analysis and interpretation of data

4.1 Process, analyse and display data using appropriate mathematical, ICT and statistical techniques

The way you analyse your data will depend on the quantity and nature of data that you have collected, and on what you are trying to find out.

- State the errors/uncertainties in measured and calculated values wherever possible.
- Record a suitable number of significant figures in measured and calculated values.
- Use standard scientific notation to represent very large and very small numbers.
- Look for opportunities to develop and demonstrate your mathematical and ICT skills.

If you have a lot of data and need to carry out several repeat calculations, use a spreadsheet to record and manipulate your data. Use settings that give correct numbers of significant figures.

Use statistical tests to explore correlations between variables. However, in most physics tasks, just finding a correlation is not enough. If two variables are correlated, look for a mathematical relationship between them that can be expressed as an equation.

Think how best to present your data and results. In many physics tasks, this will involve drawing one or more graphs or charts.

4.2 Plot a graph and use it to derive further information

In some cases, a pie chart or bar chart might be suitable, but more often you will need to plot one variable against another and produce a line graph,

MATHS REFERENCE
Units
See Maths note 2.1
Significant figures
See Maths notes 7.1, 7.2, 7.3, 7.4

MATHS REFERENCE
Significant figures
See Maths note 7.2

MATHS REFERENCE
Relationships and graphs
See Maths notes 5.1–5.5
Measurement and uncertainty
See Maths notes 7.1–7.7

When using ICT to plot line graphs, use settings that give sensible scales and labelling, graph gridlines and sharply marked data points.

Use your estimates of experimental uncertainty to add error bars and error boxes to your line graphs, and draw the 'best' trend line that passes through all the boxes. On linear graphs, draw the steepest and least-steep straight lines that go through all the error boxes; these lines can be used to estimate the uncertainty in the results.

A straight-line graph indicates a linear relationship between variables, and further information can often be deduced from the graph's gradient and intercept.

If the relationship is non-linear, the graph is a curve whose shape can indicate the mathematical relationship involved. By manipulating the variables mathematically, you can sometimes produce numbers that give a straight-line graph, which in turn can be used to deduce further information.

5 Conclusion and evaluation

5.1 State a conclusion based on experimental evidence

State a clear conclusion to your work, summarising what you have found out.

- If you set out to test a hypothesis, say whether or not your findings support it.
- If your aim was to find a mathematical relationship between variables, write an equation to express that relationship.
- If you were determining the value of a quantity, state your final result.
- If you were working to a design brief, summarise the outcome of your work.

State the uncertainty in any numerical result. If you have combined several measurements to calculate a value, consider how their uncertainties contribute to the overall uncertainty in the final result. If you have derived your result from a graph, use the graph to estimate the uncertainty in the result. Then write your result, complete with units, in the form:

result = best experimental value ± uncertainty

MATHS REFERENCE

Combining uncertainties
See Maths note 7.5
Uncertainties and graphs
See Maths note 7.7

5.2 Use appropriate scientific knowledge to explain your conclusion and comment on its validity

A conclusion is **valid** if it is based on sound reasoning using data obtained from a well-designed experiment. When discussing the validity of your conclusion, reflect on the extent to which your practical and research work enabled you to meet your original aim.

In the commentary on your conclusion, draw on your scientific knowledge to explain the outcome of your work. Refer to physics that you have studied in this course and to any additional research that you carried out, as well as bringing in relevant scientific knowledge from elsewhere (e.g. GCSE work, other AS/A-level courses, general knowledge, etc.).

Comment on whether the outcome of your work was as you expected. If it wasn't, try to explain why not.

Comment on the **accuracy** of your result. If your investigation involved determining the value of a quantity, comment on how close your result is to the accepted value (if known). Consider whether your experimental apparatus and method might be expected to produce a result that is higher, or lower, than the true value.

Comment on the **precision** of your result. Discuss the sources of experimental uncertainty in any measurements that you made, and consider which made the greatest contribution to the uncertainty in your overall results.

Where possible, comment on how the outcome of your work relates to an application of physics.

Finally, analyse the strengths and weaknesses of your apparatus and method, and make detailed suggestions for one or two improvements.

MATHS NOTES

0 Signs and symbols

0.1 Equations and comparisons

In physics, we are often interested in whether two quantities are exactly equal, or almost equal, or whether one is greater than the other. Table 1 lists the signs used for expressing such relationships.

Sign	Meaning	Notes
$=$	is equal to	
$\equiv$	is exactly the same as	used to emphasis the point that two expressions are two ways of writing exactly the same thing (as opposed to two different things being the same size)
$\neq$	is not equal to	
$\approx$	is approximately equal to	
$\sim$	is the same order of magnitude as	
$<$	is less than	the smaller quantity is written at the narrow end of the symbol
$>$	is greater than	
$\leqslant$	is less than or equal to	
$\geqslant$	is greater than or equal to	
$\ll$	is much less than	
$\gg$	is much greater than	

Table 1 Signs for equations and comparisons

MATHS REFERENCE

Order of magnitude

See Maths note 7.4

0.2 The delta symbol

The symbol Δ (the capital Greek letter delta) is used to mean 'a small amount of' or 'a change in'. Notice that Δ does *not* represent a number, so resist the temptation to cancel Δ, e.g. if it appears on the top and bottom of an expression.

For example, the symbol Δt represents a time interval and is often used when describing rates of flow or rates of change. For example, if an amount of charge ΔQ flows past a point in a time interval Δt, then the current I can be written

$$I = \frac{\Delta Q}{\Delta t}$$

The delta symbol is also used to denote an experimental uncertainty. For example, if a distance x is measured as 23 mm but could be out by 1 mm in either direction, then the uncertainty in the measurement is $\Delta x = 1$ mm. The measurement is written as $x \pm \Delta x$, i.e. 23 mm $\pm$ 1 mm.

0.3 Summation

The symbol Σ (the capital Greek letter sigma) means 'the sum of'. Note that Σ does *not* represent a number so resist the temptation to cancel it, e.g. if it appears on both sides of an equation.

The symbol Σ is usually used with other symbols representing the items to be added together. For example, the mass of a sample of gas is Σm, where m represents the mass of an individual gas molecule and the sum includes all the molecules in the sample.

When dealing with vectors, the sum is a vector sum i.e. it takes account of direction as well as magnitude. $\Sigma \boldsymbol{F}$, meaning the sum of forces in a given situation, can be represented by a vector diagram.

1 Index notation

An **index** (plural **indices**) or **power** is the superscript number which, when a positive whole number, means squared, cubed, etc. For example

$$5^2 = 5 \times 5 = 25$$

$$7^3 = 7 \times 7 \times 7 = 343$$

$$0.6^4 = 0.6 \times 0.6 \times 0.6 \times 0.6 = 0.1296$$

1.1 Index notation and powers of 10

Table 2 shows 'powers of 10'. The number in any row is found by dividing the number in the row above by 10.

$100\,000 =$	$10 \times 10 \times 10 \times 10 \times 10 =$	10^5
$10\,000 =$	$10 \times 10 \times 10 \times 10 =$	10^4
$1\,000 =$	$10 \times 10 \times 10 =$	10^3
$100 =$	$10 \times 10 =$	10^2
$10 =$	$10 =$	10^1
$1 =$	$1 =$	10^0
$0.1 =$	$\frac{1}{10} =$	10^{-1}
$0.01 =$	$\frac{1}{10 \times 10} = \frac{1}{10^2} =$	10^{-2}
$0.001 =$	$\frac{1}{10 \times 10 \times 10} = \frac{1}{10^2}$	10^{-3}

Table 2 Positive and negative powers of 10

MATHS REFERENCE

Units and physical quantitites

See Maths note 2.1

Extending the pattern gives a meaning to zero and negative indices. If you replace all the 10s in Table 2 by any other number that you choose, you should be able to convince yourself that

$$x^0 = 1 \qquad \text{for } \textit{any} \text{ value of } x.$$

1.2 Standard form

To represent very large and very small numbers, we generally use **standard form**, also called **scientific notation**.

A number written in standard form consists of a number with a single digit (not zero) before the decimal point, multiplied by a power of 10.

Large numbers

5 620 000 (five million six hundred and twenty thousand) becomes 5.62×10^6

407 300 (four hundred and seven thousand, three hundred) becomes 4.073×10^5.

Small numbers

$0.5680 = 5.680 \times 0.1 = 5.68 \times 10^{-1}$

$0.000\,702\,3 = 7.023 \times 0.0001 = 7.023 \times 10^{-4}$

1.3 Combining powers

Powers of the same number

When multiplying two numbers expressed as 'powers' of the same number, the powers add:

$$10^2 \times 10^3 = (10 \times 10) \times (10 \times 10 \times 10) = 10^5$$

i.e. $\quad 10^2 \times 10^3 = 10^{(2+3)}$

$$6^2 \times 6^2 = (6 \times 6) \times (6 \times 6) = 6^4$$

When dividing, the powers subtract

$$10^6 \div 10^2 = (10 \times 10 \times 10 \times 10 \times 10 \times 10) \div (10 \times 10) = 10^4$$

i.e. $10^6 \div 10^2 = 10^{(6-2)}$

The rules still work when negative powers are involved:

$$10^5 \times 10^{-2} = 10^5 \times \left(\frac{1}{10^2}\right) = 10^5 \div 10^2 = 10^3$$

i.e. $10^5 \times 10^{-2} = 10^{(5-2)}$

$$x^4 \times x^{-3} = x^{(4-3)} = x$$

$$4^3 \div 4^{-2} = 4^3 \div \left(\frac{1}{4^2}\right) = 4^3 \times 4^2 = 4^5$$

i.e. $4^3 \div 4^{-2} = 4^{(3--2)} = 4^{(3+2)}$

MATHS REFERENCE
Reciprocals
See Maths note 3.3

Powers of different numbers

When dealing with a mixture of numbers of different type, collect together all numbers of the same type and combine their powers by adding or subtracting:

$$2 \times 10^4 \times 3 \times 10^5 = (2 \times 3) \times (10^4 \times 10^5) = 6 \times 10^9$$

$$1.38 \times 10^{-23} \times 2.3 \times 10^3 = 1.38 \times 2.3 \times 10^{(-23+3)} = 3.174 \times 10^{-20}$$

$$3y^2 \times 7y^5 = 21y^7$$

$$5z^2 \times 3z^{-2} = 15z^0 = 15$$

1.4 Manipulating powers on a calculator

Powers of 10

Think of the EXP or EE key as 'times 10 to the power of'.

To enter 7.54×10^9: enter 7.54, press EXP and enter 9. (Notice that you do *not* type in 10 – if you do, you will multiply your number by 10, making it 10 times too big.)

Your calculator might use its own shorthand to display this number as 7.54 09, or 7.54^9, or 7.54 EE 9 (or similar). But you should always *write* it as 7.54×10^9.

Negative powers of 10

To enter a negative index, use the ± or +/−key (*not* the 'minus' key, because that will subtract the next number from the one you have just entered).

To enter 1.38×10^{-23}: enter 1.38, press EXP, enter 23 and press ±.

Squares, etc.

To square a number, use the x^2 key. For example, to work out 1.3^2, enter 1.3 and press x^2 to get 1.69.

Pressing x^2 again squares the answer, i.e. calculates your original number to the power of 4. Pressing x^2 three times altogether gives you your original number to the power of 8, and so on – each time you press x^2, you double the power.

Other powers

Use the y^x key to raise one number to the power of a second number. y is the first number you enter, and x the second.

To calculate 2.5^3: enter 2.5, press y^x, enter 3, press =.

Other negative powers

As with powers of 10, use the ± or +/−key to enter negative numbers.

To calculate 2.5^{-3}: enter 2.5, press y^x, enter 3, press ±, press =.

1.5 Powers that are not whole numbers

The square root of a number x can be written as $x^{\frac{1}{2}}$ or $x^{1/2}$:

$$x^{\frac{1}{2}} \times x^{\frac{1}{2}} = x^{\left(\frac{1}{2}+\frac{1}{2}\right)} = x^1 = x$$

so $x^{\frac{1}{2}} = \sqrt{x}$.

Similarly, $x^{\frac{1}{3}} = \sqrt[3]{x}$ (the cube root of x); $x^{\frac{1}{4}} = \sqrt[4]{x}$ and so on.

Other fractional powers can also be interpreted in terms of roots, for example:

$$x^{\frac{3}{2}} = \sqrt{(x)^3} \text{ (the square root of } x\text{-cubed)}$$

$$= (\sqrt{x})^3 \text{ (the cube of the square root of } x)$$

and

$$x^{-\frac{1}{2}} = \frac{1}{x^{\frac{1}{2}}} = \frac{1}{\sqrt{x}}$$

Fractional powers can also be written using decimal numbers, for example:

$$x^{\frac{1}{2}} = x^{0.5}$$

$$x^{\frac{3}{2}} = x^{1.5}$$

Powers that are neither simple fractions nor whole numbers are less easy to interpret, but they still exist and can be calculated (e.g. using the y^x key of a calculator. For example:

$$10^{0.333} = 2.153$$

$$10^{0.6021} = 4.000$$

$$5.6^{\pi} = 224.1$$

$$9.34^{-0.83} = 0.1565$$

(All these answers are given to four significant figures.)

MATHS REFERENCE

Significant figures
See Maths note 7.2

2 Units

The SI system of units (Système Internationale d'Unités) has been established by international agreement. In your study of physics you will use mainly SI units. The basic SI units are listed in Table 3. Notice that, when a unit is named after a person, the unit symbol has a capital but the *name* of the unit does not.

Quantity	SI unit	Notes
Mass	kilogram, kg	
Time	second, s	
Length	metre, m	
Electric current	ampere, A	Used to define the unit of charge, the coulomb
Temperature	kelvin, K	
Luminous intensity	candela, cd	Not used in this course, but included here for completeness
Amount of substance	mole, mol	

Table 3 The basic SI units

2.1 Units and physical quantities; graphs and tables

A physical quantity consists of a number and a unit. Without the unit, the quantity is incomplete. When a symbol represents a physical quantity, it represents the *complete* quantity – units and all. For example, suppose v represents speed, and a particular speed is found to be $5\,\mathrm{m\,s^{-1}}$. You should write

$$v = 5\,\mathrm{m\,s^{-1}}$$

(*not* just $v = 5$ and *not* $v\,(\mathrm{m\,s^{-1}}) = 5$).

Units can be manipulated just like numbers and other symbols. When labelling axes of graphs, and when listing physical quantities in tables, it is conventional to divide each quantity by its unit to get a pure number.

For example, you can divide both sides of the expression for v above by $m\,s^{-1}$ and write

$$v/(m\,s^{-1}) = 5$$

If you are plotting values of v on a graph, or listing them in a table, you should label the graph axis, or the table column, as $v/m\,s^{-1}$.

Large and small numbers
Suppose you were dealing with speeds that were all several million metres per second:

$$v = 2 \times 10^6\,m\,s^{-1}, \qquad v = 7 \times 10^6\,m\,s^{-1}, \text{ etc.}$$

To make the numbers more manageable, you could use the same rule as above to write $v/(10^6\,m\,s^{-1}) = 2$, etc., and label your graph and table as shown in Figure 1.

t/s	$v/10^6\,m\,s^{-1}$
1	2
2	7

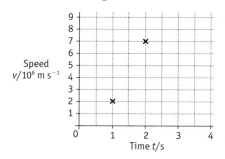

Figure 1 Labelling graphs and tables

MATHS REFERENCE

Index notation and powers of 10

See Maths note 1.1

Units and physical quantities; graphs and tables

See Maths note 2.1

2.2 Manipulating units; index notation and units

In calculations, the units should be manipulated as well as the numbers. This can help you keep track of what you are doing as well as being correct – so it is a good habit to get into.

Indices can be used with units and with algebraic symbols. For example,

$$4^{-1} = \frac{1}{4} = 0.25, \qquad x^{-2} = \frac{1}{x^2}$$

Units such as coulombs per second, or joules per coulomb, can be written either as C/s and J/C or using index notation: $C\,s^{-1}$ and $J\,C^{-1}$. Similarly, metres per second, in calculations of unit of speed, can be written as m/s or $m\,s^{-1}$. For example,

$$70\,m \div 20\,s = 3.5\,m\,s^{-1}$$

Using the index notation helps prevent table headings and graph labels having too many oblique strokes.

When multiplying numbers, units or symbols, collect together all those of the same type and add their indices. For example:

$$2\,C\,s^{-1} \times 4\,s = 8\,C$$

$$10\,m\,s^{-1} \div 5\,s = 2\,m\,s^{-2}$$

2.3 Derived units

Table 4 shows how SI units are combined to give units of various quantities. Some common combinations are given 'shorthand' names.

STUDY NOTE

In writing units, the coulomb is often treated as if it were the basic unit rather than the ampere.

Quantity	Unit name	Symbol	Equivalent
Speed			$\mathrm{m\,s^{-1}}$
Acceleration			$\mathrm{m\,s^{-2}}$
Force	newton	N	$1\,\mathrm{N} = 1\,\mathrm{kg\,m\,s^{-2}}$
Gravitational field strength			$1\,\mathrm{N\,kg^{-1}} = 1\,\mathrm{m\,s^{-2}}$
Energy, work	joule	J	$1\,\mathrm{J} = 1\,\mathrm{N\,m} = 1\,\mathrm{kg\,m^2\,s^{-2}}$
Power	watt	W	$1\,\mathrm{W} = 1\,\mathrm{J\,s^{-1}}\ (= 1\,\mathrm{kg\,m^2\,s^{-3}})$
Frequency	hertz	Hz	$1\,\mathrm{Hz} = 1\,\mathrm{s^{-1}}$
Electric charge	coulomb	C	$1\,\mathrm{C} = 1\,\mathrm{A\,s}$ $1\,\mathrm{A} = 1\,\mathrm{C\,s^{-1}}$
Potential difference, emf	volt	V	$1\,\mathrm{V} = 1\,\mathrm{J\,C^{-1}}\ (= 1\,\mathrm{kg\,m^2\,C^{-1}\,s^{-2}})$
Electrical resistance	ohm	Ω	$1\,\Omega = 1\,\mathrm{V\,A^{-1}}\ (= 1\,\mathrm{kg\,m^2\,C^{-2}\,s^{-1}})$

Table 4 Some common derived SI units

2.4 SI prefixes

When dealing with quantities that are large or small, we often use prefixes as an alternative to standard form. For example, a distance of 1.3×10^4 m could be written as 13 km, and a distance of 0.0037 m could be written as 3.7 mm. The official SI prefixes go up and down in steps of 10^3. Table 5 lists the SI prefixes that you are likely to encounter in your study of physics.

Prefix	Symbol	Equivalent in powers of 10
Tera	T	10^{12}
Giga	G	10^9
Mega	M	10^6
Kilo	k	10^3
Centi	c	10^{-2}
Milli	m	10^{-3}
Micro	μ	10^{-6}
Nano	n	10^{-9}
Pico	p	10^{-12}
Femto	f	10^{-15}

Table 5 SI prefixes

STUDY NOTE

The centimetre is not officially an SI unit [because 'centi' (10^{-2}) does not fit the pattern] but it is widely used.

When dealing with conversions involving prefixes, it is wise to write down each step using appropriate powers of 10, *and include the units at each stage*. For example, suppose light of a certain colour has a wavelength of 468 nm and you want to use standard form to write the wavelength in metres:

$$468\,\mathrm{nm} = 468 \times 10^{-9}\,\mathrm{m}$$
$$= 4.68 \times 10^2 \times 10^{-9}\,\mathrm{m}$$
$$= 4.68 \times 10^{-7}\,\mathrm{m}$$

Suppose the tension in a rope is $1.35 \times 10^5\,\text{N}$ and you want to express it in kN:

$$1\,\text{kN} = 10^3\,\text{N, so } 1\,\text{N} = \frac{1}{10^3}\,\text{kN} = 10^{-3}\,\text{kN}$$

$$1.35 \times 10^5\,\text{N} = 1.35 \times 10^5 \times 10^{-3}\,\text{kN}$$
$$= 1.35 \times 10^2\,\text{kN}$$
$$= 135\,\text{kN}$$

Suppose an electric current is $4.56 \times 10^{-4}\,\text{A}$ and you want to express it in μA:

$$1\,\mu\text{A} = 10^{-6}\,\text{A, so } 1\,\text{A} = \frac{1}{10^6}\,\mu\text{A} = 10^6\,\mu\text{A}$$

$$4.56 \times 10^{-4}\,\text{A} = 4.56 \times 10^{-4} \times 10^6\,\mu\text{A}$$
$$= 4.56 \times 10^2\,\mu\text{A}$$
$$= 456\,\mu\text{A}$$

2.5 Dimensions

The **dimensions** of a quantity show how it is related to the basic quantities listed in Table 3. Symbols M, L and T are used to represent the dimensions of mass, length and time.

For example, volume is calculated from length × breadth × height so has dimension of length³ or L^3; speed is found from distance ÷ time so has dimensions of L/T or LT^{-1}. The dimensions of force are those of mass × acceleration: MLT^{-2}.

Square brackets are used to denote the dimensions of a quantity. For example

$$[\text{velocity}] = LT^{-1}$$

$$[\text{force}] = [\text{mass}] \times [\text{acceleration}] = MLT^{-2}$$

Dimensions are more fundamental than units. You might, for example, choose to express a speed in miles per hour rather than SI units of m s^{-1}, but the dimensions are still LT^{-1}, i.e. length (miles) ÷ time (hours).

Any equation must be dimensionally consistent, that is, the dimensions of the left-hand side must be the same as those of the right-hand side. This can help you check whether a particular equation is correct, and can also enable you to derive relationships between quantities.

3 Arithmetic and algebra

3.1 Fractions, decimals and percentages

A fraction is really a division sum, e.g.

$$\frac{4}{5} = 4 \div 5; \qquad \frac{7}{3} = 7 \div 3$$

You can express a fraction as a decimal number by doing the division on a calculator.

When fractions are multiplied together, you can often simplify the arithmetic by using the fact that the multiplication and division can be carried out in any order, e.g.

$$\frac{7}{5} \times \frac{3}{14} = \frac{7 \times 3}{5 \times 14}$$

and cancelling any common factors, e.g.

$$\frac{7 \times 3}{5 \times 14} = \frac{3}{5 \times 2} = \frac{3}{10} = 0.3$$

You can think of the **percentage** sign, %, as being made up of a 1, 0, 0 to remind you that it is a fraction of 100 parts. To calculate a percentage from a number expressed as a fraction or a decimal, you multiply by 100:

$$\frac{1}{2} = 0.5 \text{ and } 100 \times 0.5 = 50 \text{ so } \frac{1}{2} = 50\% \text{ (or 50/100)}$$

$$\frac{1}{4} = 0.25 \text{ and } 100 \times 0.25 = 25 \text{ so } \frac{1}{4} = 25\% \text{ (or 25/100)}$$

$$\frac{7}{8} = 0.875 \text{ and } 100 \times 0.875 = 87.5 \text{ so } \frac{7}{8} = 87.5\%$$

For example, if a solar array produces an output power of 600 W from an input power of 4 kW (4000 W), its efficiency is

$$\frac{600 \text{ W}}{4000 \text{ W}} = 0.15 = 15\%.$$

To find a percentage of a quantity, you *multiply* the quantity by the percentage expressed as an ordinary fraction or decimal number. For example, to find 15% of 60 multiply 60 by 15/100 (or by 0.15)

$$\frac{15}{100} \times 60 = \frac{90}{10} = 9$$

or

$$0.15 \times 60 = 9$$

3.2 Brackets and common factors

To evaluate an expression such as

$$6(2 + 3 - 4 + 5), \quad \frac{12 + 8}{4} \quad \text{or } I(R_1 + R_2 + R_3)$$

you usually first deal with the additions and subtractions inside the bracket and then multiply or divide the result by the number or symbol outside. Alternatively, you can carry out several separate multiplications or divisions on each number or symbol inside the bracket in turn, then do the additions or subtractions. For example

either $6(2 + 3 - 4 + 5) = 6 \times 6 = 36$

or $6(2 + 3 - 4 + 5) = 12 + 18 - 24 + 30 = 36$

either $\dfrac{12 + 8}{4} = \dfrac{20}{4} = 5$

or $\dfrac{12 + 8}{4} = \dfrac{12}{4} + \dfrac{8}{4} = 3 + 2 = 5$

A calculation that involves several multiplications or divisions using the same number and then adding or subtracting the results can be simplified if it is rewritten using brackets with the **common factor** outside. For example

$$25 + 30 + 35 = 5(5 + 6 + 7)$$

$$3x + 3y + 3z = 3(x + y + z)$$

$$IR_1 + IR_2 + IR_3 = I(R_1 + R_2 + R_3)$$

$$\frac{7}{2} + \frac{3}{2} + \frac{6}{2} = \frac{(7 + 3 + 6)}{2}$$

$$\frac{a}{x} + \frac{b}{x} + \frac{c}{x} = \frac{(a + b + c)}{x}$$

3.3 Reciprocals

The value obtained by dividing 1 by a number is called the **reciprocal** of the number (reciprocals can be found using the $1/x$ key of a calculator). Finding the reciprocal of a reciprocal gets you back to the original number. For example:

$$\frac{1}{2}=0.5 \qquad \frac{1}{0.5}=2$$

For a wave or oscillation:

$$\text{period } T=\frac{1}{f} \qquad \text{frequency} f=\frac{1}{T}$$

Reciprocals are sometimes written using a negative index:

$$x^{-1}=\frac{1}{x}$$

To find the reciprocal of a fraction, simply turn it the other way up. For example:

$$\frac{1}{\frac{1}{2}}=\frac{2}{1}=2$$

$$\frac{1}{\frac{2}{3}}=\frac{3}{2}=1\frac{1}{2}$$

$$\left(\frac{3}{7}\right)^{-1}=\frac{7}{3}$$

This is not just an arbitrary rule. It makes sense if you think in terms of division sums. Consider the second example above. Question: 'How many times does $\frac{2}{3}$ go into 1?' Answer: 'one-and-a-half times.'

Adding and subtracting

One place where you need to add and subtract reciprocals is in calculations of resistors in parallel. To find the net resistance R of several resistors connected in parallel, you must first find the reciprocal of each resistance, then add the reciprocals together (to get $1/R$), then find the reciprocal of $1/R$ to get R.

For example, if $R_1=2.0\,\Omega$, $R_2=5.0\,\Omega$, $R_3=1.0\,\Omega$, then

$$\frac{1}{R_1}=\frac{1}{2.0}\Omega^{-1}=0.50\,\Omega^{-1} \text{ (notice the unit of } 1/R\text{)}$$

$$\frac{1}{R_2}=0.20\,\Omega^{-1}$$

$$\frac{1}{R_3}=1.00\,\Omega^{-1}$$

(notice that $1/1=1$ – the number stays the same but the unit still changes). So

$$\frac{1}{R}=(0.50+0.20+1.00)\,\Omega^{-1}=1.70\,\Omega^{-1}$$

$$R=\frac{1}{1.70}\Omega=0.59\,\Omega$$

Notice that adding the reciprocals of two numbers is *not* the same as adding the two numbers and then finding the reciprocal of their sum.

Multiplying and dividing

Multiplying by the reciprocal of a number is the same as dividing by that number. For example

$$7\times\frac{1}{2}=7\div2=3.50$$

Dividing by the reciprocal of a number is the same as multiplying by that number. For example

$$4 \div \frac{1}{3} = 4 \times 3 = 12$$

$$9 \div \frac{3}{4} = 9 \times \frac{4}{3} = \frac{9 \times 4}{3} = 12$$

For a wave,

$$f = \frac{v}{\lambda}, \qquad \text{time period } T = \frac{1}{f} = \frac{1}{\frac{v}{\lambda}} = \frac{\lambda}{v}$$

We can simplify divisions involving fractions. For example:

$$\frac{3}{4} \div \frac{5}{4} = \frac{3}{4} \times \frac{4}{5} = \frac{3 \times 4}{4 \times 5} = \frac{3}{5} = 0.6$$

3.4 Algebra and elimination

If we have two different relationships that both involve some of the same things, we can combine them to produce a new equation. This allows us to avoid measuring, or calculating, something that is not already known – we can eliminate it (remove it) from the equations. For example, we can take an expression for electrical power

$$P = IV$$

and use the resistance equation

$$V = IR$$

to write IR instead of V:

$$P = I \times IR = I^2 R$$

This enables us to relate P directly to I and R without needing to know or calculate V. Similarly, if we want to eliminate I:

$$P = \frac{V}{R} \times V = \frac{V^2}{R}$$

3.5 Adding and subtracting fractions

You can of course add and subtract fractions on a calculator – you carry out several division sums and add or subtract the results. But for simple fractions it can often be quicker to do the sums 'by hand'.

The trick is to write the fractions so that they have the same **denominator** (the number underneath the fraction). Sometimes it is quite easy to spot how to do this. For example:

$$\frac{3}{4} + \frac{5}{6} = \frac{3 \times 3}{3 \times 4} + \frac{2 \times 5}{2 \times 6}$$

$$= \frac{9}{12} + \frac{10}{12} = \frac{9 + 10}{12} = \frac{19}{12}$$

Otherwise, make a common denominator by multiplying the original denominators together:

$$\frac{1}{17} + \frac{4}{3} = \frac{2 \times 3}{17 \times 3} + \frac{4 \times 17}{3 \times 17}$$

$$= \frac{6}{51} + \frac{68}{51} = \frac{6 + 68}{51} = \frac{74}{51}$$

Another example:

$$\frac{1}{2} + \frac{1}{3} = \frac{3}{6} + \frac{2}{6} = \frac{5}{6}$$

4 Solving equations

It may sound obvious, but the main thing to understand about equations is that the '=' sign means that the two things on either side are *equal* to one another. So whatever you do to one side, you must also do to the other, otherwise they would no longer be equal. (Beware of getting into the bad habit of writing '=' when you really mean 'and so the next step is . . .'.)

One way to think of an equation is as a 'recipe' for calculating. For example, $F = ma$ tells you how to calculate the net force F if you know the acceleration a that it gives to a mass m. In this example, F is the **subject** of the equation – it is written on its own (usually on the left).

4.1 Rearranging an equation

Quite often, the quantity you want to calculate is wrapped up in the right-hand side of an equation, and you need to make it the subject. When doing this, it helps if you try to understand what you are doing rather than blindly trying to apply a set of rules. It is also wise to write down each step, justifying each one to yourself as you do so. This might sound time-consuming, but it isn't really because it helps you to keep track of what you are doing and, if you do make a slip, it is quite easy to go back and check.

Look at the part of the equation that contains the quantity that you want to know. Think what you need to do to get that quantity on its own, and do the same thing(s) to both sides.

For example, suppose you want to know the acceleration that a force F gives to a mass m:

$$F = ma$$

To get a on its own, you need to divide the right-hand side by m ($ma \div m = a$), so do the same to the left-hand side:

$$\frac{F}{m} = a \qquad \text{or} \qquad a = \frac{F}{m}$$

Another example: suppose you want to calculate internal resistance r from

$$V = \mathcal{E} - Ir$$

It is a good idea first to arrange that the thing you are interested in has a positive sign. You can do this by adding Ir to both sides:

$$V + Ir = \mathcal{E}$$

then to get r on its own you subtract V from both sides:

$$Ir = \mathcal{E} - V$$

and then divide by I

$$r = \frac{\mathcal{E} - V}{I} \qquad \text{or} \qquad r = (\mathcal{E} - V)/I$$

(Notice that you have to divide the *whole* of the right-hand side by I – hence the brackets.)

MATHS REFERENCE

Brackets and common factors

See Maths note 3.2

4.2 Simultaneous equations

Simultaneous equations arise if we have two (or more) different ways of writing a relationship between quantities. If we have two unknown quantities, then they can both be found if we have two simultaneous equations. For three unknown quantities, we'd need three separate equations, and so on.

The trick in solving simultaneous equations is to carry out some algebra and arithmetic to get an expression that involves just *one* of the unknown things, and then use that value to calculate the other one.

For example, the equation $\mathscr{E} = V + Ir$ involves two things that can be measured (V and I). If neither $\mathscr{E}$ nor r is known, then they cannot be found from a single pair of values of V and I. However, if you obtain two *different* pairs of readings (V_1 and I_1, and V_2 and I_2) for the same power supply (using two different external loads), then you can write down two simultaneous equations – two different equations that both describe a relationship between the two unknown things $\mathscr{E}$ and r. These equations let you find both $\mathscr{E}$ and r. So

$$\mathscr{E} = V_1 + I_1 r$$

$$\mathscr{E} = V_2 + I_2 r$$

Since the right-hand side of each equation is equal to $\mathscr{E}$, then they must also be equal to each other:

$$V_1 + I_1 r = V_2 + I_2 r$$

Subtracting V_1 from each side

$$I_1 r = V_2 - V_1 + I_2 r$$

Subtracting $I_2 r$ from both sides (and being careful with signs and with the subscripts 1 and 2)

$$I_1 r - I_2 r = V_2 - V_1$$

Now r is a common factor on the left-hand side, so

$$r(I_1 - I_2) = V_2 - V_1$$

Dividing both sides by $(I_1 - I_2)$ (and using brackets to keep the subtracted things together)

$$r = \frac{(V_2 - V_1)}{(I_2 - I_1)} \qquad \text{or} \qquad r = (V_2 - V_1)/(I_1 - I_2)$$

This value of r can then be used in one of the original equations to find $\mathscr{E}$.

For example: a power supply gives readings of $V_1 = 3$ V, $I_1 = 7$ A, and $V_2 = 8$ V, $I_2 = 2$ A. So

$$r = \frac{8\,V - 3\,V}{7\,A - 2\,A} = \frac{5\,V}{5\,A} = 1\,\Omega$$

and

$$\mathscr{E} = V_1 + I_1 r = 3\,V + 7\,A \times 1\,\Omega = 3\,V + 7\,V = 10\,V$$

(you would find the same value using V_2 and I_2).

5 Relationships and graphs

Graphs are extremely useful in physics for giving us a pictorial representation of how one quantity is related to another. Trends in data are not always clear from a table of results, but become immediately evident when viewing a plot of the two quantities involved.

5.1 Graphs and proportionality

Many important relationships in physics involve the idea of direct proportion.

For example, if a conductor obeys Ohm's law, doubling the potential difference produces double the current, tripling the pd triples the current ... and so on. Mathematically, we say that the potential difference is **directly proportional** to the current. In symbols

$$V \propto I \qquad \text{or} \qquad V = kI$$

The symbol $\propto$ means 'is directly proportional to' and k is called a **constant of proportionality** and has a fixed value for a particular set of values of V and I. (In this example, the constant k is the electrical resistance R.)

If one quantity is directly proportional to another, then a graph of one plotted against the other is a straight line through the origin.

5.2 Linear relationships

The equation

$$V = \mathcal{E} - Ir$$

is an example of a **linear relationship** between two variables, V and I in this case. A graph of V (on the vertical axis, the y-axis) against I (on the horizontal axis, the x-axis) gives a straight line. Linear relationships and graphs are often said to be of the type

$$y = mx + c$$

where y stands for whatever is plotted on the y-axis and x for whatever is plotted on the x-axis, and m and c are constants (they remain fixed when x and y change). This type of graph has two properties that are often useful for doing calculations using experimental results. We can illustrate these with a graph of $y = 2x + 1$, i.e. $m = 2$, $c = 1$ (Figure 2).

On Figure 2, the line cuts the y-axis at $y = 1$ (using the equation, when $x = 0$, $y = c$). The line of such a graph always cuts the y-axis where $y = c$.

If y is directly proportional to x, then the line goes through the origin and $c = 0$.

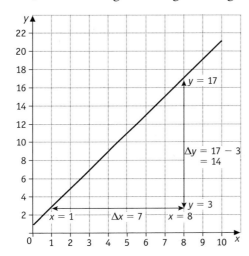

Figure 2 A graph of $y = 2x + 1$

5.3 Gradient of a linear graph

Figure 2 is a graph of the linear relationship $y = 2x + 1$.

The **gradient** (or slope) of the graph is defined as the rise of the graph (the increase in y, Δy) divided by the run (the corresponding increase in x, Δx) found by drawing a right-angled triangle as shown in Figure 2. On Figure 2,

$$\Delta y = 14, \qquad \Delta x = 7,$$

$$\text{gradient} = \frac{\Delta y}{\Delta x} = 2$$

Notice that Δy and Δx are numbers read from the graph scales (*not* lengths measured with a ruler) and that any similar triangle drawn on the graph will give the same value of the gradient.

The gradient of a linear graph of y against x is always equal to the value m in the relationship $y = mx + c$.

The graph in Figure 2 has a positive gradient. If m is negative, then the graph slopes down from left to right.

If two variables measured in an experiment are related by a linear equation, then plotting them on a graph enables you to find the values of the constants relating them. It is helpful if you arrange

MATHS REFERENCE

Error bars and error boxes

See Maths note 7.6

MATHS REFERENCE

Reciprocals

See Maths note 3.3

the relationship so that it looks as much like $y = mx + c$ as possible. For example, by subtracting Ir from both sides you can write $\mathcal{E} = V + Ir$ as

$$V = (-r)I + \mathcal{E}$$

which can be compared directly with

$$y = mx + c$$

If you plot measured values of V on the y-axis against corresponding values of I on the x-axis, the graph will be a straight line that cuts the y-axis at $\mathcal{E}$, and with a gradient $m = -r$.

5.4 Inverse proportionality

If one quantity is **inversely proportional** to another, then as one increases, the other will decrease. For example, the acceleration produced by a given net force is inversely proportional to the mass on which it acts: doubling the mass halves the acceleration, tripling the mass divides the acceleration by three and so on – and vice versa.

Such a relationship is written using reciprocals and the symbol for direct proportion:

$$a \propto \frac{1}{m} \qquad a = \frac{k}{m}$$

or

$$m \propto \frac{1}{a} \qquad m = \frac{k}{a}$$

(In this case, the constant of proportionality is the same as the resultant force F.)

If one quantity is inversely proportional to the other (Table 6), the graph of one plotted against the other is curved as in Figure 3.

But if one quantity is plotted against the *reciprocal* of the other, then the graph is a straight line through the origin, as shown in Figure 4.

m/kg	$(1/m)$/kg^{-1}	a/ms^{-2}
1	1.000	5.00
2	0.500	2.50
3	0.333	1.67
4	0.250	1.25
5	0.200	1.00
6	0.167	0.83
7	0.143	0.71
8	0.125	0.63
9	0.111	0.55
10	0.100	0.50

Table 6 Data for Figures 3 and 4

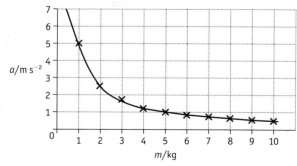

Figure 3 A graph showing how the acceleration a produced by a constant force F (= 5N) depends on mass m (data from Table 6)

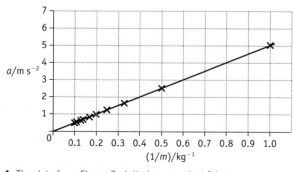

Figure 4 The data from Figure 3 plotted as a against $1/m$

5.5 Testing mathematical relationships

Sometimes we are interested in finding a mathematical relationship between two measured quantities. This usually involves some educated guesswork, based on ideas about the underlying physics and/or from looking at the numbers. Plotting graphs provides a way of testing the guesses.

Direct proportion

For example, if both quantities increase together, you might guess that one is directly proportional to the other. Plot a graph of one against the other and see whether you can draw a straight line through all the error boxes.

MATHS REFERENCE

Experimental uncertainty

See Maths note 7.1

Error bars and error boxes

See Maths note 7.6

Examples that give straight-line graphs include:

$s \propto t$ for motion at constant speed

$I \propto V$ for an ohmic conductor.

If the plot does not give a straight line, try something else. For example, motion from rest at constant acceleration is described by the equation

$$s = \frac{1}{2}at^2$$

$$s \propto t^2$$

A graph of distance s against time t is a curve, but a graph of s against t^2 is a straight line with gradient $\frac{a}{2}$ or $\frac{1}{3}a$.

Sometimes you need to use the square root of a quantity to get a straight line. For example, for a simple pendulum a plot of its period T against the square root of its length l gives a straight line:

$$T \propto \sqrt{\ell}$$

Inverse proportion

If one quantity increases as the other decreases, you might guess that you are looking at inverse proportionality, so try plotting a graph using the reciprocal of one quantity.

If this does not give a straight line, try plotting the square, or the square root, of the reciprocal.

For example, suppose you measure the frequency f of the note from a plucked string of mass per unit length μ. Frequency f decreases as you increase μ, but suppose you find that a graph of f against $\frac{1}{\mu}1/\mu$ is not a straight line.

If a graph of f against $\frac{1}{\mu^2}$ is a straight line, then $f \propto \frac{1}{\mu^2}$

If you need to plot f against $\frac{1}{\sqrt{\mu}}$ to get a straight line, then $f \propto \frac{1}{\sqrt{\mu}}$

6 Trigonometry and angular measurements

6.1 Degrees and radians

A **radian**, or **rad** for short, is a unit for measuring angles commonly used in physics instead of degrees. Figure 5 shows how the size of an angle, in radians, is defined.

For a full circle, length of arc = length of circumference = $2\pi r$.

Size of angle = $\frac{2\pi r}{r} = 2\pi$ radians, i.e. approximately 6.28 rad.

Table 7 lists some useful conversions between radians and degrees.

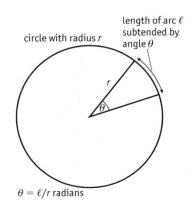

circle with radius r

length of arc ℓ subtended by angle θ

$\theta = \ell/r$ radians

Figure 5 The size of an angle measured in radians

Angle	Size in degrees	Size in radians
Full circle	360°	2π rad = 6.28 rad
Half circle	180°	π rad = 3.14 rad
	114.6°	2.0 rad
Quarter circle	90°	$\pi/2$ rad = 1.57 rad
	60°	$\pi/3$ rad = 1.05 rad
	57.3°	1.0 rad
	45°	$\pi/4$ rad = 0.79 rad
	30°	$\pi/6$ rad = 0.52 rad
	28.6°	0.5 rad

Table 7 Some conversions between radians and degrees

Note that π is a *number* (approximately 3.14) that frequently, but not always, appears in angles measured in radians.

6.2 Sine, cosine and tangent of an angle

Figure 6 shows a right angled triangle. The sides of the triangle are related by Pythagoras's theorem:

$$c^2 = b^2 + a^2$$
$$c = \sqrt{a^2 + b^2}$$

(Careful! You can't 'cancel' the squares inside the bracket.)

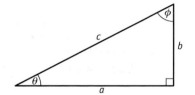

Figure 6 A right-angled triangle

All similar triangles, i.e. those with the same angle θ, will have sides in the same proportion to one another. The ratios of the sides depend only on the angle θ.

The sine, cosine and tangent of the angle θ are known as **trigonometric ratios**.

- Sine of angle θ, $\sin\theta = \dfrac{\text{opposite side}}{\text{hypotenuse}} = \dfrac{b}{c}$

- Cosine of θ, $\cos\theta = \dfrac{\text{adjacent side}}{\text{opposite side}} = \dfrac{a}{c}$

- Tangent of θ, $\tan\theta = \dfrac{\text{opposite side}}{\text{adjacent side}} = \dfrac{b}{a}$

We can combine these to give another useful relationship. Since

$$\frac{b}{a} = \frac{b}{c} \div \frac{a}{c} \quad (c \text{ cancels}),$$

we can write

$$\tan\theta = \frac{\sin\theta}{\cos\theta}$$

Also

$$\sin\phi = \frac{a}{c} = \cos\theta \qquad \text{and} \qquad \cos\phi = \frac{b}{c} = \sin\theta$$

i.e. if two angles add up to 90°, then the cosine of one is equal to the sine of the other.

Using Pythagoras's theorem leads to another useful result. Dividing $c^2 = a^2 + b^2$ by c^2:

$$1 = \frac{a^2}{c^2} + \frac{b^2}{c^2} = \left(\frac{a}{c}\right)^2 + \left(\frac{b}{c}\right)^2$$
$$1 = (\cos\theta)^2 + (\sin\theta)^2,$$

which is true for any angle and is usually written as

$$\cos^2\theta + \sin^2\theta = 1$$

6.3 Graphs of trigonometric functions

For angles greater than 90°, Figure 7 shows how sin, cos and tan are defined. For some angles, negative numbers are involved. Figure 8 shows how the sin, cos and tan vary with angle θ. Note that we have labelled the axis in degrees and in radians.

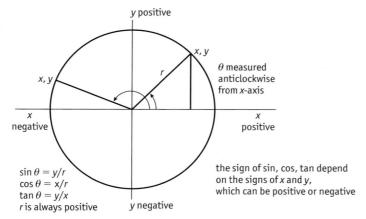

Figure 7 Defining sin, cos and tan for angles greater than 90°

Notice that sin θ and cos θ are always between +1 and −1, but tan θ is infinite for some angles (notice the different scale in Figure 8(c)).

Also notice some useful values, e.g. sin 30° = cos 60° = 0.5. Look at the values of sin θ and cos θ when θ is a multiple of 90°.

MATHS REFERENCE

Degrees and radians

See Maths note 6.1

6.4 Inverse sin, etc.

The angle whose sin is x is written $\sin^{-1} x$. We can write the relationships from Figure 6 as

$$\theta = \sin^{-1}\frac{b}{c} \qquad \theta = \cos^{-1}\frac{a}{c} \qquad \theta = \tan^{-1}\frac{b}{a} \qquad \phi = \sin^{-1}\frac{a}{c}$$

Beware! The index −1 here does *not* indicate a reciprocal:

$$\sin^{-1} x \text{ is } not \text{ the same as } \frac{1}{\sin x}$$

(The reciprocal of sin x can be written $(\sin x)^{-1}$.)

6.5 Trigonometry on a calculator

You can find the sine, cosine and tangent of an angle on a calculator. For example, to find sin 30°, type 30 and press sin.

Many scientific calculators can be switched between 'degree' and 'radian' modes. The display will indicate which one you are in.

If you switch your calculator to 'radian' mode, you can find sin, etc., of angles in radians without having to convert to degrees. Check that you know how to do this.

With your calculator in radian mode, type π, ÷, 2 (you may need to press = as well) and then press sin or cos. You should get $\sin(\pi/2) = 1$, $\cos(\pi/2) = 0$. If you have your calculator in degree mode by mistake, you will find the sin or cos of 1.57° (3.14° ÷ 2).

Try finding the sin, cos and tan of some angles in degrees and in radians. Check that you get the same values as shown in Figure 8.

If you know the sin, cos or tan of an angle and wish to determine the size of the angle, use the 'inv' key.

For example, to find the angle whose sin is 0.5, type 0.5, press inv and then press sin. You should get 30 if you have your calculator in degree mode. If you do this with your calculator in radian mode, you will get 0.5236 ($\approx \pi/6$).

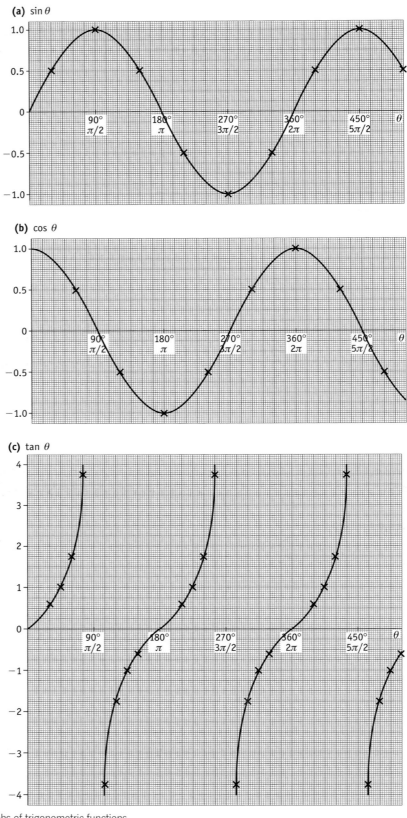

Figure 8 Graphs of trigonometric functions

6.6 The small angle approximations

There are some useful approximations involving the trigonometric ratios of small angles. These become evident when we express the sine and tangent of an angle θ in terms of the right-angled triangles shown in Figure 9.

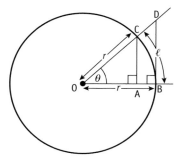

Figure 9 The sine and tangent of an angle

From the triangle OAC

$$\sin\theta = \frac{AC}{OC} = \frac{AC}{r}$$

and

$$\cos\theta = \frac{OA}{OC} = \frac{OA}{r}$$

From the triangle OBD

$$\tan\theta = \frac{BD}{OB} = \frac{BD}{r}$$

and

$$\cos\theta = \frac{OB}{OD} = \frac{r}{OB}$$

Figure 9 shows that $\tan\theta$ is always greater than $\sin\theta$ because BD is greater than AC.

As θ is made smaller, the lines AC and BD become closer together and more equal in length, and the lines OA and OD become closer to r, so *for small angles*:

$$\sin\theta \approx \tan\theta$$

and

$$\cos\theta \approx 1$$

With your calculator in degree mode, try finding the sin, cos and tan of the angles listed in Table 7, and some smaller angles. Notice that the approximations get better as the angles get smaller.

Small angles in radians

Comparison with Figure 5 shows that the size of θ *measured in radians* lies between $\sin\theta$ and $\tan\theta$ (the arc length ℓ is longer than AC and shorter than OD):

$$\sin\theta, \; \theta, \tan\theta$$

When θ is small,

$$AC \approx \ell \approx BD$$

and so *for small angles measured in radians* we have some additional approximations:

$$\sin\theta \approx \theta$$

and

$$\tan\theta \approx \theta$$

Switch your calculator into radian mode, and again try finding the sin, cos and tan of various angles. Notice that the approximation gets better at small angles.

7 Measurement and uncertainty

7.1 Experimental measurements

All measurements are subject to systematic and random effects. Such effects are often referred to as 'experimental error', though 'error' here does not mean 'mistake'. However carefully and correctly you make a measurement, there will aways be some **random error** (also known as **uncertainty**) and possibly some **systematic error** as well.

A **precise** measurement is one in which the random uncertainty is small. An **accurate** measurement is one that is close to the true value. A precise measurement is not necessarily accurate; there could be some systematic error even if random effects are small.

Systematic errors affect each reading in the same way. For example, a zero error on a micrometer produces an offset so that each measurement is too big or small by the same amount, while a measuring-tape that has been stretched leads to readings that are all smaller than the true values by the same proportion. Systematic errors can arise from instrumental effects, or observational methods, or external factors. Sometimes they can be eliminated if their cause is known, for example by checking the zero reading of an instrument.

The uncertainty in a measurement is the range within which you expect the true value to lie. Uncertainty cannot be removed completely but it can sometimes be reduced, e.g. by choice of instrument or method. Don't worry about trying to calculate a precise value for the uncertainty in your experiments - uncertainties are themselves uncertain – but you can usually make reasonable estimates to one significant figure (two at most). There are various ways to estimate the uncertainty in experimental measurements.

MATHS REFERENCE

Significant figures. See Maths note 7.2

Spread in repeated measurements

Suppose you measure a quantity x several times and obtain a series of different values:

$$x_1, x_2, x_3...x_n$$

In your A level physics work, n will usually be a small number, say 3 to 5.

Unless there is reason to suspect that one of the results is seriously out (i.e. it is **anomalous**), the best estimate of the true value of x is the arithmetic mean of the readings:

$$\text{Mean value } \langle x \rangle = \frac{x_1 + x_2 + ...x_n}{n}$$

A reasonable estimate of Δx, the uncertainty in x, is half the range:

$$\Delta x = \frac{(x_{max} - x_{min})}{2}$$

where x_{max} is the maximum and x_{min} the minimum reading of x (ignoring any anomalous readings).

You would write the result of the measurement as

$$x = \langle x \rangle \pm \Delta x$$

Instrumental uncertainty

Sometimes there may only be a single reading. Sometimes all the readings may be identical. But you cannot therefore assume that there is no uncertainty in the reading(s). The **instrumental uncertainty** is often taken as ± the smallest scale division on the instrument.

When using a digital instrument, the uncertainty cannot be less than half the smallest division of the display. For example, if you are using a digital meter to measure a current and it reads 0.357 A, you can only be sure that the current is closer to 0.357 A than it is to either 0.356 or 0.358 - it could lie anywhere between 0.3565 A and 0.3575 A. So the uncertainty in that reading is 0.0005 A. With analogue instruments, the uncertainty might be smaller if you can interpolate between scale divisions, and you need to consider the particular instrument in order to come up with a realistic estimate.

In many situations, a measurement involves the difference between two readings. For example, the length of an object measured with a ruler is the difference between one mark and another (often zero but not always). There is an uncertainty in each, and both contribute to the uncertainty in the overall measurement. The simplest way to deal with this is to add the two uncertainties and say that the overall uncertainty in the measurement is equal to the smallest scale division. For example, if you were using a ruler graduated in mm, and measured the distance, x, between two markers on a piece of wire to be 864 mm, you would write:

$$x = 864 \, \text{mm} \pm 1 \, \text{mm}$$

Other considerations

Sometimes uncertainty arises because it is difficult to judge exactly what to measure. For example, if you are using a signal generator to produce a sound from a speaker, and adjusting it to give the same pitch as the note from a guitar, it might be hard to judge the 'best' frequency. If you think it is close to 260 Hz, but are unsure by about 10 Hz either way, then (even if the generator had a scale that told you the frequency to the nearest Hz) the uncertainty in your measurement would be $\Delta f \approx 10 \, \text{Hz}$ and you would write:

$$f = 260 \, \text{Hz} \pm 10 \, \text{Hz}$$

7.2 Calculations with uncertainties; significant figures

If you carry out a calculation using a measured value, there will always be an uncertainty in your answer. You can use the uncertainties in the measurements to work out the uncertainty in the calculated value.

For example, suppose you measure a current of $I = 0.24 \, \text{A} \pm 0.01 \, \text{A}$ and a corresponding pd of $V = 0.67 \, \text{V} \pm 0.02 \, \text{V}$.

On a calculator, the resistance found using the 'best' values is

$$R_{\text{best}} = \frac{V}{I} = \frac{0.67 \, \text{V}}{0.24 \, \text{A}} = 2.791\,6667 \, \Omega$$

But, using the largest possible V (0.39 V) and the smallest possible I (0.23 A), the calculated resistance could be as large as

$$R_{\text{max}} = \frac{0.69 \, \text{V}}{0.23 \, \text{A}} = 3 \, \Omega$$

Or, using the smallest V and the largest I, it could be as small as

$$R_{\text{min}} = \frac{0.65 \, \text{V}}{0.25 \, \text{A}} = 2.6 \, \Omega$$

There are several things to notice! First, there are quite large differences between the three values. Second, the first value extends to the full length of the calculator display, whereas the others do not.

The large differences show that you *cannot possibly* say that the resistance is precisely $2.791\,6667 \, \Omega$. This value is close to $2.8 \, \Omega$, and the other two differ by $0.2 \, \Omega$ in either direction, i.e. the uncertainty in R is $\Delta R \approx 0.2 \, \Omega$. The resistance can therefore be written as

$$R = 2.8 \, \Omega \pm 0.2 \, \Omega$$

The second figure in this answer (the 8 after the decimal point) is uncertain, and so any further figures are meaningless.

Another way of putting this is to say that the answer has (only) two **significant figures** – the one before the decimal point and the first one after it. The rest of the figures in the original 'best' answer are meaningless. They are *not* significant.

7.3 A useful rule of thumb

In a calculation, the answer cannot be known any more precisely than the values used to calculate it. As a useful rule of thumb, the final answer has no more significant figures than the *least* precise value used in the calculation. (The example in Maths note 7.2 illustrates this.)

Suppose you did a calculation to find the frequency f of light whose wavelength is 468 nm (4.68×10^{-7} m). The speed of light is known very precisely: $2.997\,925 \times 10^8$ m s^{-1}.

Using speed ÷ wavelength

$$f = \frac{2.997\,925 \times 108 \text{ m s}^{-1}}{4.68 \times 10^{-7} m}$$

$$= 6.4058 \times 10^{14} \text{ Hz}$$

However, we only knew the wavelength to three significant figures, so we cannot quote the frequency of this precisely. We must stick to the three significant figures and write

$$f = 6.41 \times 10^{14} \text{ Hz}$$

There was in fact no point in using the very precise value for the speed of light. Values listed in data books are often rounded to, say, three significant figures if they are likely to be used only in calculations requiring this precision or less.

7.4 Significant figures and orders of magnitude

The speed of light to seven significant figures is $2.997\,925 \times 10^8$ m s^{-1}; the significant figures are 2997925.

Zeros in front of a number are not significant. The speed of light could be written (rather oddly) as $002.997\,925 \times 10^8$ m s^{-1} or $0.000\,299\,7925 \times 10^{12}$ m s^{-1} without making any difference to its value.

However, zeros at the end of a number are (or at least can be!) significant. If you wrote the speed of light as $299\,792\,500$ m s^{-1}, that would imply that you knew that the last two figures were definitely zeros and not some other numbers. If they are, in fact, not known, it is better to use standard form so that the meaningless zeros can be dropped.

To five significant figures, the speed of light would be 2.9979×10^8 m s^{-1}. To three significant figures, it would be 3.00×10^8 m s^{-1}. Here the zeros *are* significant and should be written down, because 2.997... rounds to 3.00.

To one significant figure the speed of light would be 3×10^8 m s^{-1}.

If a value is rounded to just the nearest power of 10, then we say we are giving just the **order of magnitude**. Two values are said to have the same order of magnitude if one is between 1 and 10 times the other. For example, the wavelengths of red and blue light (about 400 nm and 700 nm) are within the same order of magnitude. But the wavelengths of infrared radiation range from about 10^{-6} m to about 10^{-3} m – they cover three orders of magnitude.

7.5 Combining uncertainties

When calculating a quantity by adding or subtracting measurements, the actual uncertainties are added together. For example, If the starting temperature of a liquid is 18.5 °C ± 0.2 °C, and the final temperature is 30.0 °C ± 0.2 °C, the rise in temperature is 11.5 °C ± 0.4 °C.

When measurements are combined by multiplying or dividing, the *percentage* uncertainty in the result is found by adding the individual percentage uncertainties. For example, suppose a glass stopper has mass m, and volume V (measured by displacement of water) and you want to find the density, ρ, of the glass. This is how you would use the measurements:

$$m = 48.7 \text{ g} \pm 0.5 \text{ g}, \Delta m = \frac{0.5}{487.7} = 0.01 = 1\%$$

$$V = 18 \text{ cm}^3 \pm 1 \text{ cm}^3, \Delta V = \frac{1}{18} = 0.056 = 5.6\%$$

$$\text{density} = \rho = m/V = \frac{48.7\,\text{g}}{18\,\text{cm}^3} = 2.7056\,\text{g}\,\text{cm}^3$$

percentage uncertainty = 1% + 5.6% = 6.6%

uncertainty in density, $\Delta\rho = 0.066 \times 2.7056\,\text{g}\,\text{cm}^{-3} = 0.2\,\text{g}\,\text{cm}^{-3}$ (to 1 significant figure)

so density $\rho = 2.7\,\text{g}\,\text{cm}^{-3} \pm 0.2\,\text{g}\,\text{cm}^{-3}$

For formulae involving powers, multiply the percentage uncertainty by the power. This is an extension of the procedure for dealing with multiplication and division. Remember that roots can be expressed as powers e.g. $\sqrt{x} = x^{\frac{1}{2}}$, so the percentage uncertainty in $\sqrt{x}$ is half the percentage uncertainty in x.

7.6 Error bars and error boxes

When plotting a line graph of experimental data, draw a vertical and a horizontal error **error bar** on each point to represent the range of possible values. Use the bars to draw an **error box** around each point. Draw a smooth trend line on your graph which passes through all the boxes, going as close to all their centres as possible. If there is a linear relationship between the variables, you can draw a straight line passing through all the boxes, even if you could not draw one through all the points.

Figure 10 shows graphs of some measurements where the uncertainties were $\Delta y = \pm 0.5$ and $\Delta x = \pm 0.25$. If you only had Figure 10(a) it would be impossible to say whether there is a linear relationship between y and x, but from Figure 10(b) you can say that there is such a relationship within the limits of experimental uncertainty. If x and y were current and pd, Figure 10(b) would indicate that material obeys Ohm's law.

(a)

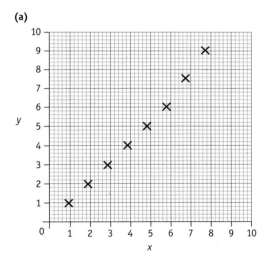

(b)

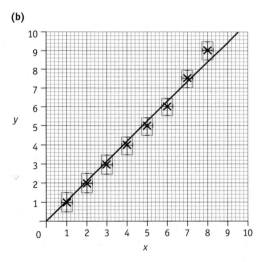

Figure 10 A plot of experimental values (a) without error boxes (b) with error boxes

MATHS REFERENCE

Percentages. See Maths note 3.1

STUDY NOTE

Verify this by finding the maximum and minimum possible densities using values of 49.2 g and 17 cm³, then 48.2 g and 19 cm³.

MATHS REFERENCE

Powers that are not whole numbers. See Maths note 1.5.

7.7 Uncertainties and graphs

When you have plotted a graph with error boxes around the points, you can draw the 'best' trend line that passes through all the boxes. The spread of points either side of the line indicates how certain you can be that the 'best' trend line shows the true relationship between the variables – the greater the spread, the greater the uncertainty.

On a linear graph, drawing the steepest and least-steep lines passing through the error boxes allows you to find the uncertainty in the gradient and intercept of the graph, as shown in Figure 11.

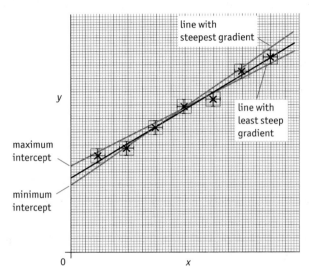

MATHS REFERENCE

Gradient of a linear graph.
See Maths note 5.3

Figure 11 Linear graph to show uncertainty

8 Logarithms

8.1 Logs and powers of 10

If a number can be written as *just* a 'power of 10', then the power is the **logarithm** of that number; strictly speaking, it is the **logarithm to base 10**, or **common logarithm**, of the number, but it is often simply called the **log**.

Table 8 lists some examples using whole-number powers.

Number x	$\log_{10}(x)$
$100\,000 = 10^5$	5
$10\,000 = 10^4$	4
$1000 = 10^3$	3
$100 = 10^2$	2
$10 = 10^1$	1
$1 = 10^0$	0
$0.1 = 10^{-1}$	−1
$0.001 = 10^{-2}$	−2

Table 8 Some numbers and their common logarithms

MATHS REFERENCE

Powers that are not whole numbers

See Maths note 1.5

In fact *any positive number* can be expressed as a power of 10, using powers that are not whole numbers. Most whole numbers have logs that are not themselves whole numbers or simple fractions. For example:

$$10^{0.6021} = 4.000$$

so

$$\log_{10}(4.000) = 0.6021$$

All numbers between 1 and 10 have logs that lie between 0 and 1. For example:

$$10^{0.333} = 2.153$$

so

$$\log_{10}(2.513) = 0.333$$

Similarly, all numbers between 10 and 100 have logs that lie between 1 and 2; all numbers between 100 and 1000 have logs between 2 and 3; and so on.

All numbers less than 1 have negative logs. For example:

$$\log_{10}(0.5) = -0.3010$$
$$\log_{10}(0.1) = -1.000$$

8.2 Logs on a calculator

To find the common log of a number using a calculator, type in the number and then press the key marked log or lg.

This process can be reversed to find the **antilog** of a number. Type in the log whose number you want to find, then press the keys marked INV and log (or lg). By doing this, you can show that 4.000 is the antilog of 0.6021, and 2.513 is the antilog of 0.333.

Notice that using the INV and log keys to find the antilog of a number x gives exactly the same result as using the y^x key to find 10^x.